# THE ADVENTURE OF BIRDS

*Other books by Charlton Ogburn*

THE WHITE FALCON

THE BRIDGE

BIG CAESAR

THE MARAUDERS

SHAKE-SPEARE—THE MAN BEHIND THE NAME (*co-author*)

THE GOLD OF THE RIVER SEA

THE WINTER BEACH

THE FORGING OF OUR CONTINENT (*Smithsonian Library*)

THE CONTINENT IN OUR HANDS

WINESPRING MOUNTAIN

THE SOUTHERN APPALACHIANS

# ___THE
# ADVENTURE
# OF BIRDS

by CHARLTON OGBURN

WITH DRAWINGS BY MATTHEW KALMENOFF

MORROW QUILL PAPERBACKS
New York    1980

**Library of Congress Cataloging in Publication Data**

Ogburn, Charlton (date)
    The adventure of birds.

    Bibliography: p.
    Includes index.
    1. Birds.   I. Title
QL676.035          598.2          76-13502
ISBN  0-688-08080-4 pbk.

Printed in the United States of America

First Morrow Quill Paperback Edition

1   2   3   4   5   6   7   8   9   10

FOR GEORGE STEVENS
*Avunculus in loco fratris,*
who has added equally to the
spice and substance of my life

# LIST OF DRAWINGS

Catbird—Rufous-sided Towhee—Robin      19

Common (Great) Egret      30

Wandering Albatross      53

Toucan      57

Different Kinds of Feathers: Flight—Shaft—
Barbs—Down—Body Feather      67

*Archaeopterex*      71

Bob Whites      125

Kingbird Chasing Crow      144

Warblers—Canada, Blackburnian, Blue-winged      233

Red-tailed Hawks      249

Winter Feeding      296

Snowy Owl      307

Spring      333

Shore Birds—Semipalmated Sandpiper, Yellow Legs      361

# CONTENTS

PART ONE    A World of Birds

1. BIRDS IN A LIFE    11

2. BIRDS AROUND THE WORLD    33
    The World to Birds and Men
    The Seafarers
    The Domain of Birds
    The Division of the Avian Treasure
    Birds of Our Cultural Homeland
    Birds of the Lonely Latitudes
    Birds of the Earth's Green Girdle

3. THE NATURE OF BIRDS    66
    Birds' Unique Advantage
    The Abandonment of Flight
    Nature's Supreme Insulator
    The Mechanics of Flight
    Structure and Sensors
    The Mental Processes
    The Variety of Food and Means of Getting It
    In Sum: Feathers
    Language

PART TWO    Birds Through the Year

4. SUMMER    123
    Birds at Home
    Flora and Avifauna: The Unrolling Carpet
    Birds and Territory
    The Ritual of Courtship
    The Musicians

The Variety of Nests
The Beginning Ebb

5. AUTUMN  213
  Arrival of the Season for Birds and Birders
  Autumn and the Shorebirds
  Autumn and the Gulls and Terns
  The Southward Tide of the Smaller Migrants
  The Distributaries
  The Procession of Hawks
  The Perils of the Way
  Pathfinding in the Skies

6. WINTER  288
  The Scourge and Its Compensations
  On Intimate Terms
  Invaders from the North
  Winter and the Ponds and Marshes
  Winter and the Ocean

7. SPRING  326
  The Glorious but Uncertain Coming
  The Stimulus to Migration
  The Flight Northward
  The Irreversible Tide of Spring
  Migration Through the City
  The Full Tide of Spring, and the Warblers
  —And the Shorebirds
  Summer Again, and Two Voices

BIBLIOGRAPHY  369

INDEX  375

# PART ONE

# A World of Birds

# ___1
# BIRDS IN A LIFE

I

I fell in love with birds at the age of eleven and have never fallen out of it. I am an ornithophile rather than an ornithologist, though during most of my adolescence I hoped to become the latter. Had I done so I should probably not be setting forth as I am to try to account for a lifelong ardor. I should have known too much about birds and have stood overwhelmed by all that could be said about them, and doubtless I should have regarded the human response to birds as irrelevant and distorting. The title would hardly have occurred to me and would have put me off if it had been suggested. What would it have meant? That birds are an adventure for life on earth to have undertaken? That the pursuit of birds is an adventure for us? (It means both, really.) Although in my youth I was often without other company than my own and that of birds, and felt consoled and elevated by the latter, I was at the same time coming to share in the general fascination and concern of my species with itself. Even the most devoted disciple of Nature must attach a high importance to human kind if for no other reason than without it the object of his fealty would be denied understanding and remain uncelebrated.

However, if my love of birds has not been pre-emptive and I have had other preoccupations, it has been constant. It preceded and has not been displaced by the others. In half a century there has been scarcely a day when the sound of an unusual bird's voice would not have brought me up short, when the form of any bird however barely glimpsed would not have registered on my consciousness, demanding recognition of what it was and what doing. And in all those years I have had to be sorely pressed indeed not to be susceptible of delight and excitement from a fresh revelation of the charm of birds or of the drama of which they are expressive.

"What are you looking at?" a young woman, many years ago, demanded of a fellow addict of mine at a moment of advanced tenderness between them. "You're not paying any attention to me at all!" In recalling the episode at a later time the young man acknowledged that the complaint was not baseless; a Hoopoe had been in plain sight over her shoulder. (The scene was the French countryside.) But what could she have expected? We wagged our heads in agreement on that.

I have never been distracted by a bird in comparable circumstances, but it did happen on an autumn afternoon in college that my attention had to be recalled from one to my immediate situation. The voice was as pettish as I imagine the affronted young woman's to have been, but it was a man's and issued from a megaphone. I was in a racing shell on the Charles River and along with seven other freshmen being lectured between trials by the coach in a nearby launch. "Well, Number Six, when you finish looking at that duck maybe we can go on." It was a female Scaup. Naturally I transferred my attention to where it belonged; in any case, I doubted that Ludlow Griscom himself (then less than a mile away) could have told whether it was a Greater or a Lesser Scaup. But I knew it would be the same the next time. One of the next times I remember particularly, for the setting was tropical. I was on the water again, nearly thirty years later, on the after-deck of a United States naval vessel in the port of the city soon to be called Jakarta. The bird then was a Brahminy kite circling at a low elevation, snowy white of head and breast in sharp contrast to its prevailing cinnamon, and the proceedings to which my attention had to be brought back were formal negotiations to end the war then being fought behind the blue volcanoes on the horizon.

But, while I have hardly been able to get along without

them, birds have not, as I say, seemed enough for a life, in themselves. On the other hand, mankind has often seemed to me too much, overwhelming in its proliferating multitudes and obsessive drive to master everything in sight.

Who with a lifelong enthusiasm for birds would not, then, respond to an invitation to commit that enthusiasm to paper, when the invitation came from a publisher prepared to make it feasible? An account of birds that would, well, tell all about them, or, if not all, what went into being a bird; what made birds of sustained interest and even fascination to their now numerous human following; what gave them meaning to man, in the needs of his soul: that was how I understood it. If no book had quite attempted this—and I could think of none that had—it was doubtless for good reason. What I was thinking of, however, was neither the good reason nor all I should not be bringing to the task. It was the justification I should have for giving in to my feeling for birds and for enlarging my acquaintance with them. I saw myself being outdoors and afield part of every week with birds my preoccupation, this *legitimately* and while others were at a desk, as I usually was. I could not resist it.

## II

Curiously, whenever the project comes up in conversation— some reply having to be given to the question of what one is doing—I feel defensive about it. It comes back to me how it was in my youth when a hostess would present me to a girl and leave us both despondent with her enthusiastic exit line: "He knows all about birds!" I was too abashed then to explain what I should like to now for any reader coming new to the subject. Birds are not just what they may be in popular fancy. They are not just the feathered songster among the apple blossoms viewed as part of a living Easter card. Birds are the albatross riding out the gales around Cape Horn. They are the Golden Plover flying 2,000 miles without a stop, and storks and cranes winging their way at 20,000 feet where a human being in an airplane needs an artificial atmosphere or tanked oxygen. They are the Golden Eagle launching from a Kirghiz Tatar's fist to attack and kill a wolf, and the Harpy Eagle of the Amazonian rain-forest with a war-mask of a face and tiger's claws for snatching man's smaller cousins from the tree-tops. They are Diatryma, the Eocene predator, which could have run down man himself and laid his skull open with its cleaver beak, and the Cassowary, which needs little provocation to rip a man apart today, as many a Papuan has learned.

They are also the owl that was Juno's and Athena's familiar, and Proserpina's, and the eagle that was Jove's; to men in the past there was no question about the importance of birds. It is on an eagle that Jove is riding when in Shakespeare's *Cymbeline* he descends to earth in thunder and lightning:

> The holy eagle
> Stoop'd, as to foot us; his ascension is
> More sweet than our blest fields: his royal bird
> Prunes the immortal wing, and cloys his beak,
> As when the god is pleased.

"Stoop'd, as to foot us"; there speaks a falconer!—as one does again in the observation of the preening of the wing and wiping of its beak with its claw by a bird of prey. Shakespeare's resort to avian imagery is so copious that a book has been written on it—*The Birds of Shakespeare,* by James E. Harting—and the example of the incomparable poet-dramatist is to me ample sanction for an interest in birds. Though Shakespeare is capable enough of fresh observation, as in his "ribald crows," much of his reference is to birds in literature and tradition. But metaphors drawing on falconry, that sport of the nobility, rise vigorously and spontaneously to the lips of his noble characters. "O, for a falconer's voice/To lure this tassel-gentle back again!" Juliet cries of Romeo—a tassel or tiercel being the male hawk and "gentle," in the sense of "noble," denoting the peregrine.

As Jove on an eagle, so Vishnu, his Hindu equivalent, is seen riding on the Garuda, a deity half raptorial bird, half human, "associated with the wide-spread symbol of the solar eagle," according to the anthropologist Carin Burrows. In ancient Egypt, where the ibis was represented as a sacred object, Horus, the son of the supreme goddess, Isis, had the form of a falcon. An early representation of Ahura Mazda, arch deity of the Persian Zoroastrians, shows him with a bird's wings and tail. The association of birds and gods must be almost as broad as religion itself. Even in a religion as indifferent to Nature as Christianity, one of the three manifestations of God is symbolized as a dove, *le pigeon* even being a name by which the French know the Holy Ghost.

The hold of birds on man's imagination would appear to go about as far back as art itself. Professor Grundy Steiner of Northwestern University writes in *Of Men and Birds*: "Modern scholarship can only debate the intentions of the prehistoric cave painter from Lascaux who placed a bird on a pole beside the man gored by the bison or the motives of the painter from the Trois-Frères Cavern who chose to sketch a front view of two Snowy Owls in the days when the mammoth ranged southern France, but either the artists or their audiences must have thought such subjects worth the effort to record. Perhaps the bird on the pole is one of the earliest surviving representations of the human soul in avian form."

Obviously it is birds' power of flight, setting them apart, that has associated them in our minds with the gods, who enjoy the same transcendence over gravity and distance. It causes us to feel about them as about creatures materialized out of spirit, of more rarefied origin than the earthbound. It has even given rise to a widespread belief, of which, as Professor Steiner remarks, the bird on the pole at Lascaux may be the first known record, that the departing human soul takes the form of a bird.

The ability of birds to come and go at will has affected our attitude toward them in other ways as well. Sir Kenneth Clark, in *Civilisation*, observing that "birds were a medieval obsession," writes that if you had asked a fourteenth-century cleric to account for all the renderings of birds by artists, "he would probably have said that they represented souls, because they can fly up to God; but this doesn't really explain why artists drew them with such obsessive accuracy, and I think the reason is that they had become symbols of freedom. Under feudalism men and animals were tied to the land: very few could move about."

So it has always been and so it remains, I think: that birds represent for us the escape from confinement and abridgement. And if we are no longer tied to the land, if our problem today is rather too much mobility, we feel as acutely as ever that longing to escape, and from "the society we have elaborated with so much effort," as D. H. Lawrence says, "only to find ourselves elaborated to death at last." If there is no rush away from our material possessions, the penalties they exact nevertheless weigh on us increasingly.

Freedom, and life itself: that is what it has seemed to me, since I began to think of it at all, that birds symbolize for us. An utterance I came to recently in rereading Conrad's *Lord Jim* has a bearing on this. Marlow, the narrator, is commenting on the self-undoing of the young protagonist. "He had not hung on; but he was aware of it with an intensity that made him touching, just as a man's more intense life makes his death more touching than the death of a tree."

Well, I cannot argue that the death of a bird is more touching than that of a man; a man's consciousness is greater. But regard the chickadee's little black coal of an eye through which its minute being scrutinizes you, the bufflehead bobbing up buoyant as a cork from the icy depths of a winter lake, the kingbird in the vocal and gyrational flurries of its aerial evening dance, the crowing cock, the hawk or falcon in its lightning pursuit. For intensity of life I should rank birds second to none. It is not for nothing that their blood contains almost double the proportion of sugar of that of mammals and their temperature ranges to 110 degrees. Few other creatures seem so alive in every fibre of their beings, so quick in response to the outer world or, in response to inner promptings, so fully given to the action, whether in song, in motion or in display. Even in quiescence they are concentrations of vitality.

Lord Jim was a romantic who found fulfillment among the people of the tropical forest of Patusan. (Whether Jim took an interest in birds is not divulged—presumably he did not—but Stein, the "wealthy and respected merchant" with trading-posts scattered through the East Indies who recognized Jim's trouble as romanticism and Patusan as the place for him and was himself the archetype of the romantic, was a lifelong and passionate collector of butterflies.) John Henry McCabe, whose story I clipped from a newspaper—the Washington *Post*—some fifteen years ago was, I am almost certain, a romantic; certainly he "had not hung on."

He was a young man of Arlington, Virginia, who "had only one interest in life—falconry—according to his mother. 'He was so crazy about falcons he spent his Army furlough while he was stationed in Germany by going to London just to see the birds at the London zoo,' Mrs. McCabe said. In 1952, he spent three months in Alaska, living alone on the tundra above the Arctic circle for as long as fifteen days at a stretch until he captured a gyrfalcon, known as the king of the family." The photograph of the young man accompanying the article shows a sensitive, intense face, a good-looking young man with full lips and an appearance of thoughtful puzzlement, perhaps only the consequence of having the sun in his eyes, though he is described as brooding and solitary. Four months after releasing his falcons, of which, amazingly, he is reported to have had eighteen, he killed himself with a bullet through the heart. The account, which was occasioned by the discovery of his body in a tract of woods some time afterward, touched me deeply. I have felt a strong affinity for the dead youth. I, too, have known the unique appeal of the gyrfalcon, perhaps the ultimate in avian supremacy over mundane circumstance. But John Henry McCabe had the initiative to journey to Alaska himself and live on the tundra to satisfy his passion for the bird. He was more courageous than I. Said his mother, "He didn't understand life. He wanted to achieve something. He reached for it, but it was always elusive."

*He didn't understand life. He wanted to achieve something. He reached for it, but it was always elusive.*

Well, men whose grasp has far exceeded John Henry McCabe's, or mine, or perhaps the reader's, have seen in birds the symbol of that elusive something and maybe had the sense of being brought closer to it by them. That, at least, one may suspect is the common denominator of the "violent men of action, or of vast political power" whose relationship with "the smallest birds" was commented on by Saint-John Perse, winner of a Nobel prize in poetry, in a conversation with Pierre Guerre. He spoke, the latter recalls, of "Alexander, the crude Macedonian, going off to war with a cage of birds wrought in gold; Charlemagne with a live starling; Genghis Khan at the edge of the desert, contemplating a beautiful tree full of small birds' nests which he gently had carried back on his chariot with its own earth so as not to upset the feathered tribe; Tamerlane in the last years of his life, sinking into sadness before his large collapsible aviaries; the Gauls, devoted to the lark and not the eagle; General Junot, Duke of Abrantes, ordering a cavalry charge against the nightingales in his park in Illyria and later on, completely mad, finally throwing himself out of a window in his château in France so as to fly like a bird. . . ."

### III

All this, it may be said, has precious little to do with birds. So it has. But the light birds throw on man may be as much a part of the truth of things as the light men have thrown on birds. As for that, moreover, I am inclined to believe that those staid and sober scientists who have told us most of what we know about birds were drawn to ornithology by a romantic view of its objects. They could not, surely, have failed to appreciate the romance of their calling when it was so evident to me as a boy, exhaled even by the endless drawers

of bird skins, redolent of camphor and of far, jungle-clad lands (like Patusan) on the fifth floor of the American Museum of Natural History. Their exhalations especially. Occasionally I used to find an excuse and the courage to ascend to those heights and hold converse with one of the demi-gods. They were receptive to any dead birds one might pick up. . . . But, I once asked, would even a starling be acceptable? Yes, even a starling. "I happen to have one in my pocket," I said, and the unseemly amusement of the Olympian fixed the incident in my memory. One afternoon with a school-mate I even saw Frank M. Chapman get into an elevator not five paces from me. I have looked upon that figure in whom it is not too much to say that ornithology was then personified.

One would think that, living where I do, my life would be full of birds without my having to fare forth to see them on the warrant of writing a book about them. And that is true, though we are only half an hour from Washington, D.C. There is a grassy slope at the end of the house and enough clearing along a five-hundred-foot driveway to satisfy Robins and promote the growth of Blackberry, Multiflora Rose and evergreen shrubs acceptable for nesting by a pair each of Rufous-sided Towhees, Cardinals, Catbirds, Brown Thrashers and Mockingbirds. But for the rest, trees stand about the house, some of them eighteen-foot spruces we raised from seedlings and brought here when we bought the land. The house fronts the belt of woods that borders Difficult Run and, like it, extends ten miles northward to the Potomac. The woods also extend backward in time, through the years of the Civil War, of which relics turn up along Difficult Run even now, past George Washington, whose journal mentions a crossing of the stream (not easy everywhere along it—hence the name), to an America before the white man. The voice of the great, wild forest of pine, oaks, hickories, beech, black tupelos and tulip trees that once held dominion from the seacoast to the prairies, and whose diminished descendants are today in limited occupation of Washington's environs, is still to be heard. It sounds in the harsh screams, half fierce, half seemingly piteous, of a Red-shouldered Hawk when the pair whose tenancy of the woods antedates ours rises to survey their preserves. By night it is in the resonant hooting and the spectral, hollow laughter and occasional, incredible caterwauling of the Barred Owls.

When the owls' voices are booming through the moonlit woods you would not think yourself in the suburbs. And you are not. Wilderness, inscrutable and inhuman, is never farther away than sundown. Let the darkness rise to swallow up the earth as the light filters from the sky and we are cave-men again, lords of creation only as far as the beams of our lamps, and beyond them blind, faltering, apprehensive, our souls maybe even charged with fear. And we may well be content to have it so. We shall be aware of the mystery that is in ourselves only as we encounter mystery without. Deprived of that, we shall find ourselves as flat, stale and unprofitable as the world appeared to a disillusioned Hamlet. Whatever we may know in our minds of its contents, the night remains as veiled and secretive to us as an underworld.

For a solitary human being to shout into the silent darkness would take courage and probably send shivers down his spine. But the Barred Owls unmistakably exult in doing so and the Whip-poor-wills lacerate the solemn stillness with breathtaking boldness. They do not, however, encourage us to presume upon the night. On the contrary, they bespeak its eerie latency, like a rain of blows on the door of a lonely house after nightfall. Once, indeed, a Whip-poor-will startled us almost as much as that by settling on the balcony of our house and giving full throat to its reiterated, vibrant, whip-lash cry, with shocking loudness; we could plainly hear the wooden note separating the whip-poor-WEELS. In almost any other time or society the recipients of this visitation would have had no doubt of its significance as a powerful omen. ("Auspice" is from the Latin *auspicium*, which combines *avis* and *spicere* and means examining the flight of birds for indications of the gods' intentions. And as Professor Grundy Steiner observes, "The noun *augur* is probably related to the verb *augere* ('to increase'), but birds were so important in the actual procedures of the augurs that the Romans regularly assumed that its first syllable came from *avis*.") I myself have a clear idea of its message—which an Indian would have so taken for granted he could not have imagined a special emissary as needed for its conveyance. It was a reminder: "From us you come, and to us you will return."

Especially in winter could one have a life rich in birds without stirring from the house above Difficult Run. I am not sure that the artificial feeding of birds is to be approved of. It partially domesticates them, encouraging a dependence on man. A diet of suet may not be of the best. Our cue with respect to Nature should probably be to interfere as little as possible. I try to justify the feeding station on the grounds that our intervention in the natural order has deprived birds of so much that a return is owing to right the balance, but this may be only rationalization of the satisfactions of being Lord Bountiful at little cost to a marvellous and vivacious array of pensioners that turn the wintry landscape into an approximation of the tropics. Actually the cost is not so little at that. The hundred pounds of sunflower seed we have bought since fall will not last till high spring restores the natural food supply, and in addition about twenty-five pounds of suet and fifty-five of cracked corn have had to be paid for. Evidently the summer was one of poor production of seed in the coniferous forests of upper New England and Canada, for the winter has brought a hungry influx of Pine Siskins and Evening Grosbeaks.

To accommodate the northern visitors while allowing the small resident birds a chance at the seed, we have to have ten feet of narrow trough on the balcony railing, and even that is not enough. And it is emptied of a pint of seed in less than half an hour. Eight or ten Goldfinches in olive winter plumage and three to five Siskins, their brownish-streaked cousins, line up like so many mice, seeming simply to mouth the seed yet somehow extracting the meat. A male Cardinal or a male Purple finch with foreparts and rump suffused with a rich wine-red—raspberry finches, Vera (my wife) calls them, accurately—bring a touch of warm color to the chill prospect that nothing else in winter does but a sunset. Bustling, thumb-sized Carolina Chicadees, their faces compressed between black cap and black throat, dart in, make their choice quickly and skipper off. The bigger, rather fairy-like, because large-eyed, Tufted Titmice are choosier, while the short-tailed White-breasted Nuthatches, stiff as if corseted, will flick three or four seed aside before making off with one.

It is a spectacle to hold anyone not used to it. But the birds with the shock value are the Evening Grosbeaks.

These were originally birds of the trans-Appalachian fir and spruce forests—their generic name, *Hesperiphona*, is from the Greek *hesperides*, "of the west"—but in recent years they have extended their breeding range eastward across the St. Lawrence. They are large, stocky, smoothly-sculptured finches, and sweeping in late in October in one of their fast-flying flocks to whir down into the treetops on flashing black-and-white wings, bringing the bare branches to sunflower-yellow bloom, they seem as exotic as parrots, which their pale, conical beaks are massive enough to suggest. (Hesperides was also the name of the daughters of Atlas, who were keepers of the golden apples.) The most indifferent observer of Nature could hardly fail to be arrested by the sight of six or eight of the boldly-fashioned birds at close range on the balcony railing—and we have had as many as fourteen on it at once—the males a rich yellow over their lower bodies and even more strikingly yellow on their smoky heads in a sharply defined patch covering the forehead and extending back over the eyes in the semblance of horns.

*Are there really such things as this, independent of man? Does this really go on?* It is that kind of response to such a sudden revelation of Nature's fertility in design and consummate artistry, an eye-opening hint of the inexhaustible, precisely organized variety of its infinitely numerous creations that is likely to inspire a lifelong susceptibility to birds.

To be without birds around the house, where in their animation they make me think even when silent of musical notes made visible, would be to me now a bereavement akin to being in a sense marooned. But neither they in their numbers nor the palisades of trees on which the windows open can make up for not being off under the sky and away—to which the active hunt for birds will lead.

Unless I am judging too much from my own case, it is our common experience to poison the atmosphere around ourselves. The air becomes cloyed with the emanations of our tiresome personalities. We find ourselves enveloped in a miasma of anxieties, disappointments and dissatisfactions with ourselves. To sap our remaining cheer, the hydras of the world's error, evil and sorrow have us cornered and beat a path to our door. The only relief is in getting out and being among fresh scenes that draw our attention out of ourselves.

And when you have been long confined, what exhilaration there is in being again out of doors in the sweep of a boundless natural landscape, in a vastly expanded world open to the winds and of roofless blue above the high and incorporeal clouds! And what comfort and peace there is in the sense one has of being restored to a place in the supreme composition, reintegrated with the elements, with hills and woodland! It is especially so today on the hill that rises west of Difficult Run a little downstream of our house. It is a bulge of the earth, a grassy dome, for it is kept mowed, with woods bordering it; and as a mother may lift a child above the heads of a crowd that it may see about it, it opens up to you the all but forgotten greatness of the sky. The time is the eve of spring. After days of cold, raw, blustery weather the temperature has risen into the sixties. The heavens are of such a blue you are ready to surrender your soul to them. Distillations of it, too, compressed into jewels, are in some bare trees—Bluebirds, all but one a male. They cannot settle down, being driven by an unease not to be relieved until they have gone on somewhere and claimed a bit of orchard or woodland edge as their own for the breeding-season. But they are delicate in their movements as they flutter from tree to tree, like flowers come to life, and their intense and burnished blue seems almost too much for mortal eyes. The wind over the hill is from the southwest. It is the voice of an undefiled openness, and it plays through the cords of one's being as through the rigging of a ship. A Turkey Vulture is being borne swiftly across the sky before it, on crooked wings. So large a bird in our heavens is a survival, an anachronism, but a sign that the old gods have not altogether given way. . . . One is as much possessed by the air as if one were oneself a sail billowing out with it.

## IV

The binocular around my neck and the separation from extraneous harassments it connotes in my mind take me back to a time when I could be whole-souled in the pursuit of birds, and in pursuit of all the far reaches of the earth—far lands that the explorer knew—as only youth can be whole-souled. The sun is bright, and I am led to think, as so many have, how in its course across the sky it marks the progress of a life. Marching with the sun, you have it behind you in youth. Your shadow precedes you and you see your form cast upon the landscape of the future. In age, advancing toward the declining sun, you cast your shadow behind you, and that is where your place is, in the landscape of the past. Not that I am morbid about it, or even particularly bothered. It is the way of nature; and being encompassed in the unity of Nature seems, as I feel just now, a fulfillment in itself. And the truth is that I have no sense of remoteness from that time of morning.

To have contracted early in life such a passion as that for birds is, I think, to be fortunate, if it lasts. Then in later years the prepossession provides a bridge with one's younger self; one has not ceased entirely to be what one was when the fresh and radiant earth was opening up around one. It must have proved so in many cases, for, as Roger Tory Peterson has observed in *Wings Over America*, an enthusiasm for birds is likely to have been kindled by the age of ten or eleven— and, he adds, is evidently much more likely to take hold among boys than among girls.

Wild creatures are independent of man's world and deeply at odds with it. Being, as well, simpler than man, they are a youngster's natural emotional allies against the overbearing adult establishment, which, in the form of school, already has him at its mercy. In children, too, there may be a throwback to the youth of the race when men and animals were close before civilization alienated us, one from the other. When at the age of eleven I was given Ernest Thompson Seton's *Wild Animals I Have Known,* I must have had a predisposition to its animal heroes—nurtured by Kipling's *Jungle Books,* I dare say—to account for the rapidity and completeness with which I was won to it. In a few weeks I had exhausted the New York Public Library's collection of Seton's works. Going on to what looked like the next best choice, I took out a book called *Bird Life,* by Frank M. Chapman, illustrated by Louis Agassiz Fuertes—neither of which illustrious names had I ever heard before. As nearly as I can pin it down, it was the painting of a Fox Sparrow, having the effect I have imagined the Evening Grosbeak would have on a newcomer to birds, that turned the course of my life.

The Fox Sparrow was not startling in appearance. A larger-than-average member of the tribe, it was a bright reddish brown on the wings and tail and streaked and blotched with the same rusty hue on its contrasting, soft grey head and back and white underparts. It was distinctive in shade and pattern, certainly, but not so much as to make it a bird you heard of, like a Cardinal or Bluebird; it came as my own discovery. It was a small bird, too, not like a swan or eagle. On both counts it fitted into the private, interior world of childhood. It had a further magnetism in that it illustrated Nature's faculty for working small, deft variations of a theme from one species to another—for the Fox sparrow was simply a larger and brighter Song sparrow, as the Savannah and Vesper sparrows were alterations in other directions; assortments of likes varying in details appeal to a budding mind reaching out for patterns in the confusing hubbub of the world.

I nurtured the Fox Sparrow and its similarly-qualified fellows in my imagination. Reading all of *Bird Life* and other works of popular ornithology, I gave myself up to birds, brooding on them and going out to seek them, armed with Chester Reed's pocket *Bird Guide* for identification. Within a year or two I had acquired a homeland of the spirit as intimate as the sphere of lamplight in which I pored over Chapman's *What Bird Is That?* and William T. Hornaday's *The American Natural History* and as vast as the uncrowded reaches of arctic and alpine tundra, desert, seacoast and tropical rain-forest, the periphery of which I was beginning to explore on weekends and summer vacations. Life does not permit one to remain in such a realm, invulnerable, but neither can it altogether uproot one who has been naturalized to it.

From my experience, which must parallel thousands of others', I should guess that the tinder from which an ardor for birds is fired in the young is partly the collector's zeal, which delights in the filling out of categories, the accumulation of integers in a series—as of sparrows, warblers, gulls and birds as a class—and the propensity to discovery and adventure: roving. These urges are likely to make themselves strongly felt at just the age Peterson cites and may well be more characteristic of the dawning male consciousness than the female. Both may represent an impulse to assimilate the world, to acquire a power over it, even a secret power. Birds have a double appeal to the incipient rover. Not only are they, in their free-ranging lives, the expression of the roving spirit, but the collecting of birds (in a figurative sense) leads to and warrants roving oneself. By "collecting" I mean adding birds to those one can name by sight or sound and has thus made one's own, and racking up birds that are special in one way or another—though photographing them would come nearer the meaning of the word. A bird may be new to the day's list when you are out to make a good dawn-to-dusk showing. It may be new to your year's list or life-list. More notably, it may be unusual in the locality in which you find it, or at least at the time of year at which it has appeared.

Regarded strictly as striving for records, "looking for birds," as it is generally called among those who engage in it, is no more than a game. One has to realize that this seeking for the out-of-the-way among birds is a means of giving a pleasure form and structure, such as derive from having concrete goals —the purpose served by meets and competitions among those who love swimming and diving or horseback riding for their own sakes. It is a device for dealing with the stirrings that birds arouse in us, and all they represent to us. There must be a term for this in the jargon of psychology. "Objectifying" or "externalizing," perhaps.

It can be an absorbing business, akin to prospecting, only for symbolic rather than material prizes. In its aspect as collecting, the satisfactions it affords depend to a large extent on your being in communication with others who can appreciate your coups as you theirs. Looking for birds is often a solitary affair. You are alone with the meadow and the bordering woodland, the marsh and wind-swept beach, with the chill of dawn, the piercing cold of the winter wind and the close heat of a summer bog, and with the god of natural places and the natural elements; and ultimately it is between you and this god, whom you celebrate and who is your judge. But association with other human beings with whom reports of the hunt may be exchanged in the confidence of a common understanding of the finest points—companionship with the like of heart—adds greatly to the rewards: Most of us have someone whom we rush to tell, even if it is only the secretary of a bird club, by mail.

I have only to pick up an issue of *Atlantic Naturalist*, the quarterly of the local Audubon Society, and turn to "Birds of the Season" to be reminded of the old thrill when patience, dedication and—yes—prowess were rewarded by the exceptional, the enviable encounter. "Jack Abbott noted all the pertinent field marks in identifying a nonbreeding-plumaged eared grebe on Bombay Hook NWR [National Wildlife Refuge], Del., Nov. 26. . . . Carlson saw 2 pomarine jaegers Oct. 25 and different single parasitic jaegers Oct. 23, 24, and 25, and 2 on the 26th, on the N. C. Outer Banks. . . . On Oct. 24 Rowlett carefully identified a sage thrasher on the north end of Assateague Island, Md. He made detailed notes and photo-

graphed the bird. This is the first record for Maryland."
Identifications of aberrants—birds outside their normal range—
are far commoner than when I was a beginner. The ornithological contemporaries of my boyhood would be amazed by
the dispersals reported in *American Birds,* a journal of the
National Audubon Society which every two months publishes
notes from the field bearing on the status of the North American avifauna—how our roughly 645 native species are faring
and how their distribution may be changing and what incur-
sions from abroad have come within the ken of assiduous and
fortunate observers. Today there must be fully ten times as
many birders, as we call ourselves. We have more leisure and
can get about in motorcars on superior highways; street-cars,
trains and shank's mare were the conveyances when I was a
boy. We have better binoculars, while improved and handier
telescopes have revolutionized the identification of birds at a
distance—those nearer, too, that will remain within their field.
Birders are better informed and have much better guides to
identification, thanks to innovations wrought by Peterson,
whose first field guide came out in 1934. That there are so
many of us today is also owing in unique measure to Roger
Tory Peterson as painter, writer, photographer and lecturer.*

I was thirteen when, mastering a nearly paralyzing weakness
of nerve, I stood up in a meeting of the august Linnaean So-

---

* In October 1975 at Toronto, after a thousand persons had filled an
auditorium in which Peterson was to show a film he had made in the
Galápagos Islands, the police had to be called to subdue some of those
who had been shut out when the doors were closed and had started to
rough up the guards. Not only have we become more numerous—and
avid—but we count for more. The Washington *Post* on January 8, 1976,
gave fifty-three square inches of its first page to the presence of a Smew
at Newport, R.I.—the first record on the Atlantic Coast of North America
of this small merganser from extreme northern Europe. And four days
later, when the possibility of the bird's having escaped from a local
waterfowl collection had been eliminated, the *Post* gave almost half as
much of its first page and twenty-seven column-inches of an inside page
to reporting on the birders who had congregated around the "bitterly
cold, windswept marshland" for a sight of the wanderer. Times have
changed.

ciety of New York during a period of reports from the floor
of significant sightings and gave one of my own. On August
13th I had observed a Great Egret at the edge of a lake near
South Salem in Westchester County. I came as close as my
condition permitted to the phraseology I had planned and that
was *de rigeur*, namely that I had examined the bird at leisure
through an eight-power binocular and noted the distinguishing
features, which were the yellow beak and dark legs. The
egrets had by then made only a very partial comeback from
their near extermination at the hands of the plume-hunters
and were among the southern herons only beginning to return
to the northern part of their former range; my bird was very
much in the van.

Twelve years later I made my supreme record. It was again
in August, the bird was again at the edge of a lake—this one
three miles north of the other, in a thousand-acre tract of
woods. Against that northern background of sugar-maples and
cherry birches it glowed like an ember of a land of fierier
exuberances—as it was. "My God!" I groaned with the marvel

of it, with trembling incredulity, with ecstasy. It was a bird not even part of American avifauna, a native of South America recorded as "accidental" on the Gulf Coast, as I was to find—a Scarlet Ibis. "And I had a very big emotion," said Stein, the wealthy merchant and lepidopterist in *Lord Jim*. "You don't know what it is for a collector to capture such a rare specimen. You can't know." Stein's knees gave way beneath him from weakness. I braced myself against a tree and, suiting the word to the action, framed the phrase to myself, "Studied at leisure through eight-power binocular." * When I had absorbed the sight I ran the three-quarters of a mile back to the house and, winded, snatched up the telephone. A fellow enthusiast of mine lived seven miles to the south. Having gasped the electrifying news to him, I hurried back to the pond, where the ibis had scarcely moved. Louis J. Halle was a ferocious driver at ordinary times and on this occasion I could hear his Ford convertible a long way off, first on the asphalt, then on the gravel. At the end it was nip and tuck. The Ibis had taken to the air. In one direction at some distance off I could see my friend vaulting from his car, in the other the departing bird—which vanished just as he reached the spot where I stood, from which he could have seen it.

I have been fortunate in having friends, and later a wife and daughter, with whom to share the excitements of birding. In Louis, with whom the association began in college and was to extend over decades, I had one in whom were apparent from the start the powers of observation and expression that were to make him an outstandingly fine writer on birds. (I have always been proud of appearing, albeit under a cryptic nickname, in his classic *Spring in Washington*.) Earlier, as a

* And so I reported. But I never received credit for my record. My note to *The Auk*, journal of the American Ornithologists Union, was rejected on the grounds that the ibis was too likely to have escaped from an aviary. The editor was almost certainly mistaken. The color of the Scarlet Ibis is known to fade quickly in captivity and that of my bird was intense. The next issue of *Bird Lore* (now *Audubon Magazine*) reported the sighting of the ibis near Ridgefield, just across the Connecticut line, two days later.

boy, I had three contemporaries with whom birds could be endlessly mulled over and excursions made into the more accessible green pastures—Central and Van Cortlandt Parks and the exurbs of the city, between the Overpek marshes of New Jersey and Long Beach. Most of these we were introduced to after we had constituted ourselves the Junior Linnaean Society and been taken in charge by a veteran member, a stocky little man named George E. Hix, an insatiable birder, with thick glasses and a sudden grin that never varied in character.

In the summers I was on my own, however, on the farm where I worked and where the egret appeared. Here I remember at the age of twelve beginning the composition of a book, a harder task, it developed, than I had anticipated and quickly aborted. It seemed the natural thing to do, I was so immersed in reading. In particular was I in thrall to *Two Little Savages*, Seton's tale of two boys who went off into the woods to live like Indians, so much so that in finishing the last page I would turn without a pause back to the first, as if I were reading a continuous scroll. (The influence of that book among boys of my time was, I think, incalculable.) However, the novel I had planned owed rather more to *The Swiss Family Robinson*, to which I was also very partial. It was to turn upon a shipwreck, but one of an uncommon sort in that the prime part of the cargo was an assortment of North American gallinaceous birds. Notable among these from my point of view were the Western quails: the Scaled, California, Gambel's, Mountain and Montezuma quails. The purpose of the shipwreck was to enable the protagonist to possess, to cultivate and to treasure, on a paradisiac island, a variety of lively but domesticable birds that each resembles the finished work of an imaginative master lapidary. And is not what I had in mind, I would ask my fellow birders, what in part we all seek in this quest of ours—to take to our hearts the poignancy, the beauty, the spirit, the subtle harmonies and vivid patterns of the living world that come to a focus in these vital creatures?

## 2
# BIRDS AROUND THE WORLD

### The World to Birds and Men

Between birds and men, so much more unlike in general than man and other mammals, there are yet parallels. They and they alone are bipeds. Some other animals are capable of bipedal movement, but for man and birds on the ground any other is awkward and unnatural. In their characteristic posture they have heads up and are looking around. And in this they draw our attention to their most important similarity. Outstandingly among all other forms of life they take in their impression of their surroundings through the senses of sight and hearing. Both, too, are keenly color-perceptive. Almost all mammals other than man are colorblind, a red flag to a bull being, except for metaphoric purposes, no different from a green flag or a grey. The odor of carrion is said to assist vultures in its detection and the Kiwi, a nocturnal denizen of New Zealand's damp tree-fern forests resembling a wig of straight hair ambulatory on over-sized feet, has nostrils at the tip of its extra-long bill and presumably locates earthworms by scent; but in comparison with mammals and most insects the olfactory sense seems in birds generally as in man but little developed. Broadly speaking, the kinds of things that attract a bird's attention are those that attract a man's. To that extent the two bipeds inhabit comparable universes. Studies of their navigational abilities suggest that birds even take in the pattern of the night skies, making them surely the only other creatures than men, and perhaps bats, on whom the stars register.

That in turn points to a further similarity. A number of other

animals are great travelers, notably inhabitants of the oceans—
some of the fish, squid, turtles and marine mammals. Salmon
that range the northern seas swim as much as a thousand miles
up rivers to spawn. Eels do the opposite. The reproductive
instinct sends them down the rivers in which they dwell on
both sides of the Atlantic, then on to spawning grounds in the
Sargasso Sea, south and southeast of Bermuda. From there the
young, slight as they are, somehow accomplish the perilous
oceanic journey to the rivers whence their parents had come
and swarm up them. Some reach headwaters or ponds as high
as 8,000 feet above sea-level. (Young and old, eels can travel
overland through wet grass.) It is an amazing hegira. None
of the marine travelers, however, knows the great vistas of the
earth's varied landscapes, snowy mountains, lush dales and
deserts, prairie and rain-forest. This is reserved for the flying
animals and—since he first raised fabric wings upon the seas—
for man. Bats of the temperate zone that do not hibernate
necessarily migrate to escape the winter and a few butterflies
do. But no other migrants in the skies can compare with birds
in numbers and distances traveled or in the perception they
bring to the earth's changing face below. Birds and modern
man are pre-eminent in global perspective. The curvature of
the planet enters into their experience as the curvature of the
hill into the fox's. Of only one other animal—man—could such
an observation as Donald Griffin's about the extent of bird
migrations be made, that it "is limited not by the capabilities
of the birds, but by the size of the planet."

### The Seafarers

It is a bond between birds and men that in their respective
navigations of the oceans each has helped in the achievement
of the other's ends. Numberless migrating birds, exhausted by
battle with the winds and perhaps blown off course, have
found safety in the superstructure of ships. Though a hummingbird may hurtle its minute being across 600 miles of the
Gulf of Mexico, birds have no store of magic but only flesh
and blood on which to call in their perilous journeys. Ships,

except when they discharge oil on the seas, are generally good news to birds. Beyond offering refuge to weary travelers they may be accompanied for days by gulls or albatrosses for the marine organisms their propellers cast up and scraps of food in the refuse of the galley, or, in the case of fish- or whale-processing ships, more substantial fare. For their part, birds may have shown venturesome mariners the way to most of the lands that lay below the horizon. Probably no other agency could have accounted for the peopling of the far-flung isles of the Pacific by the Polynesians.

Writing of the oceanic explorations of those seafarers, a New Zealand historian, G. S. Parsonson, contends that "they must have relied to an increasing extent upon migratory birds, in particular the long-tailed cuckoo, the sooty shearwater, the golden plover and possibly also the godwit, whose flight, spread out over several weeks, they had long studied." The migrations of the Lesser Golden Plover between its breeding grounds on the two sides of the Bering Sea and its winter haven in the south Pacific islands are believed to have drawn the Tahitians on to the Hawaiian group. It was a bird, too, that led to the discovery of New Zealand by a certain Tahitian, if C. Percy Smith, a New Zealand ethnologist, is right. "Kupe," he declares in *Hawaiki, The Original Home of the Maori*, "had observed in his many voyages the flight of the *kohoperoa*, or long-tailed cuckoo, year after year, always coming from the southwest and wintering in the central Pacific islands. He and his compeers would know at once that this is a land bird and consequently that land must lie toward the southwest."

We can only speculate whether it was the flight of birds out of the featureless, grey water-world of the West and their return into it that beckoned the Vikings to the discovery of the New World. Two species they would have known to fly only from land to land regularly cross the North Atlantic between the continents. One is the Wheatear, a black, white and grey thrush of buff-colored underparts, a champion over-water migrant among small birds, and the Arctic Tern, champion of all. We do know that birds gave Columbus and his men their first intimation of land on the far side of the Atlantic. The many that they sighted shortly after entering upon the blue waters flecked with golden seaweed of the Sargasso Sea were probably of the same species believed to have led to the discovery of Hawaii—Lesser Golden Plovers. These would have been on their fall migration between the Maritime Provinces of Canada and South America. Two days later they saw other birds, among them West Indian Gannets, or, as ornithologists elect to call the tropical relatives of the Northern Gannet, adopting the sailor's epithet, Boobies. Columbus set his course by theirs to his landfall on Guanahani Island. In doing so he was following the example of the Portuguese who had come upon the western Azores (from *açores*, Portuguese for "hawks," by the way) by following the flight of land birds.

### The Domain of Birds

The two great adventurers over the restless waters that overspread two-thirds of the earth's surface and that have taken incalculable toll of the invaders' lives: such are birds and men. And as no immensity of ocean, so no barrier of *terra firma* has confined the range of either rover; the whole globe, virtually, comes within the ken of the one as of the other. The South Pole, at the heart of the most forbidding terrain of all, is known to have been overflown by the Skua, a heavy, brownish, predatory relative of the gulls. The Skua, which breeds in the arctic as well as the antarctic, and is the only bird that does so—with the two populations remaining distinct, so far as is known—may have been at the North Pole as well. Its trimmer cousin the Parasitic Jaeger (German for hunter) is one of several birds seen at or near it. Another is the pure white Ivory Gull, which, with the lovely Ross's Gull of pink underparts, passes the winter in the unspeakable desolation of the open leads among the floes. (It was one of the latter that created such a sensation when it turned up at the mouth of the Merrimack River in Massachusetts in March 1975, bringing birders to the spot from all across the country and even being prominently reported in the press.) The frigid waters of the antarctic are home to the albatross-petrel order and of course to penguins. The Snow Petrel may not only surpass the Ivory Gull in whiteness but inhabits a world of white, the consort of snow and ice, nesting on the antarctic continent as much as 186 miles inland on rocks that break through the glacier. The Emperor Penguin chooses to nest on the Great Ice Barrier and to incubate its single egg in the dark of the antarctic winter in temperatures that may fall to 80 degrees below zero. Only a creature of its stature and vitality could hope to succeed in such a regimen; Emperors weigh when grown between 50 and 90 pounds, and one, in an early encounter with our race, was reported to have thrown off five men attempting its capture.

Between the earth's icecaps are regions that man invades at his peril or only if burdened with elaborate sustaining and protective paraphernalia, and in all of them he finds birds in confident occupation. At least that is true within limits. Taking a bubble of the atmosphere with him in a metal capsule, man may descend to depths of the sea or rise to altitudes at which no unarmored inhabitant of the earth's surface could survive. Yet birds with no life-support systems (in the jargon of the space age) but those inherent in them endure a vertical range beyond the tolerance of any other class of animals. The eagle-like Lammergeier, a vulturine bird of the mountains from Spain eastward, has been seen at 25,000 feet in the only range reaching such an elevation—the Himalayas. There, the one time I have been there, I saw my one Lammergeier! At Gulmarg, in Kashmir, on leave from the Army, I labored one day to a height not much more than half the species' observed maximum, though at the end I was barely setting one foot before the other. That was when the magnificent bird came by on swift wings, wings narrower than an eagle's and seven or eight feet in spread; it is one of the fastest of birds, having been timed at approximately 80 miles an hour. A memorable encounter! Another bird of the Eurasian mountains, the Red-billed Chough (pronounced *chuff*), a small, slender-billed crow, is believed actually to have reached the 29,000-foot summit of the tallest of mountains, Chuma-lungma—Everest—while geese have been reported over Dehra Dun, India, at 29,500 feet.

At the other extreme, no one knows how deep some of the aquatic birds may dive, or could with strong incentive. Loons and Old-squaw ducks have been recorded at depths of up to 200 feet. The record would probably be achieved by the penguins. These are of all birds the most thoroughly adapted to marine life. Having branched off early from the main line of avian development, abandoning flight, they have had ample time to perfect their adjustment to the medium: about 60 million years, by the fossil record. Stream-lined and supple, their wings transformed into powerful flippers, they are virtually small seals in build and style of locomotion. Capable of zipping through the water at 25 miles an hour and of leaping like salmon, they pop out of the sea as if shot from it to land on ice floes as much as five feet above it.

Large parts of the ocean, especially in the tropics, are almost lifeless. They may be known by their deep blue color. This is the consequence of the diffusion of light at the blue end of the spectrum by water molecules, which absorb light from the rest of the spectrum where there is no particulate matter in suspension to reflect it; it is in accordance with this principle that a clear sky is blue. Marine deserts, these seas are shunned by birds though even here vagrant, far-ranging flyers may be encountered. As for the earth's arid deserts, few stretches are so devoid of vegetation as to be birdless as well. Even these, places of wind-sculptured dunes conjured up in the minds of most of us by the term *desert*—exceptional among deserts though they be—are likely to come within the purlieus of soaring vultures and other hawks, not to mention the birds of passage that may cross them. The greatest of the dune-deserts, the Sahara, harbors over 80 species of birds exclusive of migrants, these ranging in character from the sweetly-singing Desert Lark to the Ostrich. Deserts, in fact, are often richer in avifauna than some coniferous forests, though in forests of other kinds—those of tropical rain belts—the number of bird species reaches a peak.

Short of the planet's extremes of inhospitality, birds generally abound—if in the present century decreasingly. They are numerous individually and, as compared with other animals of their size, in variety. The figure usually cited for the number of their species is around 8,600. That is enough to keep any pursuer of birds occupied for a lifetime. Such a one would find his hunting particularly good in lands where year-around warmth and plentiful rain foster a copious vegetation, for this in turn ensures an unfailing supply of fruits, seeds and insects, which are the principal items of diet of the major part of the Class Aves and of the quarry of the birds of prey. Among these fecund lands the quest would yield the greatest returns in the Congo basin and in the lusher tropics from central Mexico southward through the Amazon basin, the greatest of all in Colombia, where 1,700 species have been recorded. Conversely, he would find the number of species thinning out markedly toward the poles, toward the interior of great arid deserts, in coniferous forests and outward from the major land masses to oceanic islands.

Density of numbers may be a very different matter where individuals rather than species are considered. The Passenger Pigeon had an enormous habitat to range through—the eastern North American deciduous forest—and one highly productive of acorns, beechnuts and other seeds and fruits on which it lived. Being an extremely strong and rapid flyer it was able to make the most of the bounty. Before the white man came, its numbers amounted to several billions, probably exceeding those of all other birds of the continent put together.

In the Arctic and Antarctic Oceans a simple but fruitful environment sustains hosts of birds of a few species well adapted to it. Upwellings in these seas bring to the surface the waters of the bottom, holding nutrient minerals in solution. The causes are various. The confluence of currents or their deflection by bodies of land may bring lower layers to the top.

So may the sinking of surface water rendered heavy by contraction in the cold and the salt concentrated in it by the extraction of fresh water in the formation of ice. In Antarctica fresh water draining from the continental glacier drifts northward and is replaced by water flowing southward below, which is forced upward by rising land. In any case, the fertile waters on reaching sunlight nourish a tremendous growth of diatoms and dinoflagellates, the unicellular plant-life of the plankton—the "drift." These pastures of the sea sustain the minute animal organisms of the plankton, especially the little crustaceans called copepods, which (according to Ritchie R. Ward) make up 80 per cent of the animal life of the oceans. These in turn feed the larger, among which the shrimp-like krill are the staple of sea-birds as of baleen whales. Alcids (the penguin-like auks and their relatives), Gannets and Kittiwake gulls nest by the thousands and tens of thousands on rocky islets in the northern seas; Murres (an alcid) resorting to Three Arches Rock on the coast of Oregon have been estimated at three-quarters of a million.

In the cold southern ocean, however, the number of birds is greater. Colonies of Adélie Penguins have been calculated at half a million birds to 500 acres, and the species nests all around the rim of Antarctica. In places, the sea even hundreds of miles from land is thronged by penguins and procellarines—members of the order of petrels, shearwaters and albatrosses: birds of the *procella*, or storm. The smallest of these, the size of a bluebird, the Wilson's Storm-petrel, nests on antarctic islands and escapes the antarctic winter by migrating northward as much as 10,000 miles to the waters off Great Britain, Labrador and California. In the good old days when travelers crossed the Atlantic by ship, the scattered flocks of the sooty-black, white-rumped pitterals (as the name, taken from the bird's cry, originally was) flittering to the waves to patter upon them, was a familiar and charming sight from the taffrail. James Fisher and Roger Tory Peterson consider the Wilson's Storm-petrel the most numerous species of bird in the world. Some others might make this claim on behalf of the little shearwaters, blue-grey over white, called Prions or Whale-birds, of whose flights Robert Cushman Murphy of the American Museum of Natural History writes in his classic and encyclopedic *Oceanic Birds of South America* as "filling the air like the flakes of a snowstorm and stretching in all directions toward the circle of the horizon from daybreak until dark."

Where the cool Humboldt Current moves northward along the Pacific bulge of South America, antarctic concentrations of sea-birds come with it. These are owing less to the drift from the southern ocean, however, than to the prevailing southerly winds, which blow the surface water offshore and thus bring cool water from the depths laden with phosphates up along the precipitous coast. The result is a plankton "bloom" giving the waters the consistency of thick soup. Feeding upon the plankton are herring and especially the little anchovies, and, upon these, larger fish, seals and birds in hosts that have made the bird islands of Peru synonymous with avian abundance. "The long lines of pelicans, the low-moving black clouds of cormorants, or the rainstorms of plunging gannets probably cannot be equalled in any other part of the world," the American ornithologist Robert E. Coker wrote half a century ago. "As for the birds," Frank M. Chapman was moved to exclaim a decade later, "who can describe them in their incalculable myriads?" Robert Cushman Murphy computed the number of cormorant nests on one small island at a million, representing four or five times as many birds. In the course of thousands of years the droppings of the Humboldt seafowl on their island roosts along that largely rainless coast had accumulated, packed hard, up to a depth of 180 feet. Between 1848 and 1875 more than 200 million tons of the guano were exported. Farms all over Europe and the United States, as well as the Peruvian treasury, were enriched by it, for it proved to be the most potent, and the cheapest, fertilizer in commerce.

Yet a few miles off shore the warm waters of the tropical Pacific reassert themselves and with them the swarms of birds disappear. Blue and largely empty, the ocean rolls by for hundreds upon hundreds of miles . . . until the vessel nears an island or archipelago where interference with ocean currents again brings up the nourishing lower waters. While "one may travel for days across the tropical oceans and see no birds at all," as W. B. Alexander observes in his *Birds of the Ocean*, "many small, desolate, sun-baked islets off the coasts of the continents, and numerous coral islands in mid-ocean, swarm with sea-birds whose cries may be heard for miles across the water and which may appear at a distance like a column of smoke rising from the island."

### The Division of the Avian Treasure

Rich in birds, hence rich indeed, rich beyond realization: such is the ornithophile's view of the earth. He finds enough to keep him going for a lifetime, as I say, and to beggar him in journeys afar. With travel today made easier all the time and wild-life tours organized to most parts of the world, he is in fact apt to have seen a variety of out-of-the-way places. ("The Seychelles turned out to be islands of all the main types of geological origin," an attractive middle-aged woman, a fellow birder, said to me last winter. Before World War II we should neither of us have ever heard of them.) Year by year more countries are treated in adequate bird books, some of them delights in themselves, so that there are more and more places one can visit without the torturing frustration of not knowing what one is seeing.

*Not knowing*. It may be an unworthy consideration. The wholly free mind should perhaps find satisfaction enough in the impression of things as they are in themselves. If one truly takes in the actuality of the bird before one—the tree, the flower—then what can knowing its name and relationships add? There it is, all it is in its instantaneousness, in all its beauty and vitality, fully achieved. How can the dusty labors of taxonomists enhance that quintessentiality?

I can ask these questions but I am still, like the unfree spirit in Buddhist belief, bound to the wheel. I am one of those who have to know names and where the named object fits into the scheme of things. Thus we come into possession of the world around us, as far as we are able to, and as we seem to need to. "That's a Golden-crowned Kinglet!" I exclaimed of the restless little being on the lower branch of a tree in Central Park: I had just turned twelve and had a sense of fulfillment, keen if small. It was one I was to know many times. "That's a Chaffinch!" I recognized three years later when by good fortune business took my parents to Europe and I followed at the end of the school term. (The thrill during the voyage over of the occasional shearwater gliding along the leading slope of a comber is with me still.) But often enough when it has been given to me to be abroad I have been stumped. I have had either no book to go by or been left at a loss by merely verbal descriptions. Even for Britain and Europe there was no satisfactory guide until the 1960's, or until the excellent Peterson and Hamlyn guides came out, pocket-sized and with every species illustrated in minutely accurate color. As the creators of bird books have added to their fields of operations—and today eight or ten bird painters do work of which only Louis Agassiz Fuertes was capable in my boyhood—the boon is not for travelers alone. There are books to be pored over by the stuck-at-homes, like seed catalogues by gardeners in winter. I cannot open one of the new guides or either of two sumptuous volumes of global compass, *The World of Birds*, by Fisher and Peterson, and *Birds of the World*, by Austin and Singer, without danger of being lost to the world of duties and responsibilities among the Fulmars and Pintado Petrels, Least Auklets and Ancient Murrlets, Lanner and Red-footed Falcons, Ornate and Long-crested Hawk-eagles, Winchats and Stonechats, Touracos, Cotingas, Crested Swifts . . . all 8,600 species. "Little is known about the sharpbills beyond what the few scattered museum specimens reveal," I read in Austin and am a goner.

Here is the place to take notice—since not to do so might be considered remiss—that ornithologists divide the world's birds into seven avifaunas, with overlaps, in accordance with the zoological areas derived from Alfred Russell Wallace's delineations. The designation of these areas exhibits scientific nomenclature at its most inept, which is saying something. It requires us to consider the furnaces of Mexico's deserts and the Lybian desert, where the highest temperature yet known on the surface of the globe was recorded, as part of the arctic and the glacial mountains of Tierra del Fuego, lashed by sleet and snow on screaming winds, as part of the tropics.

The regions as named are these:

1) Nearctic, which science has decided is Greek for "New World Arctic." (Comprising North America down to central Mexico, it might be called Ameri-boreal.)

2) Neotropical. (Amer-austral would be more fitting for a region extending from central Mexico to the waters below Cape Horn.)

3) Palearctic: sciencese for "Old World Arctic." (Eurasia-boreal would be analagous with the above and give a much better idea of what is meant.)

4) Oriental. (Southeast Asian.)

5) Ethiopian. (Sub-Saharan African. To avoid confusion with the country of Ethiopia, Afro-austral would seem preferable.)

6) Australasian. (Australo-Newguinean.)

7) Oceanic. (Pacific-Oceanic.)

### Birds of Our Cultural Homeland

The areas that science calls the Palearctic and the Nearctic together make up a super-region it calls the Holarctic. (Holo-boreal might be preferred by those who can consider the deserts of Arabia as northern in a hemispherical sense but not as parts of the "whole arctic" in any sense at all.) The two avifaunas certainly have much in common. Americans crossing the Atlantic will find most of the sea-birds they left behind and be reminded by the breeding colonies of alcids, Gannets and Fulmars on the British coast that they are at the latitude of Labrador. Even those that are different are far from unknown on the other side of the Atlantic. This is true of some less marine water-birds as well. The Black Duck, Ring-necked Duck, American Green-winged Teal and other ducks, Killdeer and other shorebirds from the west and Black-headed, Lesser Black-backed and Little Gulls, European Teal, European Wigeon, Barnacle Goose and Ruff and other shorebirds from the east are continually turning up in the company of other species on the other side of the ocean, after a journey which those who know the vast, storm-ridden expanses of the North Atlantic must wonder how in heaven's name some of them achieved, especially little seven-inch-long sandpipers. The occasional occurrence of North American warblers, vireos, finches and thrushes, including Robins, in Europe would seem even more amazing. That they are blown off course by the prevailing, often very strong westerlies of our latitudes is evidenced by the almost wholly one-way nature of the trans-Atlantic traffic in small land-birds; and one may suspect that those that make it all the way have done most of it after taking refuge on a ship.

For such strong flyers as most waterfowl, hawks and eagles, ravens and crows on one side of the ocean to have counterparts on the other is not very surprising. What is more so is finding close affinities among many small birds so far separated. The Pine Grosbeak, both species of Redpolls and of Crossbills, Lapland Longspur, Snow Bunting, Winter Wren (*the* Wren of the Old World), Brown Creeper, Horned Lark, Northern Shrike and Three-toed Woodpecker are native to both hemispheres. But these are all birds of the higher latitudes. Circumpolar, as the term is, they do not so much bridge the Atlantic as the Bering Strait. As you move south in the two hemispheres the affinities become weakened. Of species that breed widely in the United States only the Black-billed Magpie, Barn Swallow and Bank Swallow are conspecific, as they say, with their Old World equivalents. Still, an American in Britain or on the Continent finds much to make him feel at home, even among the small birds of park, garden and farm. The woodpeckers, titmice, nuthatches, jays, many finches and swifts have the same ways and personalities on either side of the ocean and often look alike. The Goldcrest, *Regulus regulus,* an Old World warbler, extends with minor modifications across northern North America as the Golden-crowned Kinglet, *Regulus satrapa,* and across Asia to Taiwan, where it rejoices in the priceless scientific name of *Regulus goodfellowi.*

Perhaps, however, the strongest impact made on a returning American by the birds of his ancestral lands—if they are his ancestral lands—is neither of the similarities to those of North America nor of the provocative differences. (Redshank? Black Kite? Wood Pigeon? Eagle Owl? Hoopoe? Green Woodpecker? Wryneck? Ring Ouzel? Brambling?!!) It is of returning to that which goes far back in our past. These birds are the familiars of hill and wold, heath and marsh and fen that were home to us over a vaster time by far than ever we have put in remaking the New World. We go back together to a time when—and even long, long before—the Anglo-Saxon who had been "with the sea-flood over the whale's domain" sang that "I took my gladness in the cry of the gannet and the sound of the curlew instead of the laughter of men, in the screaming gull instead of the drink of mead" and recalled that "There storms beat upon the rocky cliffs; there the tern with icy feathers answered them."

As we think of our individual past, moreover, we are likely to recognize that Matthew Arnold's "wet, bird-haunted English lawn" has indeed "Lent it"—that past—"the music of its trees at dawn." Literature begins for us with "Sumer is icumen in, Lhude sing cuccu"; the bird was Wordsworth's "blithe new-comer" that he thought perhaps "but a wandering voice" —and our introduction to books is sure to include

> The north wind doth blow,
> And we shall have snow,
> And what will poor robin do then?

We learn in time that the robin is not ours, which flies south before the snow-bearing winds, but the bird—also a thrush— that Wordsworth addressed:

> Art thou the bird whom man loves best,
> The pious bird with scarlet breast,
> Our little English robin:

It may well be the bird whom Englishmen love best, for as Oliver L. Austin, Jr., points out in *Birds of the World,* wherever Englishmen have settled they have named a local species after it; "So we find robins, related and unrelated, the world around, in America, Australia, India, Africa—wherever English is spoken." Izaak Walton had the sentiment returned: "the honest robin that loves mankind, both alive and dead." The reference is to a solicitude for humankind assigned to the Robin in legend, of which John Webster wrote in 1638:

> Call for robin-redbreast and the wren,
> Since o'er shady groves they hover,
> And with leaves and flowers do cover
> The friendless bodies of unburied men.

In Shakespeare's *Cymbeline* Arviragus alludes to the same attribute of the "ruddock"—an old name for the little bird—in the lovely speech in which he promises to sweeten Imogen's sad grave with pale primrose, azured hare-bell and leaf of eglantine and adds:

> . . . the ruddock would
> With charitable bill, . . . bring thee all this;
> Yes, and furr'd moss besides, when flowers are none,
> To winter-ground thy corse.

As for the "four and twenty blackbirds baked in a pie," we learn in time, too, that these were not the Red-wings of our marshes but the bird Shakespeare called "The ouzel-cock, so black of hue,/With orange-tawny bill." The English—or European—Blackbird is in all but its sable color virtually a replica of our Robin and fills the same place in the scheme of things. It frequents lawns and, in a similar rollicking way, "sings as loud as a lady's piano," as the poet John Clare has it, albeit "with a yellow ring round his violet eye."

The Blackbird is one of the five songsters we hear most often in English literature. Michael Drayton has three of them in a couplet in *Shepherd's Garland:*

> Crave the tuneful nightingale to help you with her lay,
> The ousel and the throstlecock, chief music of our May.

Throstle is thrush, here the Song Thrush, or Mavis. Edmund Spenser in *Epithalamion* completes the roll:

> The merry larke hir mattins sings aloft,
> The thrush replyes, the mavis descant playes,
> The ouzel shrills, the ruddock warbles soft, . . .

It was the Song Thrush, a spotted thrush but otherwise much like the Blackbird and our Robin, that Robert Browning epitomized so engagingly:

> That's the wise thrush; he sings each song twice over,
> Lest you think he never could recapture
> That first fine careless rapture!

But the star is of course

> O nightingale, that on yon bloomy spray
> Warbl'st at eve, when all the woods are still.

So exclaims John Milton. And Matthew Arnold:

> Hark! ah, the Nightingale!
> The tawny-throated!
> Hark! from that moonlit cedar what a burst!

It is an ingredient of Robert Louis Stevenson's dream of contentment:

> A little river by the door,
> A nightingale in the sycamore!

(That of course is not our sycamore but a kind of European maple.) It is Keats's "light-winged Dryad of the trees" that

> In some melodious plot
> Of beechen green, and shadows numberless
> Singest of summer in full-throated ease.

No other bird has received such tributes from poets. Yet a writer of prose, and a simple man, spoke more closely to the mark than any of them, over 300 years ago. We can hear in Izaak Walton's tribute a response to nature characteristic of much later times, when, after the industrial revolution, nature was no longer to be taken for granted.

> The nightingale breathes such sweet loud music out of

her little instrumental throat, that it might make mankind to think miracles are not ceased. He that at midnight, when the very laborer sleeps securely, should hear, as I have very often, the clear airs, the sweet descants, the natural rising and falling, the doubling and redoubling, of her voice, might well be lifted above the earth and say, Lord, what music has thou provided for the saints in heaven, when thou affordest bad men such music on earth?

It is curious how consistently the singing nightingale was represented as she. "By this, lamenting Philomel had ended/ The well-tun'd warble of her nightly sorrow," Shakespeare writes. James E. Harting suggests in *The Birds of Shakespeare,* no doubt correctly, that this was because of the myth recounted by Ovid in which Philomela—"Lover of Song"—daughter of King Pandion of Athens, was transformed into a nightingale, her sister, Progne, at the same time into a swallow. So do the familiar birds of the Old World come into our ken out of ancient memory in kinship with man, like the animals of the New to the Indians.

Keats in his *Ode to the Nightingale* is moved by a consideration that the voices of the Old World songsters must awaken in all of us and, for the Old World's far-flung children returning to the fold, set their discovery apart from all other avian encounters. I have to quote the entire stanza for the sake of the rhyme, though I have never been able to make anything of the last three lines, musical as they are.

> Thou wast not born for death, immortal Bird!
>   No hungry generations tread thee down;
>     The voice I hear this passing night was heard
>   In ancient days by emperor and clown:
> Perhaps the self-same song that found a path
>   Through the sad heart of Ruth, when, sick for home,
>     She stood in tears amid the alien corn;
>       The same that oft-times hath
> Charmed magic casements, opening on the foam,
>   Of perilous seas, in faery lands forlorn.

The self-same songs: who has not heard them before us? I stood once on Salisbury Plain as a Skylark—Shakespeare's bird that "tirra-lirra chants"—rose singing over the inscrutable monoliths of Stonehenge, by which prehistoric Britons computed the movements of the heavenly bodies over 3,000 years ago, and I knew then how brief was a two- or three-hundred-year tenancy of the Redman's continent measured against the balance of the whole.

Shakespeare must have been especially susceptible to the lark, for the lines it inspired in him seem to soar with its own flight:

> . . . My state
> Like to the lark at break of day arising
> From sullen earth, sings hymns at heaven's gate.

And, of course, not Shakespeare alone. It is probably, indeed, the lark, beginning with Chaucer's "bisy larke, messager of day," that of all birds comes most often to the imaginations of English poets—Milton's "herald lark" that leaves "his ground-nest, high-towering to descry/The morn's approach, and greet her with his song"; the lark that is "on the wing" for Browning when "All's right with the world"; that for Shelley pours out "his full heart/In profuse strains of unpremeditated art," flying "higher and higher," until, with Tennyson, "Drown'd in yonder blue," it "becomes a sightless song." There can, in truth, scarcely be a conjunction of two such brief words with more power to lift the spirit than *sky-lark*.

It is not only that the birds of Britain are celebrated in the reading we have grown up on, but that they appear in that reading in a landscape that has awakened more love, or been loved by those with the words to move us more, than any other we know of. Yes, the first two lines may have become trite enough, but go on with Browning to the end of the stanza:

> Oh, to be in England
> Now that April's there,
> And whoever wakes in England
> Sees, some morning unaware,
> That the lowest boughs and the brushwood sheaf

Round the elm-tree bole are in tiny leaf,
While the Chaffinch sings on the orchard bough,
In England—now!

Or, better yet, read the other stanza as well. It helps make clear why the birds of Britain have another claim on us, or those of us who cherish our own landscape and see it ruined and lost unless a nation can be aroused to care for it more than it has yet seemed to. It was the English, beginning with Shakespeare, who more than any others opened our senses to the landscape of nature, to which birds had been instrumental, in two meanings of the word, in opening their own.

### Birds of the Lonely Latitudes

It is for almost opposite reasons that another of the world's avifaunas exerts a hold on the imagination. If that of Europe is the most domestic, most intertwined with our long past, that of the far South Atlantic and antarctic could be considered the most alien to man. The partially grass- and brush-grown, storm-lashed islands and icebound, virtually plantless shores of the South Polar continent and, more than those, the literally endless seas between, beyond the frontier of permanent human habitation, or all but its farthest outposts, make up its habitat. It has, of course, its antipodean counterpart; and perhaps the arctic and antarctic avifaunas, in their character, should be grouped together from the point of view from which I am writing. If quite different in origin, their components, through contending with similar conditions, have come by convergent evolution to resemble each other. (Little Auks of the arctic and Diving-petrels of the antarctic, though of wholly different stock, could scarcely be told apart at any distance if they occurred together.) Alcids and the gull-tern family (included by science in the same Order) predominate in the far north, two more primitive Orders (only distantly related to each other) in the far south: the procellarines—albatrosses, shearwaters and the several groups of petrels—and the penguins.

There has, however, been intermixing. The gull-tern tribe

has colonized almost all the coasts of the world (not to mention the continental interiors) down to and including the Antarctic Peninsula. It has, moreover, contributed to far southern lands their scourge. The Skua is in effect a gull that has turned into a hawk, says Robert Cushman Murphy, whom Louis J. Halle calls "the greatest of all observers and students of seabirds." It "has left, I believe, a more vivid impression on my memory than any other bird I have met," Murphy declares. "The skuas . . . fear nothing, never seek to avoid being conspicuous, and, by every token of behavior, they are lords of the far south. . . . Not only are they the enemies of every creature they can master, living almost entirely by ravin and slaughter, but they also have the appearance of a bird of prey in the general color of their plumage, the pointed, erectile hackles on the neck, the hooked bill, and the long, sharp, curved claws, which seem incongruous on webbed feet."

The success of the gulls in spreading southward has been paralleled by that of the shearwaters in the opposite direction. (Of the more than 50 species of these the majority are called petrels, like the Snow Petrel and Pintado Petrel, creating confusion with two other families called petrels.) Named for their habit of coasting along the front of waves with one wing-tip appearing to skim the surface, shearwaters breed on the coasts, somewhere, of all the oceans or on islands in them. Some of the family of little storm-petrels breed on far northern coasts and some albatrosses on islands in the Pacific as far north as the latitude of southern Japan. With all the dispersion, however, it remains true, as Halle says in *The Sea and the Ice*, that as land birds reach their peak of numbers in the tropics, sea-birds reach theirs in the cold of the high latitudes, above all, those of the south, where "there are small fowl and middle-sized fowl spread over the waves in their myriads, wandering this way and that, moving carpets of birdlife, such an abundance as has never been known in the waters of the familiar world."

For persons subject to a sense of the press of things, of being closed in upon and beset by too many demands on their responses, cloyed, as it were, by an over-richness on life's part,

human and natural together, more prone to claustro- than agoraphobia, avian trails lead above all to the realm of the sea-birds, and among the sea-birds above all to the procellarines. It is a varied Order, *Procellariformes*, certainly as to size. In no other are the extremes greater. The smaller storm-petrels are no larger than swallows, which they resemble in their swerving, darting flight, while the Wandering Albatross has the largest wing-span of any existing bird—up to ten feet or even more. Murphy writes, "Because of a certain uniformity of habitat, and the possession of incomparable specializations for pelagic life, the Tubinares [as the Order was once called owing to its members' having nostrils opening from tubes along the top of the bill] are almost without rivals in an enormous geographic field. Their range in size, therefore, tends directly to relieve the pressure of competition among their own kind."

Of whatever proportions, the procellarines exhibit in their ultimate degree the qualities that set sea-birds apart. More than any others they are wide-roving birds of the open ocean. They come to land only to nest, and some of the world's most inaccessible and inhospitable islands are favored by them for this purpose, the Snow Petrel resorting to mountain heights deep in Antarctica, some even above 6,000 feet. Their true home is the homelessness of the circumpolar ocean's unland-marked, limitless vastness. The desolation of endlessly rolling waves, from horizon to empty horizon; cold, hard, blue skies lifeless but for their kind, or chill, sullen overcasts dimming the light of the low sun; icebergs, sometimes many miles across, of a preternatural whiteness with luminous depths of aquamarine and azure; the perpetual wind of the sea and the storm that rears monstrous breakers raging as far as the eye can reach, silvered with racing spume: those are their connotations—and space, above all, space.

Some of the large albatrosses, the eminent British ornithologist James Fisher believed, may spend the first nine years of their lives without resting on land at all. A Wandering Albatross that was banded off the east coast of Australia in August

1959 was at its breeding ground on the island of South Georgia, on the opposite side of the world, in February 1962, was off the east coast of Australia again in August of that year, was there again in July 1963 and then was back in South Georgia for the next nesting season. Referring to these records, Halle remarks that "It could not have beat its way against the west wind, either to go from South Georgia to Australia or from Australia to South Georgia, for that is not the manner of its flight. It went, rather, like the wind around the world, knowing intuitively that going on would bring it back." An albatross, he notes, may circumnavigate the globe again and again. One sees it, with Matthew Arnold,

> Sail and sail, with unshut eye,
> Round the world for ever and aye.

And how they put the miles behind them in the process! An albatross shot off the coast of Chile at 43° south latitude on December 30, 1847, had a message around its neck attached on December 8th by the whaler *Euphrates* at the same latitude about one-third of the way between New Zealand and Chile. Even if the bird had traveled by the shortest route it would have covered almost 5,000 miles in 22 days. Presumably it covered substantially more, and while routinely drifting. A little Manx Shearwater taken from its nest in Wales, flown to Logan Airport in Boston, 3,250 miles away, in an area quite unfamiliar to it, and released was back at its nest in 12½ days.

No birds are such far-rangers as the procellarines. The Greater Shearwater nests, so far as is known, only on islands of the Tristan da Cunha group, on the spine of the mid-Atlantic ridge about as far as one can get from a continent in the South Atlantic, and moves northward after breeding to the cold fishing-banks of the North Atlantic. Frederick C. Lincoln of the Fish and Wildlife Service estimates that in the seven or eight months of the year the birds of the species may spend at sea without making a landfall they may fly between 50 and 100 thousand miles. The Slender-billed Shearwater annually circumnavigates the Pacific. Leaving their nesting sites on the shores of Bass Strait, between Australia and Tasmania, the flocks wing their way to New Zealand, thence, passing off the Bismarck Archipelago, to the waters off Japan and on to those below Kamchatka, from there to the Aleutians and, skirting the west coast of the United States, back again across 7,200 miles of ocean. (The migrants have been known to swing in-shore so that, in the words of the San Francisco *Chronicle*, "Thick black streams of birds—sometimes so thick they seem to darken the sky—have been spotted off Ocean Beach and the Golden Gate.") The young spend their first three or four years on this odyssey.

I have never known anyone more susceptible to the idea of the procellarines than Louis Halle. It was a description in William Beebe's *Arcturus Adventure* of an albatross coming in for a landing after months at sea that started him on an interest in birds. It was to take him forty years to get to the Southern Ocean, but the result has been *The Sea and the Ice*, of which Brooks Atkinson (a literary and dramatic critic turned discerning naturalist) says, surely with warrant, that it "will eventually become a classic of Antarctic literature, if it is not already a classic." It has confirmed my feeling that the oceanic birds, culminating in the procellarine hosts of the waters under the Aurora Australis, offer us one of the three great fields of avian discovery outside the United States.

His affinity for the sea-birds, wanderers free as thought on the winds of everlasting distances, was indicative of the clarity of view in the largest perspective that was to be the hallmark of Louis's writing on the affairs of men and of birds. In the way of this life, I was to have a glimpse of the edge of his southern ocean and see eye to eye with Wandering Albatrosses before he had a chance to, while he was to have a full season of the tropics before I had ever been south of Georgia. And the tropics were the object of my dreams—the disarming warmth of perpetual summers and fragrant airs, outpourings of flora and fauna, vine-hung forests of giant trees from which strange calls issued. To me, today, one of the fecund tropical land-masses—any one—offers the third of the triumvirate of

irresistibly alluring avifaunas. As a young man I should have put it first, and I think I still should.

### Birds of the Earth's Green Girdle

> I've never sailed the Amazon,
> I've never reached Brazil. . . .

So we sang in the eighth grade. I should have been electrified to know that ten years later I was to do just that.

To say that the anticipation as the small freighter rolled with me down to Belem (Rolled really down to Belem . . .) and the actuality of a trip by a small, shore-hugging boat up the greatest of rivers, past the greatest of forests (of giant trees, vine-hung), stand in their way as a supreme experience of my life not involving relations with other human beings would be to neglect the larger truth. They stand in their way as a supreme experience of man's term on earth.

Parrots there were, big, stocky ones, green touched with brighter colors on their heads, smaller ones of tapering forms, mostly green, too, with brighter colors on their wings, and stately, massive macaws bearing regally their masquerade garb of primary colors so little in keeping with their ancient, naked faces rounded with great hooked beaks. Birds of prey watched from bare limbs of the unending forest, disappeared in its shadowy defiles or winged across the side channels of the great tawny flood the vessel mostly navigated: hawks and eagles beyond my identification, to my despair. Tanagers the hue of a misty blue sky, others wine-red rich as velvet; toucans conceived in a mood of child-like intoxication with color and design on the Creator's part; chocolate-backed, buff-breasted, pheasant-like Hoatzins, phoenix-crested, whose infant young climb about—young *Archeaopteryxes*—with claws at the bend of the wing; herons of all kinds and tree-ducks; huge-billed white Jabiru Storks of bare, black heads and necks; flights of Scarlet Ibises: in the dawn hour especially I was in ecstasy, and much I could not see reached out from the forest to stir primal senses as I had anticipated, only more varied, more musical or more brazen, more human and more inhuman. I later saw much more of the forest than a river trip disclosed, moved by a ferment within me that the years would not subdue. . . . But enough of that. Let me move on to somewhat safer ground.

I have been fortunate in being allowed a passing view of some part of Asia's great tropical avifauna, too, first in the Second World War. If Rudyard Kipling had never reached Brazil, he had certainly been in India—and I had known about Darzee the Tailor-bird before I had ever heard of the Song Sparrow.

> Ere Mor the Peacock flutters, ere the Monkey-People cry,
> Ere Chil the Kite swoops down a furlong sheer,
> Through the Jungle very softly flits a shadow and a sigh—
> He is Fear, O Little Hunter, he is Fear!

I never saw Mor the Peacock in the wild, but once at the head of a column of troops crossing a ravine I came on one of the great feathers of its tail (strictly, upper tail-coverts) such as Cleopatra bore to crown her pomp, burning green in the sun with its blue eye rimmed in gold just short of the crescent tip. The Monkey-People we heard cry rather too often, and too abruptly, too shockingly loud, in the hills of Burma when Fear was indeed flitting through the Jungle as a shadow and a sigh. And tense times were made a little more unnerving by the call of the Brain-fever Cuckoo—its song, actually—which spirals off into nothing in a way that does sound touched with delirium. However, the war was man's doing, not monkeys' or birds', and I was recompensed for any inconvenience it caused me by a train trip, in various stages, clear across the sub-continent, from Bombay to Calcutta and Assam. Here again was enchantment. The train jogged on, car windows open to the blessed warmth (the bloody heat, there may have been some justification for calling it at times) and to the vendors of tea and cakes at every station, and all India passing by, its countless palm-clustered villages, its humped Brahma cattle, its lean, brown-skinned men in white dhotis, its emerald rice fields, its ruins. . . . But this is an account of birds.

Yes, I saw Chil the Kite, many times. I even saw him swoop down, perhaps not quite an eighth-mile sheer, to snatch food from a human hand. Once it was from a fellow soldier's messkit at our training camp, where we used to toss pieces of bread up to see the kites catch them in the air. The other time it was on a crowded street in old Delhi from an Indian. That was the country for me, I thought, where birds were on such terms with men. Birds in India did seem uncommonly trusting, perhaps because the heathen religion of the country stays the killer's hand.

Pariah Kites—the Black Kite of Europe—seem to take over from the gulls in Indian Ocean ports, and you could count on seeing them continually from the train. So you could also White-backed Vultures with their bare brown heads and necks craning out of ermine coat-collars, small, white Egyptian Vultures, their pinched yellow faces tapering to thin beaks, and grey-and-black House Crows dealing as energetically with life as crows do everywhere, except South America and New Zealand, where there are not any—yet. Besides the Little Egrets, which are found on all the major continents (if you count our Snowy Egret as one of them) were stockier Cattle Egrets, marked with buff, which I little realized were then consolidating the bridge-head they had gained in the New World by crossing from Africa to the Guianas and would soon be expanding across the United States. Astonished as I should have been to know that twenty-five years later I should see a wild Cattle Egret in northern Virginia, I should have been no less so to learn that Rose-ringed Parakeets, whose screaming bands enlivened the banyans on the cities' outskirts and the coconut palms of villages all across India, would a few years after that establish a breeding colony (doubtless of escaped cage-birds) at the northern tip of Manhattan Island. (So reports Katharine Scherman, who writes eloquently of very different islands.) As in the Amazon river-boat, so in Indian trains: I was apprehensive of what I might miss if I withdrew my attention for a moment from what was slipping by—an Adjutant Stork (ugliest of birds) or black-headed, white Paradise Flycatcher with foot-long central tail-feathers. However, I was to have a much more intimate introduction to the Southeast Asian avifauna—the Oriental, as ornithologists call it—four years later in Java. And I was to have impressed on me as I had not had since Brazil the qualities of a great tropical country that for those responsive to nature make it every morning an excitement to awaken to.

The first of these likely to strike the attention is that the life-force in the neighborhood of the Equator is so strong as to make deep inroads into cities, which elsewhere are barrens. This rejoices the heart, as life's ascendancy over confinement and negation does, being—for us—the drama of the universe. Cities like Belem and Jakarta create hardly a break in the bird-life, unless I am out of date on them. "The only city I know in the temperate zone of which this can be said," I thought at the time—and this certainly is less true today—"is Washington, D.C., which has justifiably been termed a city in the woods." I know I thought it because my enthusiasm for Java overcame even the inertia that in the absence of compelling incentive prevents one from putting one's impressions into writing. "At night in Batavia [as Jakarta was then called], I have been electrified by the owls that flew over the main streets, their forms dimly illuminated from below, their protracted, strangled screeches sounding loud above the noisiest traffic. After returning from Java I twice met with the same phenomenon on the outskirts of Washington [in Alexandria] and have concluded that in both cases it was the Barn Owl, *Tyto alba*, whose distribution is almost world-wide.

"Among the birds that take over Batavia by day are the swifts that nest in hundreds under the bridges spanning the city's canals. These are Cave Swiftlets of the genus *Collocalia* [the kind found to use sonar in navigating], related to the swift that builds edible nests. . . . A huge flock as thick as gnats swirled every morning, for the ten months I was in Batavia, around the crown of one of the great shade trees in the courtyard of the Hôtel des Indes." I remember watching them at breakfast and "four or five Glossy Starlings of the genus *Aplonis* —very handsome in their jet plumage with its green sheen and with their ruby eyes—that inhabited an iron lamppost by the dining terrace." And I would hear the bird sounds of Batavia, "the outpouring of the bulbuls, the not unmusical efforts of the Pied Starlings and the hollow cooing of doves." The Black-capped Bulbuls, which gave the impression of regarding the city as theirs, reminded me of Kingbirds in size and pattern and in their restless vitality and raucous notes; but they had a voluble, melodious song.

"Wherever you find a full-grown specimen of one of the giant native trees you have a fragment of the forest—even among the quadrangles of the Hôtel des Indes, where a number of waringins with trunks formed of aerial roots, like banyans, hold their canopied branches high above the roofs. A complete avifauna had its existence in the foliage of these trees, not to mention gecko lizards, like baby alligators, that would wake one from the deepest sleep with their cry of '*TOK' EH* . . . TOK'-EH . . . *tok'eh* . . . tok'eh,' gradually subsiding like a bagpipe running out of air. I even found fruit-doves in the trees, the males resembling Neapolitan ice cream, with pistachio predominating. These I discovered while lying on my back on the hood of a jeep in my perennial quest for the source of a song, . . . a soft *too-too-too-too-too,* delivered without emphasis, without hope, without meaning, and certainly without surcease —one of those sounds that could have come from a great distance or from inside one's head. . . . The perpetrator finally turned out to be a bird that dwelt exclusively in the tree-tops and which I had never seen—a Crimson-breasted Barbet, a chunky little beauty with brilliant crimson on the crown and breast and with yellow throat and cheeks and dark green upperparts." It is called a Copper-smith in India, from the sound it makes.

"It was in the trees of the Hotel des Indes that for the first time in Java I saw Fruit-bats, or Flying Foxes. Java abounds in bats, bats like our Little Brown Bats, bats only half as large, and silver bats. There are bats as big as Screech Owls that dash through your open window for a quick circuit of the room and out again, in that intermingling of nature with civilization that gives the tropics part of their appeal for those whose tastes incline that way. But the Fruit-bat is like nothing else in this world. Indeed, with its dog-like or fox-like head and its wingspread of three feet, it seems more than any other animal to be of another world. Picture a flock of these bats outlined from your hotel window by the full moon, flapping around a waringin tree—and flapping is exactly descriptive of their flight— squeaking and gibbering, alighting with much shaking and rearrangement of their leathery wings, walking upside down among the terminal branches, which bend beneath their weight, and you have a sight worth traveling halfway around the world to behold, or to avoid, as some people would have it."

That is one aspect of the tropics: the intimacy into which they bring you with a prodigal Nature. And of course it is this prodigality of Nature's where there are no seasons but those of greater and lesser rainfall that is their primary distinction: the profusion and variety of the forms of life they breed. Of that my remembered impression is rekindled as my eye travels down the pages—of that and of other elements of that spell of the tropics under which one's soul seems to become to a degree unfettered. It comes back to me especially as, here at home under a grey March sky, I recall bicycling out the road to Tangerang after work, "in the last hour of the day, when the townspeople and villagers were bathing in the canals and rivers and water-buffaloes being brought back from the wallows [and] it was easier to believe that the road led to paradise, such were its avian wonders and the splendors of its incomparable sunsets."

Jeweled kingfishers that Europeans are familiar with but that amaze Americans—mites with bodies smaller than your thumb . . . and with colors of turquoise, amethyst and coral—Golden-backed Woodpeckers, like small, gilded Pileateds—Black Drongos which appear three parts flycatcher and one part crow, with long tails curling out on either side at the tip. . . . Throngs of little chocolate White-breasted Manakins which small naked boys with long poles go paddling out in the rice fields to drive off. . . . A Tree-swift of a family all its own, which has the perching habit, coloration and deeply forked tail of a swallow but the long scimitar wings of the swifts and a clean, lunging flight combining the best features of both families. . . . White Kites, their flight between a falcon's and a small gull's. . . . Chestnut-headed Bee-eaters like foot-long swallows, mainly metallic green and blue, with long, thin bills, long tails and, when volplaning, the purposeful lines of fighter aircraft. . . . Dyal Thrushes resembling Mockingbirds in formal black-and-white attire. . . . Orange-headed Thrushes compounding the build and proclivities of our Robin with the soft and dreamy quality of the Bluebird. . . . A Malay Eagle-owl, with enormous talons and hooked beak in a visage from a totem pole, its presence betrayed by the vociferous attacks of a pair of Large-billed Ravens and the screams of Bulbuls. . . .

So it goes until I come to the Black-naped Oriole, which moved me to as near an avowal as I dared come in an article for *Audubon Magazine* of the sense I have, where the tropical fertility of plants and birds seems to breathe upon the moist and scented air, of a profound and tantalizing, close yet elusive spirit epitomizing and resolving it all—everything—the observable and the unknowable together. I saw the oriole and heard its voice in the great botanical gardens of Buitenzorg, now Bogor.

"The song is short and beside the extended performances of the Dyals and Bulbuls is to be compared to a six-note finger exercise, the alternate notes sharply ascending the scale, those intervening falling back a tone or two. It can be imitated with poor fidelity if you whistle with your jaw lowered as far as possible, using your tongue as a stop. A comparison for the rich and reverberant tone of the notes is impossible to find, however. Sounding from the dome of one of those mighty, buttressed trees, mingled with the dripping of the foliage from the last rain, the golden, flute-like notes of that golden bird, unmuted by distance, evoke the mood in which one first read Hudson's *Green Mansions*. It is as if some forest being, to whose voice humanity has long been deaf, were calling from a world before time began."

Wherever you go on this earth—or very nearly—you will find birds closely resembling if not identical to those at home; the Common Swallow pacing the train out of Amritsar is the swallow Charles Algernon Swinburne and Alfred Lord Tennyson wrote of and the one that nests in cowsheds across the United States as the Barn Swallow, *Hirundo rustica;* the nuthatch upside down on the frangipani tree at Buitenzorg essentially the one on the oak in Bronx Park but with black velvet on its forehead. You will find others recognizably kin to the familiar, still others greatly different. Yet even the least alike are totally birds, exemplifications of the avian, with which a basis of acquaintance already exists. Foreign avifaunas make the appeal of variations on a theme—ingenious, subtle, daring, inspired, infinite—which is close to the appeal of music and as difficult to define. They also help us see afresh, as the novel and unexpected do, where habit dulls perception. The incentive to travel is inexhaustible for ornithophiles—or so we must judge from the case of Barbara and Roger Tory Peterson, who have probably seen more of the earth at eye-level than any other couple alive or dead.

Yet the opposite is true, too. Ornithophiles have special reason for contentment if required to remain at home. For birds bring much of the world to us. Where most of us live, the arctic reigns for part of the year, the tropics for another, and as we follow birds we appreciate how much this is so. They are a conduit to the woods, fields and watersides where Nature rules out of sight of man. They are themselves, too, in large numbers creatures from afar, coming to us from treeline and tundra, orchid-decked rain-forest and coral beach. Among them, now and again, will be a wanderer or rider of the gale, a true exotic, which ordinarily we should have to travel a thousand miles or two to see. You never know what day, what hour may bring one. I had no premonition when on a walk near our house I looked up to behold with heart suddenly drained, flying steadily northward, a large black-and-white bird long and tapering of wings and tail I had last seen in spirited flight above the Amazonian forest—a Swallow-tailed Kite! (High in favor with the gods I must have stood that day; ten seconds later I should have missed it.) But with our regulars, too, there is a perennial newness. It may be, as Shakespeare says, that "the cuckoo in June,/Heard, not regarded," but winter will come, and after it April again. The freshness of birds, as of the first time seen, is as unfading as that of spring flowers and the autumn coloring of leaves.

# ___3
# THE NATURE OF BIRDS

### Birds' Unique Advantage

Of all the classes of animals, I believe that birds would be most sorely missed if they vanished—and I should explain that I am speaking not of practical consequences and am excluding domesticated breeds. Mankind, like other species, has been habituated through its long history of struggle for survival in conditions of nature to respond to natural phenomena. We need sensory stimuli, and of the kind nature affords, it seems to me, to feel wholly alive. The animated presences of birds lend movement, variety and warmth to vistas of land and sea. The living earth seems to speak to us through them in accents we understand and find congenial; they make us feel part of that earth. There are human beings, it is evident, who can get along without that reassurance. They would not suffer a demoralizing sense of deprivation in a world lacking birds or other creatures to fill the void the departure of birds would leave. They would not be dispirited in an inert natural landscape. The excitations of the metropolis serve for them: the glitter and throb, the pace, the press of myriad-faced humanity, the very absence of repose without anodynes. Yet one may suspect that a keyed-up dependence on artifice means living on the nerves and that the race as a whole could not long endure it.

Birds account for a disproportionate amount of our perception of nature not only because their flight, song and colors make them noticeable as well as appealing but because they are nearly ubiquitous. And as it is human invention that has enabled men to extend their realm to the farthest reaches of

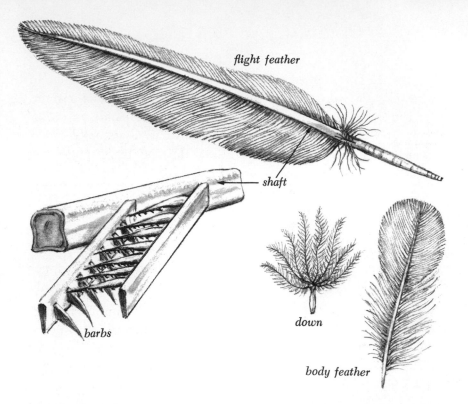

flight feather

shaft

barbs

down

body feather

the planet, it is a masterpiece of Nature's that has enabled birds
to do so: the feather.

Fine feathers will not alone make fine birds, Aesop tells us.
I should think they would go a long way toward it, however,
for it is feathers that make birds. All birds and no other creatures have them. To examine a feather, to see it as it is, is to
marvel that engineering skill, let alone a mindless one, could
have designed from the horny substance of which fingernails
are made an instrument so beautifully answerable to the varied
and exacting demands made on it.

The form ranges from the fluffy to the stiff (you can sleep in
down or write with a quill) and from the nearly round and
cupped to the nearly linear. But characteristically the feather
is an oblong plane, a vane, given longitudinal rigidity by a
median hollow shaft extending almost to its end. To precisely
the required degree it is elastic and flexible, especially toward
its margins. So fine in structure as to be translucent and if not
too heavily pigmented even almost transparent, it is also extremely strong for its weight—and it provides our simile for

*The Nature of Birds* /67

lightness. The muffled thunder of a grouse's whirring wings in the take-off expresses the force the frail-seeming sails sustain.

The vane is a web of fine ribs rooted to the shaft on either side and called barbs because they extend diagonally backward from the point of the feather, the end from which the shaft projects. The barbs are themselves very like feathers. Each consists of a central shaft fringed on either side with what might also be called barbs but are known as barbules. These bear microscopic hooks on one side and flanges on the other. The hooks of one barbule engage with the flanges on the adjacent barb, somewhat as the two sides of a zipper interlock. When the vane of a feather is rent a bird need only pass the two edges through its beak to rejoin the barbs on either side and heal it, as a zippered opening is closed by running the slide up it. A large flight feather may have 500 barbs on either side of the shaft and as many barbules, on the average, on either side of each barb.

Feathers, writes Joel Carl Welty in *The Life of Birds* (a foundation in ornithology for any serious birder), "exhibit the most highly evolved and precisely adapted epidermal structures known." That they originated as reptilian scales, such as still cover the tarsi and feet of most birds, there can be no doubt. In the absence of any other explanation it must be supposed that the transformation took place by the process of natural selection. That is to say, each deviation in the form of scales in the direction of feathers occurring in an individual by freak of birth—an abnormality—tended to improve the individual's chances of survival and, passed on to some of its descendants, theirs also. That a scale's stark simplicity could have been turned into a feather's subtle, complicated, ingenious artistry by so hit-or-miss a process is at first blush incredible, at least to me. But . . . imagine the transfiguration as being brought about by several thousand successive, minute changes in design, each change requiring a thousand years to appear and become established. It begins to come within the conceivable. And two or three million years, while far beyond human grasp, are not an immoderate withdrawal from the earth's store of time. Nature could spend twice as much for the passage of a miracle and scarcely notice the difference.

No fossils have been found of epidermal structures intermediate between scales and feathers. Nothing in the fossil record foretells feathers. Feathers appear, evidently fully evolved, on the first discovered bird. But then we know the raven-sized *Archaeopteryx* itself—the "ancient wing"—from only three fossils and have no idea how widely it was distributed or what came after it, let alone before, for millions of years. *Archaeopteryx*, which climbed, glided and flew weakly and with an effort among cycads and tree-ferns when it was not walking about beneath them in what is now Bavaria 140 million years ago, was not a fully evolved bird. It retained three claws at the bend of the wing and a slender tail like a lizard's from which feathers grew laterally. Its snout-like beak was toothed. Still, it was a bird; it was feathered. There in the middle chapter of the Mesozoic—the Jurassic—the die was cast. Evolution had taken a decisive turn. From a proliferation of avian species in the last chapter of the Mesozoic—the Cretaceous—in which dinosaurs yielded to mammals and flowering plants took over the land, came, with gathering momentum, the triumphant, multiform, winged hosts of the past 60 million years—the Cenozoic.

Because feathers serve the purpose of flight uniquely well it is natural to assume that they developed as an adjunct to wings. There rises in the mind the picture of a small, slightly-built reptile leaping squirrel-like from tree to tree, spreading its forelimbs to give itself added planing surface. Such a habit on the part of certain arboreal mammals led to the Flying Squirrel and Flying Phalanger, neither of which fly, and bats, which do. It is hypothesized that the practice was favorable to the attenuation and fraying of the scales on the hind edge of the forelimbs, turning them eventually into feathers, on wings.

But this explanation presents difficulties. It hardly accounts for the transformation of the body scales into feathers; feathers do not spread by underground runners like grass. It leaves unanswered, moreover, the question of why the gliding ability was not achieved by the progenitor of birds as it was among other vertebrates that took this course. In these, the skin, which was already available, was extended in a membrane joining the limbs on either side. Winged reptiles—pterosaurs—did of course come into being through just such an adaptation, and some were giants. One with a wing-spread of 26 or 27 feet was believed for many years to have been the largest. Fossil bones discovered in the American west in 1975, however, have been interpreted as relics of one with an incredible span of over 50.

Had the ancestors of birds evolved as did the flying reptiles, there, probably, would have been the end of it. While the pterosaurs may have been capable of remaining in the air by the hour, it is doubtful that they actually flew. They evidently depended on the power not of their wings but of the winds to carry and sustain them aloft. We may picture them launching from the ledges of sea cliffs to coast above the waves and snatch up food, then ascend on the wind, no doubt with some beating of their leathery wings. Albatrosses, which have similarly long, narrow wings, depend correspondingly on ocean airs to do most of their work for them. They may be seen borne along above the combers that deflect the wind upward or create wind of their own in their passage. Accompanying a ship, they hang in the air above it for mile upon mile with scarcely a motion of their wings, playing gravity off against the impetus of the wind. An albatross requires a brisk head wind to lift it from the water, and even then must run along the surface into it, while on land it requires at least a slope from which to launch itself. Much too weak-legged to run, a downed pterosaur might have been raised from the crest of a wave by a strong wind under its great sails. On land, it would have had to claw its way back up to some kind of eminence. Any monster of 50-foot wing-spread, even a dry-land carrion-feeder, as the newly reconstructed one is thought to have been on the strength of its long neck, would surely have been under this necessity.

What the winged reptiles lacked for true flight was the bony

keel to anchor the powerful pectoral muscles required for aerial propulsion and, probably, the metabolism required to fuel the muscles. They could not have become flyers like bats. They were cold-blooded. Or at least so most students believe. And therein, we may believe, lies the clue to the development of feathers.

If so, it was the advantage of warm-bloodedness, which requires insulation, that commenced the remodeling of scales into the soft, filmy coverlets that clothe a bird. Feathers cloaking a body enable it to maintain a high temperature even in sub-zero cold. That, elongated and strengthened by a thickening of the shaft, they also make flight possible, would have been secondary.

Mammalian creatures had appeared well before *Archaeopteryx*. Warm-bloodedness, though birds were to achieve it independently, had already been invented, presumably beneath insulating hairy coats. It was only their ability to function in the cold, which reptiles could not, that enabled the mammals to hold out in the reign of the dinosaurs and eventually to triumph over them. But our furry forerunners were furtive, skulking, shrew-like little animals. Birds, being descended from bipedal reptiles with strongly developed hindquarters— unlike the pterosaurs, by the way—may be imagined in their early form, before we should have called them birds, escaping their predators by sprinting for cover or hopping up among the branches of trees, assisting themselves with their fore-claws. (They may also have run down and consumed their predators' newly-hatched young.) The more the survival of the fittest—in this case the fleetest or most agile—changed scales to make them more like feathers, the faster the proto-birds could get about and the less they were handicapped by cold. We may visualize them dashing over uneven ground with lengthening stride and clearing wider depressions as they ran, or leaping from a tree to a lower part of another. Those that spread their forelimbs performed better than those that did not, and those with longer feathery projections from the hind edge of the forelimbs and the tail better than those without. It might be said that when the first proto-bird drew its legs up on taking off from a height, the eagle, the swallow and the hummingbird were inevitable. By the time *Tyrannosaurus* appeared to spread terror across the land, there were birds in the tree-tops to give warning cries of its approach. The dinosaurs did not survive the Mesozoic, and fairly early in the Cenozoic birds produced some rather fearsome carnivores of their own. *Diatryma* stood about seven feet high and struck with an axe-blade beak; *Phororhacos*, which came a little later, about five feet and had the head and massive, hooked beak of a griffin. Both were of course flightless.

### The Abandonment of Flight

The virtues of the feather warrant an encomium. While enlarging on them, however, an admirer must acknowledge that in the course of evolution many species of birds of diverse orders have abandoned flight. Some have done so for the advantage of size, like *Diatryma* and *Phororhacus*. The largest living birds capable of flight, according to Fisher and Peterson, are the big swans and the Great Bustard of the lower half of Eurasia, and the neighborhood of 50 pounds is the record even for these; individuals in the 30's would be considered large. Even *Gigantornis*, a contemporary of *Diatryma*'s and supposedly an albatross-like bird with a wingspread of around 20 feet—almost twice that of today's largest albatross—probably weighed no more.

The limit to the size of flying birds is set by a physical law of crucial importance to the forms of living things. As size increases, volume increases much faster than surface—one as the cube of the diameter, the other as the square. In a two-story building with four rooms on a floor, each a corner room, all eight rooms will have three outside surfaces: two walls and a floor or ceiling. But double the size of the building in all dimensions so that it is four rooms wide, four rooms deep and four rooms (or stories) high. Of the 64 rooms it now contains, still only eight will have three outside surfaces—one-eighth of the total—while three-eighths of the total will have but two outside surfaces, another three-eighths but one and one-eighth no outside surface at all. Room for room, the larger house will require much less heat in winter. So with animals: the larger they are the smaller their surface in relation to volume and the easier for them to keep warm. Thus cold-climate forms tend to be larger than their warm-climate equivalent. The farther north you go, beginning in the tropics, the larger grow the bears, wolves, mice and falcons. Of the penguins, the smallest breed in Australia and on the Galapagos Islands, within six degrees of the Equator, while the largest, the Emperor, is the most exposed to antarctic cold. Tropical elephants are large, yes, but not as large as Ice Age mammoths—or Bengal tigers as Siberian.

Volume is of advantage to birds in helping them maintain warmth, resist predators, overcome prey and vanquish rivals. (If a large animal has to eat more, absolutely, than a similar small one, it can eat more at once and not have to eat as often.) But if they are to fly they also need a lot of surface in proportion to volume. As their size increases, so does the effort required to get them air-borne. A turkey much larger than those in the wild could not get off the ground no matter how much muscle it developed; its growing weight with the added muscle would be increasingly more than it could lift, given its form. Up to a point birds can overcome the surface-volume bind by spreading out, just as all the rooms in a large building can be given outside exposure by making the building only two rooms deep. Employing the principle of the glider, birds larger than any ever seen in the skies could remain aloft almost indefinitely with little muscular exertion, at least in favorable conditions. But they would have to put down sometime. And the difficulty would be in rising again. Species of great wing area require a long taxiing surface, strong head winds or a height to drop from. With increasing size, these needs become exorbitant and over-restrictive. In the Frigatebird, with a seven-foot spread of narrow, tapering wings, the weight of feathers and flying muscles makes up almost half the whole. The black marauder is supremely adapted to the air, or so one is convinced who has seen it coasting high overhead, as unmoving as a painted silhouette on a pane of glass drawn across the sky, or overhauling with dazzling speed another sea-bird trying to get by with a newly-caught fish. But, too weak-footed to run for a take-off as swans, bustards and most sea-birds do, whether on land or water, it has great difficulty rising from either and ordinarily puts down only on trees or shrubs or channel-markers.

The largest birds outgrew flight far back in avian history. The Ostrich of Africa, the Rhea of South America, the Emu of central Australia—all plains-dwellers—and the Cassowary of the New Guinean and Australian tropical forest have massive bodies carried horizontally on powerful legs and relatively small heads on long necks. Among them, however, only the Emu and Cassowary have a resemblance possibly traceable to relationship. For the rest, their similarities derive from their common approach to life: all might have set out to model themselves on the hoofed animals. They can run at the speed of a racehorse; and, like a buck at bay, an Ostrich or Cassowary can disembowel an enemy, including man, with slashing strokes of its heavily-nailed feet. An Ostrich can even run with a small human being on its back. The largest of existing birds, it achieves a stature of eight or nine feet in height and weighs up to almost 350 pounds. But two groups of similarly-built birds, wiped out by man in the past five to seven centuries, were much larger. The greatest of the New Zealand Moas stood 13 feet high and must have weighed over 500 pounds, the greatest of the Elephant-birds of Madagascar, though three or four feet shorter, almost half a ton. The eggs of the latter, which are still being found, had a volume of two gallons, equal to over eight dozen chickens' eggs. Incidentally, the smallest hummingbird is only two and one-quarter inches in length, including bill and tail, and weighs but one-twelfth of an ounce, less than one-fortieth the weight of a Goliath Beetle. High in surface relative to volume, it has to eat half its weight in food a day to maintain itself. Some hummingbirds actually get through the chill Andean night by sinking into torpor with greatly lowered temperatures. The smallest mammals, the tiny shrews, must spend virtually all their time in quest of food, and the fact that the tiniest is the same weight as the smallest hummingbird suggests that nothing smaller is possible for warm-blooded life.

Not only the pursuit of size has cost birds the power of flight. More have lost it in the absence of predators requiring them to fly; in nature's exacting economy, that which is not used atrophies. Some, including a teal, two steamer-ducks, a cormorant, several rails and the illustrious Dodo with two of its relatives, are or were inhabitants of small islands. Some evolved, or retrogressed, if one prefers, in New Zealand, which is without native mammals, among them the Kiwi, *Notornis* (a strange, gallinule-like bird); the wattled crows (which can hardly fly); and even a large nocturnal parrot, the Kakapo. Some exchanged aerial flight for aquatic.

The sea, in which life originated, seems never to lose its attraction for its progeny. Reptiles, with their dry, impermeable skins and leathery-shelled eggs, had freed vertebrate life from the necessity of direct association with water and opened the continental interiors to conquest. But then some were drawn back to the sea to become huge marine lizards called mosasaurs, plesiosaurs with paddle-limbs, shark-like ichthyosaurs and—still surviving—sea turtles. To the seas of the last chapter of the Mesozoic, which these creatures inhabited, birds also returned. One group at least, to which the name *Hesperornis* has been given, became not only flightless but wingless; loon-like in appearance, but six feet long and toothed, the Hesperornids propelled themselves with large, lobed feet evidently sticking out to the sides like Charlie Chaplin's. They lasted a long time, 25 million years, and witnessed the appearance of another group of birds making an irreversible commitment to the marine environment: penguins. With these the wings became powerful flippers. The adaptation was so complete that no vestige of flight quills remains on them, and some ornithologists have believed that the penguin stock had always been flightless. The discovery of rudimentary flight quills in penguin embryos would appear to confirm what others had maintained, that the change came about in the long course of time because the proto-penguins used their wings to fly under water. The stockier those appendages became, the more poorly their wielders performed in the air and the better in the water.

Today we can see another group of sea-birds apparently midway in this evolutionary process, though we cannot know that they will proceed farther with it. The black-and-white divingbirds we call alcids may be considered the Northern Hemisphere counterparts of the penguins. They fly well, though presumably not as well as their ancestors, from which the gulls are also descended; but, heavy-bodied and feeble-gaited, they are more at home in the water than anywhere else. The largest of them, the Great Auk—which, by the way, was the first bird to bear the name penguin—was of course wholly flightless. It was also so helpless on land that sailors putting ashore on the island sites of its breeding colonies were able simply to herd the luckless and usually unsuspicious fowl to their doom. This they did for the fish-bait, feather bedding and oil the small bodies provided. Thus we rewarded the species whose flesh had helped Neanderthal man and our Neolithic forebears through the terrible Ice Age winters, as the bones at their camp sites attest.

The fate of the Great Auk illustrates the peril to which the flightless birds have been exposed by man's appearance on the scene and the recent explosive extension of his dominion. Any animal that hoped to share the earth with its new lord would, it was evident some time ago, have had to be adept at escape and preferably more valuable to our kind alive than dead. (Fortunately for our fellow animals, this value in some human quarters anyway may be non-material—aesthetic, emotional, of a kind no other animal could recognize—man being an ambivalent creature who, mired in carnage, gropes for the infinite.) The penguins might well have gone the way of the Great Auk but for the remoteness of their haunts. As it was, one reads of horrifying slaughters of penguins, as in the Falkland Islands. There the number butchered and rendered for their oil in the past century is said to have run to the scores of millions. Many flightless species have been exterminated by man and the predators he has brought with him, intentionally or otherwise; the Dodo, for instance, fell victim to the combined depredations of sailors and pigs released in an island home, Mauritius. In the gloomy chronicle of extinctions one reads with perhaps disproportionate gratification of the return of two species from the dead. *Notornis*, the gallinule-like bird of New Zealand, was believed wiped out by the turn of the century, then in 1948, astonishingly, a few breeding pairs were found in a remote fastness of the South Island. In 1974, in a similar area of the South Island, five remaining Kakapos—the flightless parrots—were found.

### Nature's Supreme Insulator

However many birds have abandoned flight, and for what varied reasons, none that we know of ever abandoned feathers. Feathers are too satisfactory a solution to too many needs to be given up. The Cetaceans—whales and dolphins—found hair inadequate as a protection against the cold of the sea and exchanged it for a veneer of blubber. Blubber also protects seals, whose fur is chiefly of use out of the water. But feathers are what serve the purpose with birds that brave the depths, forming a sleek, streamlined, water-repellent envelope, flexible and padded, keeping the bird within dry and warm. Penguins, the most marine of birds, are uniquely well-equipped in this respect, for where in other birds feathers grow in separate tracts, in penguins they grow solidly, in unbroken ranks. Because their flippers provide their sole means of propulsion, penguins at the surface generally remain submerged to their backs. The contrary is true of other swimming birds. In most of these the broad feathers of the flank form pockets into which the wings fit, flight pinions protruding behind, so that, as the Heinroths, Katherina and Oskar, ornithologists of Berlin, remark in *The Birds*, "they swim around in a kind of canoe which keeps the body and wings dry."

In one marine mammal, the sea-otter, fur holds air and keeps the water away from the swimmer's body as feathers do. But it does not hold so much. No mammal or, for that matter, any other creature can ride high in the water like a bird. And retention of air is the secret of insulation; no solid resists the transfer of heat and cold as still air does. A bird moves about in a captive atmosphere, and two kinds of feather structure play a part in its containment. Shield-like contour feathers make up a shingled outer surface. Beneath this is down, which, like the vanes of feathers, is formed of barbs, but barbs lacking barbules so that they stand free, soft yet springy. The lower part of the contour feathers is downy and there are special feathers wholly of down. By fluffing up a bird can expand the layer of still air around it and gain further protection from heat loss.

For retaining air a coat of contour feathers over down has no equal. No mammal or, again, any other form of life—or any but the simplest in a state of dormancy—could endure the cold that birds face in the Polar regions. Least of all could any stand, almost unmoving, for two months through the bitter antarctic winter as male Emperor penguins do, and without eating, lashed by gales and wind-driven snow, each incubating an egg in a fold of skin between the legs, until "the females, sleek, glossy, fat and full of food, come tobogganing in over the ice"—in Oliver L. Austin, Jr.'s charming vignette in *Birds of the World*—"to relieve their mates and care for the chicks." That the ordeal costs the males between 30 and 50 per cent of their weight, according to Michael Fedak of Duke University, is not so surprising as that they survive at all.

The same epidermal structures that fit birds to come through Polar blasts keep them active and chirpy in desert sunshine that sends other creatures to their burrows or into the deepest shade. Contour feathers repel the punishing rays. Flight feathers take birds to the tops of shrubs or tall cacti and to temperatures as much as 50 or 60 degrees below those on the ground, where any animal unable to escape would soon be fried.

## The Mechanics of Flight

Birds did not invent flight. Insects did, two hundred million years before the first bird took wing, even before reptiles had appeared. But in what we think of as mastery of the air—the ability to turn the properties of air and its movement to the greatest advantage—birds are supreme. Insects, lacking mass, cannot develop the momentum that birds' evolutions require. With the exception of moths and butterflies, some of which flap and glide momentarily, superficially in the manner of birds —and have been found fluttering along, hundreds of miles at sea—insects practise a whirring or buzzing flight. In the sense in which birds and airplanes have wings, insects in general have not. They have propellers. In principle, they are helicopters, as are hummingbirds, not with revolving blades, of course, but with reciprocating.

Like winged reptiles and bats, birds almost certainly began as gliders, coasting from a higher elevation to a lower. Probably much of their evolution to their present form took place while their aeronautic capabilities did not much exceed those of the flying-squirrel today. *Archaeopteryx* would suggest as much. Gradually the changing use and design of their outer wings gave them propellers—reciprocating, again—and the planet was open to them. They became powered gliders, like conventional airplanes though far more efficient and adept and in harmony within themselves and with the medium in which they operate. With the notable exception of the hummingbirds, they did not go all out for power as the generality of insects did, and had to if they were not to be encumbered by sails, like a butterfly, and be incapable of speed.

The more of its time a bird spends in the air (again excepting the hummingbirds), the more its design is that of a glider. At one extreme are the flightless runners like the Ostrich, in which there is nothing the least glider-like. Farther along are the gallinaceous birds. By preference they use their legs for locomotion, but they can launch into the air with dramatic rapidity and fly well if not far. They are somewhat bee-like in proportions and in their high-powered, whirring flight, but they can sail on set wings for short distances. At the top of the form are the albatrosses that can sail by the hour with only trifling movements of their extremely long, narrow wings, which man has copied in the gliders he has fashioned for himself.

As a glider should, a bird that is much on the wing has the form that offers the least practicable resistance to the air through which it must pass. Its body in flight is streamlined, close to the shape a drop of water assumes in falling, the shape, that is, in which the pressure of the air is evenly distributed over the body and thus has the least possible retarding effect on it. Its wing in cross-section is also streamlined, and in this, too, the bird has provided man with a model in the design of his airplanes. The leading edge, thickened by the bones and muscles just behind it, is further thickened and rounded by the tightly-packed, sickle-shaped little feathers that grow out from it and bend back. From there the feathering is so disposed that the wing tapers to the rear, or trailing, edge. The principal feathers of the wing, the flight feathers, are themselves tapered. Of these, the secondaries, which are set at right angles to the bone, chiefly forming the vane of the inner wing, have the same direction as the air-stream and are tapered from stem to end. The primaries chiefly form the vane of the outer wing. The initial primaries have the same direction as the bone, which in effect they extend, and are at right angles to the air-stream. Not only are they tapered from stem to end, like the secondaries and the wing itself, but, again like the wing itself, they are streamlined in cross-section from the leading edge to the trailing. This is the effect of the placement of the shaft close to the leading edge and the tapering of the barbs that extend back from it.

To glide, an object must have momentum as well as a planing surface, such as wings or lateral membranes provide. Otherwise it will simply tumble to the ground, planing surface or no.

In simple gliding from a higher to a lower elevation, gravity provides the power that the glider turns into forward momentum. The drawback here is, of course, that the glider must climb to an eminence before each glide or fly to a greater height; as Leonardo da Vinci noted, "When there is no wind stirring in the air, the kite beats its wings several times during flight and acquires impetus; it then glides down with that impetus, going slowly without beating its wings; and when it has come down, it repeats the action." (The aerially-versatile kite was Leonardo's favorite bird.) It does not invalidate the principle to recognize that the generality of birds in flight are gliding continuously, between and during wing-beats, which is what distinguishes their flight from the generality of insects'. While their gliding is dependent on their wing-beats to recover the elevation lost between beats, their flight is still much more efficient than power-flight alone would be, just as ice-skating is much more efficient than running. That is to say, the one takes you much farther for the same expenditure of energy than the other.

Certain categories of birds are gliding *virtuosi*. Among soaring and sailing birds, gliding has been freed of dependence on power-flight. Such skilled aeronauts, of which the Turkey Vulture is one of the most familiar, can coast at will as long as you keep them in sight without a wing-beat or loss of elevation, if conditions are right. They are like ships that sail the seven seas under canvas alone, with the big difference that they must utilize the air currents not only to propel them forward but to maintain them aloft. Human pilots of man-made gliders have proved able, where the air currents are favorable, to remain borne on them for many hours. They are hardly, however, in a class with birds that travel for thousands of miles without use of their wings for propulsion except from time to time to give them a start when they have had to put down, Broad-winged Hawks from Canada to South America, Wandering Albatrosses around the world of the southern oceans.

Soaring means circling higher and higher in more or less the same place, sailing keeping more or less the same elevation but moving from place to place, both without wing-beats. Each being gliding, birds that are good at one are good at the other. The soarers, of which the vultures, Buteos and storks are typical, exploit the lightness of warm air, which causes it to rise, to do their work for them. It enables them to glide continuously on a downward slope in a medium that is going up faster than they are descending. Carried high by such an updraft, they can coast to the next and repeat the performance.

Sailers depend on the winds, but on one of two special conditions of wind. Wind striking an obstruction and being deflected upward provides a rising billow of air upon which a sailing bird can coast, again gliding downward in a rising medium. Migrating hawks utilize the updrafts thus created on the windward side of mountain ridges and sea-birds the updrafts created on the windward side of combers, also, as chance may offer, the upward deflection of the wind by ships. Regions of the ocean where steady winds prevail offer sea-birds another source of energy to exploit. Strong at a height above the water, such winds will be slowed near it by the braking action of the waves. A sailing bird, like a gull or a procellarine, can glide to leeward down nearly to the surface of the water, picking up momentum and then, swerving around to face in the direction from which it had come, convert its momentum into forward impetus and be borne upward, like a kite, by the lifting force of the wind, which, accelerating with height, compensates for decrease of momentum. "If a bird descends toward the south while there is a north wind" and "makes its reflex motion into and on the wind, it will rise much more than it would from natural impetus, since it is favored by the wind." So observed the astonishing Leonardo over four and a half centuries ago. "But when it is at the end of its climb it will have used up its impetus," he added, "and will have only the favoring wind left." Having regained its previous elevation, however, it will be in a position to repeat the maneuver. By the hour from decks of ships I have watched gulls execute the maneuver—not for purposes of travel, since they returned to the ship each time, but evidently just for sport—but I can still only assume that the official explanation is correct in assigning crucial importance to the increase in speed of the wind with elevation.

In sum: if you were designing a glider you would recognize that power would have to be applied to it to keep it moving through the air, if not the power of a propeller, then that of air currents. You would also recognize that the more streamlined the body and the wings in cross-section the less power would be required for the same ends. However, you would also do well to recognize (as you doubtless would) that if the wings were perfectly streamlined and set horizontally, the glider would sink to earth no matter how much forward impetus it were given. (Regardless of its muzzle velocity, a bullet fired from a horizontal barrel and one dropped from the barrel at the same time will hit the ground simultaneously.) Some of that forward impetus has to be converted into lift. Birds achieve this through two departures from streamlining, both followed by man in the design of his airplanes.

First, the upper surface of the wing is made more convex, slightly bulged out, and the lower is flattened or even made slightly concave. The result, says John H. Storer, a motion-picture photographer, in his classic *The Flight of Birds*, is that "the air stream over the curved upper surface must go farther, and hence faster, to keep pace with the shorter lower stream and rejoin it at the rear or trailing edge. With its higher velocity the upper stream will put less downward pressure on the upper surface, and the greater upward pressure from below will then exert a lifting force." Again, I am not sure I understand, but the bird's wing, so designed, does work.

That the second departure from streamlining should provide lift is obvious. The wing is tilted—given an upward slope to the front. In consequence, the air-stream, hitting the lower surface at an angle, pushes it upward and, overshooting the upper, tends to create a vacuum above it, which sucks it up. Clearly there is a price. That potential vacuum above and behind the canted wing, which provides most of the lift, also applies a drag. When the wing is set at a low angle to the air-stream, drag is very small compared with lift. As the angle increases, increasing lift, the potential vacuum expands, increasing drag, until the air-stream parts from the upper surface of the wing and breaks up into turbulence. We have all seen how in a rapids the water will in some conditions flow smoothly over a boulder, in others eddy foamingly behind it. In the case of a wing moving through the air, when turbulence develops it creates a drag sufficient to overcome forward impetus and cause the bird or glider to stall, as the term is. The higher the angle of the wing, the greater the speed required to prevent turbulence from developing.

For a bird as for an airplane the danger of stalling is greatest at low speed and therefore in take-offs and landings. The problem is to maintain headway at such a speed with the wing angle high enough to provide lift. Since I could not think of even a theoretical solution to the problem, I might expect the undirected processes of evolution to have been utterly incapable of coming up with one. But that would be to underestimate the powers of invention that go with those processes. Nature discerned that what was needed was to increase air speed over the upper surface of the wing without having to increase the speed of the wing, and that this could be done by forcing the air-stream through a slot in front of and above the wing. That was very smart. But where was the slot to come from? Nature picked on the bird's free-standing thumb for the role. By the growth of a set of stiff feathers from it, it was made over into a little auxiliary wing—the false wing or alula, we call it—which when raised compresses the air-stream and deflects it down against the wing. (This device, too, has its parallel in a comparable structure on the leading edge of airplane wings.) The first primary, when it rises above its mates, may also serve this purpose.

Leonardo did not overlook the alula, but he thought it served to maintain equilibrium. His keen interest in flight made birds a natural object of his attention, and he gave them a great deal. He liked them for themselves, too, and would buy caged birds at the market to give them their freedom—not neglecting to observe the action of their wings as they embarked upon it.

Yet it appears that he mistook that action. "When the bird wishes to rise by beating its wings," he wrote, "it raises its shoulders and beats the tips of its wing toward itself and condenses the air between the points of its wings and the bird's breast, and the tension thereof lifts the bird up." If Leonardo did not grasp the mechanics of a bird's propulsion we may be sure that no one else did, either, or was going to for a long time—until, as far as I know, the invention of high-speed photography. (Not that they are fully understood yet.) And Leonardo left some suggestive observations on the subject. "The hand of the bird is that which causes the impetus," he declared, correctly; for it is the bones of the hand, simplified as they are in birds, that the instruments of thrust, the primaries, are attached to. Of them, he wrote, "That the expanse of the wing is not all employed in compressing the air; and to see that this is so, note that the interstices between the primary feathers are much greater in width than the breadth of the feathers." That was an important clue.

The original view, which Leonardo evidently held, was that birds progressed by rowing motions, drawing their wings up and extending them forward only to deliver the powerful back-thrust which sent them forward. We now know that the telling thrust is delivered on the down-and-forward beat of the wing. This is so because of the design and action of the primaries. They are louvered, and the pressure of air against them as the wing is pressed forward and downward causes them to separate and slope upward from front to back. Biting into the air like the propeller blades they are, they pull the wing after them and the bird with it. Other feathers also play a part. The secondaries and adjacent primaries, which grow more flexible from stem to tip with the narrowing of the shaft, bend at the ends under the pressure of air during the wing-beat and this, too, impels the bird forward. In this they act like the flexible flippers that divers attach to their feet and work up and down as they swim. The impetus is delivered on both strokes.

The wing in the recovery stroke is brought backward (not forward as it would be in rowing or swimming) but chiefly upward. At the same time it is flexed at the mid-wing joint—the wrist—so that the outer wing is drawn inward toward the body as the inner wing rises. When the inner wing reaches its maximum elevation the outer wing is pointing downward; the bird seen end-on approximates the form of an M. In a continuing movement the outer wing is pulled up and back, the wing straightening out. In this process the primaries in small birds open at such an angle that they cut through the air edge-on, knifing through it with negligible effect on the bird's progress. Larger birds, in which the wing has to do more work in relation to its size, cannot afford to let their propeller blades remain in neutral during half the wing movement. Accordingly, on the recovery stroke the wings are so twisted as to bring their upper surface to face almost as much rearward as upward, with the result that the primaries now slope *down* to the rear and open out (remember that they overlap in an order the reverse of shingles) to press upward against the air and propel the bird forward.

The primary is a marvel of nature—a cliché one tries to use sparingly despite the abundant occasion for it. As Storer reminds us, every point on a moving propeller, whether the blade revolves or beats back and forth, goes through a wider arc than the points nearer the inner end. And that means that "each fraction of the blade moves faster than its inner neighbor." But to do its work best, the greater the speed of the propeller, the less its slope should be with respect to the air into which it is biting, and the less its speed the more its slope should be. "To be efficient," as Storer observes, "the blade must be designed with its angle, or pitch, constantly changing from hub to tip, in order to give an even amount of forward drive through its whole length. A bird's propeller feathers achieve this changing pitch, or twist, by an ingenious design of quill and vanes which gives the proper angle in response to the pressure of the air." Moreover, "a bird's propeller can swing through only a semicircle; it must then return to its former position and start over again, completely changing its shape and pitch while doing so. It must be ready to go into reverse or to become a helicopter blade to lift the bird straight upward." Finally, "if the bird wants to glide, the propeller changes its function and becomes merely a part of the main lifting wing, with the added job of keeping the bird balanced." Withal, "it must, of course, take the right shape for each job automatically in response to changes in air pressure."

The design of the wing itself depends on the use to which it is put. Moderately long wings tapering to a point and somewhat bent back give falcons, shorebirds, swallows and swifts exceptional speed combined with endurance—but are inferior sails for soaring and unhandy among trees. Short, wide, cupped wings enable gallinaceous birds, and others to the extent that they share them, to take off fast and zoom between branches but require high energy output. So do a hummingbird's insect-type wings, which, as Storer puts it, seem "to be all propeller, set on a swivel joint at the shoulder" and "can be rotated to drive the bird forward, upward or backward, or to permit hovering in the air." (A hummingbird's wing-muscles may account for 30 per cent of its weight, and its fuel consumption for its size is the highest in the Class Aves.) The longest and narrowest wings are the best for gliding—and the poorest for getting off the ground or water.

Small birds, with the exception of hummingbirds, tend to have larger wings proportionately than do birds of greater size. Joel Carl Welty points out in *The Life of Birds* that if a Mute Swan had the same wing area for its weight as a Barn Swallow, its two wings would have 81,000 square centimeters of surface instead of the 6,800 they do have and if of the same shape would be seven meters long, giving the bird a wing-span of 46 feet. That is just about what the newly-discovered pterosaur is said to have had, but with wings only a quarter that length a swan could not get into the air at all in a calm from a lake or level ground. Moreover, to flap wings of such extent would require bones and muscles of such size as to make them prohibitively heavy. On the other hand, a Robin with wings proportionately as small as a swan's would quickly exhaust itself in flight if it could take off at all. Large wings are more effective than small, relatively as well as absolutely. This is shown by the rule that the larger the bird, in general, the more slowly it beats its wings. Part of the explanation, I judge, is that when the length and breadth of a bird's wing are doubled, the area of the wing thus quadrupled, the volume of air it will displace on a downbeat through the same arc will be octupled. Another part is cited by Welty when he notes that small birds have "relatively larger proportions of their wing areas devoted to inefficient margins."

Welty is referring particularly to the hind edge of the wing at which the air-stream, passing beneath the wing, is drawn up into the low-pressure area above and behind it. The eddies thus created, which are especially pronounced at the tips of the wings, are said to impose a drag on the flyer, and certainly they represent a loss of energy. The long, narrow, pointed wings common among sea-birds evidently cause the least amount of eddying and make superb gliders of Frigate birds, albatrosses and shearwaters. Land birds would find such wings awkward to manage and those that depend much on gliding —White Pelicans along with storks, most of the larger raptorial birds and ravens—have relatively wider, blunt wings terminating in primaries that open in flight like spread fingers. These, being each a long, narrow wing in miniature, probably serve to reduce tip vortex, as it is called. To do so further may be why the vane of the primaries in soaring birds characteristically narrows abruptly for the last third or half of its length.

### Structure and Sensors

As a youth, if I had thought about it at all, I should have considered the anatomy of birds to be as irrelevant and as unworthy of attention as that of the girls who engaged my emotions—and let me hasten to explain that by anatomy I mean such things as skeleton, lungs and digestive organs. Now, seeing it as the framework of the extraordinary accomplishment that birds represent, I am less disdainful. I am, indeed, struck with admiration by it.

It is of course not feathers alone that make birds the flying-machines they are. In almost every way the reptilian structure has been radically redesigned for flight—except that at the same time provision for ambulation has had to be retained. As well as fly, birds have to walk, hop or run. Or they do with few exceptions; and even those exceptions—Frigatebirds and swifts—must be able to clutch a support. Strong legs mean bone and muscle that are dead weight in the air. They have made more imperative the most thoroughgoing adaptation of a bird's other organs to the promotion of flight and the sacrifice of every anatomical non-essential to save weight.

Toothed, bony jaws, being too heavy, especially so far out in front, have been replaced by a beak, light but strong, fastened to a skull pared to translucent thinness but strengthened by internal struts; such chewing as is necessary is done in the gizzard. The conventional vertebrate tail with its heavy links had to be dispensed with. But the tail had served as a counter-weight to the body in bipedal posture and had to be compensated for. Accordingly, the hind legs have been set forward, except in some diving-birds. (These, of upright stature on land, can afford to waddle awkwardly in order to have legs that project rearward under water, where they can serve best as propellers or rudders.) The need has been to have both wings and legs join the body close to and above its center of gravity. So contrived, the bird will be neither front-heavy while walking nor rear-heavy while flying and not be top-heavy at any time. This has been achieved by foreshortening the body and affixing the wings and legs at its top, by the backbone. Perching, a bird has the rearward part of its chest between its knees. In flight or on foot its weight is evenly distributed fore and aft.

Compression of the anatomy from front to rear has forced it to spread out laterally. A bird's body is chunky. Its breadth has the virtue, however, of making another planing surface of its underside and giving water-birds swimming on the surface a shallow draft, like inflated rubber rafts.

Evolution has both suppressed parts of the higher-vertebrate skeleton in birds and developed others to bear greater stresses. In both fore- and hind-limbs bones have been eliminated and fused. Wrists and ankles have been especially modified. The fourth and fifth fingers have disappeared. The second and third, reduced in parts and connected, make up the narrow "hand," into which the outer flight feathers are set—the primaries. (The next rank, the secondaries, are set in one of the two forearm bones.) One toe has been dropped in all birds, two in most ground-dwellers and three in the Ostrich, giving it the semblance of a cloven hoof. Development and fusion of shoulder bones has produced a strong pectoral saddle, into which the wings fit. Except in the neck, which is outstandingly flexible, the vertebrae have been compressed or fused together, up to 23 of them in the strong pelvic saddle, containing the hip-joints. The pectoral assemblage, the compressed back vertebrae and the carapace-like pelvis form the top of a light, firm skeletal basket, of which the sides are the ribs (each with a lateral projection overlapping its neighbor behind) and the bottom is the breastbone. In the basket are contained the internal organs.

In flying birds the breastbone is deepened into a keel, to which the powerful wing-muscles are attached. Among the muscles that pull the wings down and bear the brunt of flight are, most surprisingly, those that raise them. These taper on the outer end to a tendon that passes between the shoulder-blades and attaches to the upper side of the wing-bone so that contraction of the muscle is equivalent to pulling down on a rope that passes over a pulley: the object on the other end goes up. This ingenious contrivance, by which all wing muscles, which make up a substantial part of a flying-bird's weight, are beneath the back, contributes to a low center of gravity and stability in flight.

Except in the smallest birds and in diving birds, the larger bones are hollow. On the principle that a tube is stronger than a rod of the same amount of material, this gives strength with lightness. The bones bearing the primary feathers of large, soaring birds are reinforced by an internal truss-like system of struts that makes them worthy of exhibition as works of art in functional or abstract design—either one.

An efficient engine keeps the avian apparatus operating at the high level of output required. The two-chambered reptilian heart has been enlarged to four, as in mammals, so that incoming blood may be completely relieved of its burden of waste products from combustion and be wholly charged anew with oxygen before being recirculated to the muscles and other organs. Birds have gone beyond mammals, however, in carrying the same principle over into breathing. Air taken into mammalian lungs is drawn into a multiplicity of dead-end pouches. With every breath, fresh, oxygen-bearing air is mixed with stale air charged with carbon dioxide resulting from combustion, which is only partially evacuated with exhalation. In avian lungs air is pumped through a network of passages. To help produce a more copious and evidently a one-way flow is one of the functions of a remarkable system of air sacs, five or more in number, that branch off the lungs to occupy much of a bird's body and, in large, soaring birds, extend even into the hollows of the major bones. In Frigatebirds and some of our Western grouse the neck sacs are visible and highly colored and are inflated in courtship display; the Spruce Grouse and Prairie Chicken expel the air from theirs to make a booming or moaning sound. Acting as bellows, the sacs supplement the lungs, which they greatly exceed in volume, and make possible the supply to the blood of the relatively huge amount of oxygen a bird requires. Bellows and lungs must work fast, moreover. A bird's respiration may reach 300 or 400 breaths a minute, or four or five times the rate while the bird is at rest; it is slower in the larger birds. To move the oxygen-bearing blood to the needy tissues a bird's heart is large, muscular and super-paced. Even during inactivity a chicken's heart-beat is 300 a minute, a small bird's twice that. The latter may increase to 1,000 or more when the system is taxed. Where our hearts pound, a bird's trills.

To fuel their engines at the tempo demanded of them, birds depend for the most part on energy-giving foods high in proteins—insects and other forms of animal life, seeds and nuts—or rich in sugars. Processing is swift: fruit given to young Cedar Waxwings, an investigator (M. M. Nice) found, was passed through the digestive system in 16 minutes. The amount consumed is also great, especially in a relative sense among small, active birds: hummingbirds have been known to take in daily twice their weight in nectar, the most directly energy-producing of all foods. With such stepped-up metabolism, there is the problem of temperature. Conversion of fuel to energy produces heat. This is as true of the combustion of blood sugar in animal tissue as of the combustion of gasoline in a motor. And the excess must be got rid of. Even birds, adjusted as they are to internal temperatures that would kill us in short order, would burn up in flight without an exceptionally efficacious heat-dispersal system. This the air sacs provide. In cooling the blood they play as vital a role as in supplying it with oxygen.

Two other properties are essential for successful flight whether by living organisms or self-guiding missiles. There must be sensors capable of accurate, constant apprehension of what is ahead and a computer to receive the information and instantly instruct the guidance mechanism of needed changes in course. That birds are well endowed in both respects cannot be doubted by anyone who has seen them shoot swervingly through networks of branches or visualized nocturnal birds navigating and locating their prey in forests too dark to reveal the hand before the face to a human being. Robert Galambos and Donald R. Griffin of Harvard University, who discovered that bats guide themselves by "sonar"—emitting a series of high-pitched sounds and detecting objects in their path by the echo—have demonstrated that the cave-dwelling Oilbird, a distant relative of the Whip-poor-will's from northern South America, employs the same device. Since then a cave-nesting swift from the Philippines and Indonesia has been found to do likewise. The hearing of birds by human standards is preternaturally acute. A Barn Owl with eyes sealed can zero in on a mouse by its faint rustling in the leaves and strike it. And it is indicative of the refinement and novelty of adaptation that have gone into birds that the apertures of the ears of many owls are different in shape, the one on the right from the one on the left. The consequence must be to register the sound from the two sides in slightly unlike tones, and make for more accurate gauging of the direction of its source. But undoubtedly it is the light-gathering power of their eyes that chiefly serves the navigational needs of nocturnal birds. Owls' eyes, which may be as large as a human being's, are ten times or more as efficient in this as ours.

The quality of a bird's vision was brought home to me many years ago by a dwarf macaw I had as a pet and used to take for walks on my shoulder or wrist. Its attention would be riveted by an object approaching over the horizon before I could see anything at all. What was remarkable was that it would recognize the imperceptible dot as a hawk. Any other kind of bird—a crow, for instance—it would ignore. Very often in winter today it will happen that the birds congregated around the house for the food we put out will suddenly disappear, except for a few caught at a distance from cover, and these will freeze. This is the sign of a Sharp-shinned or Cooper's Hawk in the vicinity. Whenever I notice this I go out to frighten off the intruder; but only *very* seldom can I see it.

There is no eye like a bird's eye. Change of focus in human vision depends on a muscle to contract and thicken the lens and on the natural resilience of the lens to restore it to its original shape. In birds there are muscles to do both jobs and others that change the shape of the cornea as well. They make possible an all-but-instantaneous shift in focus from sharp perception of objects at the limit of visibility to those a few beaks' lengths away. And a bird's perception is sharp indeed. Where the human eye has 200,000 visual cells per square millimeter in the place of greatest concentration in the retina

—the fovea—G. L. Wall in his study of the vertebrate eye reports that these reach as high as one million in the European Buzzard (the equivalent of our Red-tailed Hawk), which he believes gives it a visual acuity at least eight times ours. On top of that a bird has two fovea. One is centrally located for lateral vision and quick detection of danger in any quarter, the other posteriorly for concentrated forward vision by the eyes together on an object for attack.

Birds' eyeballs are so large that they nearly meet at the septum. Adding musculature to move them would mean a larger skull and increased weight, and it has been dispensed with. Birds' eyes are fixed. The handicap, as it would be for us, is overcome in the great majority of birds by the placement of the eyes well back on the sides of the head. Here they command a nearly full field of view. A bird has almost all its surroundings under observation simultaneously and continuously, half with one eye, half with the other. It is not readily taken by surprise. The price is that there is not much overlap of the fields of vision of the two eyes. We see objects with both eyes together—that is, with binocular vision—through an arc amounting to about a quarter of a full circle, most birds through an arc only about a third as much. The Woodcock, which obtains its living by probing the mud for worms with its face close to the ground, has eyes so far up on its head and to the rear that it has wider binocular vision above it and behind than to the front—though not very wide anywhere. The habit of birds of cocking their heads is the corollary of monocular vision; they can best get a fix on an object with the direct stare of a single eye. The need to make certain demands more. As Louis Halle observes amusingly in a poignant account of the Adélie Penguin in *The Sea and the Ice*, "What is irresistibly comical, like the clown's smile, is the eye, one on each side of the pointed black face, which looks like a round white stone with a black disc in the middle, and the habit the penguin has of never trusting completely to either eye, so that, turning its head first this way and then that, it uses first one and then the other eye for a stare of apparent astonishment at the object to be observed." Owls are different. With forward-looking eyes and protruding corneas they have a complete overlap; everything they see, they see with both eyes. Because their field of vision is relatively narrow and their eyes immobile they are constantly swiveling their heads when on the alert; and they have the advantage of being able to look straight behind them. (All birds are compensated for their fixity of gaze by extreme suppleness of neck.) Hawks stand midway between owls and other birds in the placement and scope of their eyes.

An advantage of binocular, or stereoscopic vision, in movable eyes is in facilitating the gauging of distances; the eyes, working together, converge on close objects, the more so the closer, the less so the more distant. If you close one eye and reach out, quickly, to put a finger on a spot at arm's length you are apt to find that you miss it. In monocular vision distance must be judged by the diminution of the apparent size of an object with remoteness, by its position on an imaginary tape-measure laid out on the ground between the viewer and the horizon or by the difference between its apparent movement and that of other objects nearer and farther when the viewer, or at least his head, moves. (Children are fascinated to discover in a moving vehicle how objects on the horizon seem to be keeping pace with them—an illusion arising from the much faster apparent movement of objects in the foreground.) An owl's abrupt, rather ludicrous shifts of head from side to side while its gaze remains fixed on a target may have the purpose of exploiting this principle, as, it has been suggested, may the bobbing of heads by shorebirds. Whatever the correlations birds make to determine distance, they seem to do very well.

If the messages streaming from a bird's retina into the optic nerve are comprehensive and clear, its brain is well designed to handle them. To receive and classify the rapid fire of images there are large optic nerves, indicating a capacity for visual association—we are told—comparable with man's. The cerebellum is also large and well developed: it provides for precisely ordered responses to incoming stimuli of all kinds, automatically, instantaneously, through reflex action. A bird need not stop to think.

### The Mental Processes

Whether birds can think is moot. They are not well equipped for thought. The deficiency of their brains as compared with those of mammals is in the cerebrum, which governs the ability to learn. The pattern of behavior in birds is largely, some would say all but wholly, instinctual. In reasoning, an animal has a goal in view and takes the actions that in its judgment will lead to its attainment. Where instinct is controlling there is no end in view at all; the animal acts as it does because circumstances have triggered in it a compulsion to do so. Similarly, it is said that a human being directed while under hypnosis to take a certain action in response to a certain stimulus after being restored to consciousness will do so even though the action may be illogical, and without knowing why. Certainly a human male brought up in ignorance of sex would none the less, come puberty, respond to the incitement presented by a nubile female by undertaking action obedient to the compulsion set up in him. It would not be that a specific goal had commended itself to him. He would have no knowledge of the goal. If he were genetically imprinted with sufficient precision to be set on the appropriate course—as a wild animal would be, though with perhaps some trial and error in store— he might well be astonished or incredulous at the nature of the goal. Nevertheless, he would strive to achieve it. He would do so—God knows the human record teaches us this—even if considerable risks to his welfare had to be run. The driving force would be an inner tension, an itch, which demanded relief. So it must be with all instinctual behavior. The sexual impulse may be, and is, strong because its satisfaction is essential to the reproduction and perpetuation of the species, but few males in obeying it have the future of the species in mind. A bird, influenced by stimuli internal or external or both, itches to fly south, or north, or to assemble grasses and mud and interlard them in cup form. It then itches to in-

cubate the eggs resulting from its itch to mate and to stuff
worms into the maws of the young brought forth by incubation. It does all these things because that is the only way it can
allay these itches, or hungers.

Birds have a rich repertoire of instinctive responses, or
"fixed action patterns," as Konrad Lorenz calls them, with
which to meet the demands of their existence. So appropriate
are these to the circumstances that bring them into play—the
"releasers," in Lorenz's term—that they often suggest reasoned
action. Many examples come to mind: the feigning of a broken
wing by sandpipers and plovers and some other ground-nesting
birds to lead a predator away from eggs or young; the fitting
of acorns into cavities in trees for storage by a handsome
red-white-and-black woodpecker of the Pacific states, which
chisels out the receptacles when it cannot find enough; the
storage of insects and morsels from a feeding-tray in crevices
in bark by titmice and of acorns and nuts by the peck in
concealed piles by European Jays and Nutcrackers; the incubation of eggs by the male Australian Mallee Fowl in piles
of decaying vegetation, which generates heat and which he
adds to or subtracts from as more or less heat is required.
Gulls fly with clams to hard-surfaced roads on which they
drop them to break their shells. To the same end, the European
Song Thrush beats snails on a favorite anvil stone. The Stagemaker Bowerbird of Australia picks up a stone and uses it as
a hammer to smash the snail shell, and the Egyptian Vulture
uses one as a missile to break open Ostrich eggs.

These are cases of tool-using, which few mammals are
capable of. And there are more arresting ones still. The male
Satin Bowerbird, having constructed an open corridor of
curved twigs, daubs it with crushed colored fruit pulp or even
applies colored fruit juices and masticated charcoal with a
brush of grass or fibrous bark. He also decorates the entrance
with baubles, particularly blue ones, which match his eyes:
flower petals, feathers, bits of cloth or glass. And with one of
these in his bill he dances before the female. Then there is
the astonishing Galapagos Woodpecker-finch, of a group of

species descended from a common ancestor from the mainland, as Charles Darwin deduced, but quite different from one another today, especially in the kind of bills they have evolved to deal with their diverse diets. (The Darwin finches, as they are called, helped provide the key to the origin of species.) The Woodpecker-finch has a bill enabling it to hew through the bark of trees to the tunnels of insects and their larvae but lacks the woodpecker's long, extensible tongue for extracting the occupants. To do so it takes up a thin twig or cactus thorn and with it probes the burrow. Among mammals, probably only man and the chimpanzee are equally resourceful with an implement.

On the other hand, those who view birds as essentially automata do not lack for supporting evidence. An Acorn Woodpecker appears less far-sighted and provident when it seeks repeatedly to plug a knothole in the siding of a cabin with an acorn and deposits a pile of them out of reach on the floor within. The solicitude of a Herring Gull for her eggs appears less thoughtful when, given the choice of incubating her own or a fake in which its size and colored markings are exaggerated, she will uncomfortably straddle the giant fake. The seemingly high-minded ferocity of a Skua in defense of its young must also be seen in a different light when one of the two strays a little from the nest and is killed and devoured by its parent. Where in the case of the gull's adoption of an impostor egg the normal releaser has been eclipsed by a super-releaser, in that of the Skua's turning upon its own off-spring there has been a switch of releasers: the infant, by departing from the charmed circle within which it releases the action pattern of fierce parental protectiveness, releases the pattern of response to young penguins, on which the Skua habitually preys.

The woodpecker in trying to fill a cabin with acorns is responding to the right releaser in the right way but beyond its applicability. So is the goose that admirably rolls a dis-placed egg back toward its nest but continues the rolling process when the egg has been removed. And most country-dwellers are familiar with the bird that fights its reflection in a window as it would a rival. At our house in Virginia we have had two birds that would dash at themselves for fifteen minutes at a time, day after day, month after month. One was a Mockingbird, the other a female Cardinal, a species in which, as in the European Robin, the female is prone to display male characteristics of territoriality, including song. The Cardinal quit after a couple of years, probably because she had been killed, while the Mockingbird I trapped and transported after it had commenced to drive other birds from the feeding station. Otherwise they would probably still be at it, incapable of terminating the performance despite its demonstrated fruitlessness.

Such stupidity, as we should call it, is irritating; the two birds got on our nerves. It is hard not to feel contempt for the Budgerigar that snuggles up to a mirror. (Correspondingly one delights in Robert Cushman Murphy's report of the Galapagos Penguin in the New York Aquarium that, like its fellows, was much interested in its reflection in a mirror but "took to looking behind the glass when it failed to make a satisfactory *rapprochement* with its image.") Yet instinct is not the less marvellous for the feats intelligence achieves. A bird that had to take time to think would be doomed to quick extinction. The first hint of aggressive movement by a cat or hawk must find a bird in full flight, a variety of complicated muscular actions fully coordinated. An oriole that depended on reasoning to instruct it how to weave its nest would have to have a man-sized brain and then could hardly accomplish the feat with nothing to work with but a bill. And how would a human infant fare if, like the young of precocial birds, within an hour of its birth—given comparable physical development— it was expected to traipse after its mother responding appropriately, and fast, to the perils and opportunities of the world? Suppose, like the young Mallee Fowl, it was obliged to make its way without ever even laying eyes on its parents?

I recall the noted case of the female European Robin that attacked a tuft of red feathers (the red of a rival's breast is evidently the releaser) which had been displayed on her territory and kept on attacking the place where it had been after it had been taken away, and I wonder if her behavior made any less sense than the practice of some human beings of making little replicas of an enemy and sticking pins in it to afflict the original with pain and kill it. (If I am told the practice works, I can only say that it reflects instead on the common sense of the victim, who, when he hears of it, accommodatingly pines away.) The study of human irrationality could absorb lifetimes. Most human beings obey conventions that differ from the fixed action patterns of birds chiefly in that they make no sense in any circumstances. Think of the multitudes who have starved in the presence of wholesome food unfamiliar to them or barred from them by arbitrary taboos, and of the many whose lives have been sacrificed to propitiate gods that had never once registered on the senses of a single human being. Think of all the buildings around us embodying the latest advances of technology but with a floor numbered 13 omitted (which of course makes number 14 the 13th—but never mind.) Think of the discomfort endured in expensive, awkward and often ludicrous garments under the dictates of an abstraction called fashion. All this is not to say that convention serves no purpose. For one reason and another it may be essential to a society's survival, as the psychic well-being of colonial sea-birds on their breeding grounds seems to be enhanced by quarreling and clamor and by spells of common behavior; we find them all preening, sleeping, wing-exercising together or, in the case of terns, suddenly all launching out for a flight over the water.

I was about to say that the practice of breathing in the fumes of burning tobacco, to which half the American people are addicted at the probable cost of shortening their lives, would be incomprehensible to a bird. But that would not be true. Cigarette-smoking is readily explicable in terms of avian psychology as a form of what animal-behaviorists call substitute or displacement activity. This is irrelevant and inappropriate activity to which an animal resorts when frustrated

—that is, when prevented by some countervailing force, internal or external, from carrying out an impulse or instinct. Not only smoking, but chewing gum or straws and striding the lecture platform have been suggested as other human examples. Among birds, embattled rival males, apprehensive of the consequences of pressing the issue, may leave off combat and preen their plumage, as a human being under tension may stroke his hair. Or they may go through the motions of feeding, as men and women would be better advised to do than to take out their frustrations in continual actual eating.

Starlings familiar with my suet-holder stand by vigorously stropping their bills on a branch before venturing to close with it and may finally fly off without doing so. Hunger and fear conflict within them. They know the holder is rigged with a kind of wire-mesh jaw that may fly up and pin them against it. (This it does when I pull a string from my window. When I let up the jaw opens and off the Starling flees, sadder and I hope wiser.) A Catbird from whose pillaged nest I once yanked a Black Snake broke into hurried song, as a Japanese, in a situation of tragedy, expressions of suffering blocked by a syndrome, may smile. The Dutch animal-behaviorist Niko Tinbergen observes in *The Herring Gull's World* that "One often gets the impression that birds call when they are strongly activated by an internal urge, and yet cannot satisfy that urge by performing the activities to which it drives them." Such is a displacement activity; and one wonders if artistic creation among human beings is not a supreme example, the resort of those whose passionate response to life, whether of ecstasy or anguish, or simple, deep impressionability, can find no means of fulfillment in ordinary, overt action.

"Stereotyped behavior has reached a high degree of evolutionary development in birds, and for the most part has served them well," writes George J. Wallace of Michigan State University. "Most mammals, by comparison, meet new situations more intelligently, but biologically mammals (except man) are no more successful." Yes, man is the planetary success. Yet one must be sanguine to anticipate that after 150 million years he will still be thriving, as birds are. Given the probable frequency of life's occurrence through the universe and its drive toward intelligence, if the earth is an example, we have seemed warranted in supposing that we may well pick up electronic signals beamed into space by other civilizations, some of which, we are generous enough to concede, are likely to be more advanced than our own. The possibility must be allowed for, however, that technological civilizations are inescapably of such short duration that the chances of one's communications coming just in time to reach another are negligible. Thought, analytical and creative, still seems to me the glory of the universe as we know it, but as Sophocles recognized to be true of all great things entering into the lives of men, it comes with a curse. As it gives us the power to devastate the planet, the curse may soon prove fatal. It is dangerous enough in what it does to us directly, leading those who are sicklied o'er with its pale cast through labyrinthine processes of the mind to insights we were better to have been spared. That is why we may be glad birds are as they are, unbrooding and unreflective, charged with life, creatures of the present moment, as direct and self-contained as the breezes of their airy realm.

The impression must not be left, however, that birds' behavior is wholly pre-set and inflexible. That is not so. Birds can learn and adapt themselves, though the capacity to do so varies with species and with individuals. Threading mazes should come more naturally to rats than to birds, but according to Welty birds can be taught to make their way through them just about as well; M. P. Sadovnikov brought various small birds to negotiate the fairly complex Hampton Court maze in from 20 to 50 trials. Captive Baya Weavers have been taught to thread beads on a cord, though this must have taxed the patience of the Indian trainers. More readily, titmice and European Goldfinches can learn to draw food hanging at the end of a string up within reach of their bills, which requires holding the slack to the perch with a foot while reaching down for another length. Having learned of this trick from a motion picture, I went home and suspended a piece of banana on a string below a pet parrot of mine, a Yellow-fronted Amazon. It required no instruction. Within half a minute, albeit by somewhat hit-or-miss methods, it had the food in its foot and was holding it up to eat—an interesting employment of that member which parrots share with owls; both, incidentally, have two toes opposed to two. Almost unbelievably, Hooded Crows in Scandinavia have been reported (by L. Homberg) to avail themselves of fish snared on lines that anglers have left suspended through holes in the ice of frozen lakes: they seize the line and march off with it away from the hole, then walk on it back to the hole, thus keeping it from slipping, and repeat the process until the fish is brought up.

No one who has had a parrot or a crow for a pet will be surprised to learn that its kind is notable among birds for size of cerebrum. I have had both. My crow, raised from a nestling, was one I had so long ago I have to rely on what I wrote then to bring him fully back to me.

"He mastered every turn of the household routine. . . . Even before he could fly properly he was supervising all outdoor operations. The car could not be polished until he had eaten a mouthful of the wax and wrestled with the rags. If work was being done in the garden, he would be there, squirming perilously under our legs and leaping upon our backs. . . . Once while setting out some seedlings I discovered him quietly following me down the row, uprooting each one and tearing it to bits. So acute were his powers of observation and mimicry that he had remarked my inattention to the surrounding weedlets; he disturbed none of them. He was equally quick in making aural associations. While cows, horses and cats sometimes never learn, or learn only after a long while, to come to a food call, the Crow grasped the idea on the second trial and afterwards would respond to the rustle of the brown paper in which his beef was kept."

I have remarked this same facility in the wild crows around our house. Putting meat scraps out for them on a shelf nailed to a tree 40 feet from our back door, I took to cawing to let them know when I did so. Not only did they catch on quickly and come to the tray when they heard me but even after five months without being fed would respond at once to a repetition of the call. But to resume:

"In divining purely mechanical cause and effect the bird had genius. A moment or two was all that he required to master the secret of a safety-match box, to open it, remove the matches, and close it again—this on the initial trial. His first glance at a lighted cigarette disclosed to him its dangerous property. I have seen him pick up or steal many of them, but never one by the wrong end. . . . He regarded people as merely complicated, and hence more entrancing, matchboxes and he devised marvellous methods of working them. . . . Observing someone walking down a path, he would station himself on a hidden overhanging branch until the passer-by had proceeded a few paces beyond him. Then he would launch out and down, and, with a mighty swish of his wings and the momentum of a cannon ball, would clear the subject's head by a bare two inches. The magnificent result of the experiment—and no amount of experience ever mitigated the victim's near collapse from the sudden terror—would bring forth an ecstatic burst of cawing. . . .

"[He] flew daily to my window to rap me out of bed with the dawn. . . . [He was continually] falling into our laps, pulling our hair, snatching at matches, teacups, pens, and watch-chains, tearing up flowers, turning the pages of a magazine with care only to rip it to shreds a moment later, . . . baying his excitement from morning till night, and even accompanying us on our walks, flying ahead and then back close over our heads to spur us on, I suppose."

In retrospect, what comes as most significant from my familiarity with that bird was, I think, its curiosity and gusto, its appetite for life. These are qualities of the mind ordinarily left out of account in tests or analyses of mental capacity, whether of wild animals or of human beings; they defy statistical measurement. Yet surely as much as any they differentiate the autonomous from the automata and appeal to us wherever displayed. It is because these traits are more marked in dogs than in cats that I find the former easier to warm up to. Obviously there is a correlation between them and general mental development; as man among animals, so the family of crows and jays among birds is pre-eminent. Arthur A. Allen, the famous Cornell University ornithologist, says in *The Book of Bird Life* just what I should have about Crows: "If it is possible in a 'dumb animal,' I should be willing to credit them with a sense of humor." And he goes on: "One of our pet Crows learned to laugh as well as to talk, and used his laughter so appropriately on numerous occasions that I could scarcely credit it all to coincidence. He was very observing and when children were not present he used to roll their balls and play their games by himself. He was very fond of teetering which he accomplished by running up one side of the see-saw until it went down and then turning and running up the other."

You cannot observe birds for long without finding some of them putting two and two together. Starlings caught in my suet-holder trap acquire a nice discernment about the reach of the jaw: they sneak in cautiously from the side. One that suffered an injury to its wing in the trap taught me further to respect his species while I had him in the house pending his recovery. Most birds brought in from the wild as adults and caged continue for a long time to dash against the bars when approached, if they ever desist. The automatic response is all but proof against the repeated demonstration that the human presence is innocuous and the cage inescapable. Not so with the injured Starling. It learned both lessons within a few days and, while remaining apprehensive, took its captivity on the whole philosophically, having from the beginning indulged the excellent appetite of its kind. One would expect no less, to be sure, of a bird that has defeated so many well-laid schemes of the arch reasoner to dislodge its vociferous and excretory flocks from their roosts on buildings.

Kent Durdin, in his *Gifts of an Eagle,* an account of an extraordinary experience of sixteen years' duration with a tame female Golden Eagle, wrote of his subject that "beneath that overcoat of black feathers and behind those sharp talons was a proud creature of high intelligence, a creature with a capacity for being tender and loving, a creature possessing a distinct personality." And it hardly seems excessive to attribute intelligence to a bird that was quick to learn how to open the door to a shed full of rats by pulling on a string and, when her food was hidden under one of three identical pails, had no trouble remembering which it was an hour later. She may have been even more human, however, when, wearying of the effort of memory, she responded to the test by brusquely knocking over all three pails.

G. Köhler demonstrated that a Raven could count up to six. This he did by marking five boxes with irregular spots, one with two, one with three, and so on. Food was concealed in one of these and the Raven taught to tell which when shown a key card having the same number of spots, but of *different shapes and arrangements*. H. Braun trained an African Grey Parrot to pick up three or four pieces of food depending on whether it was given three or four auditory signals. In this remarkable feat of correlation between the messages of separate senses, the bird, as Welty states, "was dealing with the abstract concept 'three'" and demonstrating "the conceptual nature of the bird's behavior."

Some years ago a spreading habit of titmice in Britain was widely reported in the press, and with understandable astonishment. The birds had learned to take the caps off milk bottles waiting at doors and drink the cream; there have even been reports of bands of tits following the milk-delivery wagon on its route. It has been a striking case of the adaptability of birds to novel sources of food—a trait that many but not all share. Gulls in flocks follow the harrow across the fields for earthworms and refuse-scows out to sea for food scraps, throng city dumps and after rains that drive earthworms to the surface repair to golf courses and other expanses of greensward; when, after World War II, mines were being exploded off Holland, they followed the sound of the detonations for dead fish. Crows, having learned long ago all about newly-planted corn, have since discovered that highways mean dead animals and picnic grounds delicacies new but welcome to corvine tastes. Grey Jays are notorious camp robbers, making off with snacks from a table, and I have seen kites in India snatch food right out of unsuspecting hands. Various birds have learned that car radiators yield dead insects. The giant parrot of New Zealand called the Kea took to gnawing through the backs of sheep in severe winters to get to the kidney fat—a costly discovery, however, leading to its near extermination by ranchers.

## The Variety of Food and Means of Getting It

A bent for exploiting new sources of food must say something about the mental range of birds. Surely it has given the Class Aves its variety of diet. And with that we come to the fourth and final characteristic of birds that has particularly made them nearly ubiquitous. Not only can they endure extremes of climate. Not only are they matchlessly mobile. Not only is their internal apparatus—machinery and controls—highly efficient. One or more of their species can find nourishment in just about any organic matter.

Seeds, nuts and fruit; insects and their larvae and spiders; fish, amphibians and mollusks; the smaller mammals and other birds: such form the bulk of avian diet. They mark only the beginning of the diversity, however. Hummingbirds of the New World, Honey-eaters, Sunbirds and Flower-peckers of the Old suck up nectar. Honeyguides—rather drab, largely African relatives of the woodpeckers—specialize not only on wasps and bees but on the wax of their honeycombs; they have the amazing habit of leading Honey-badgers and human beings to the hives with loud, chattering cries so that they may feast on the leavings when the hive has been broken into for the honey. The African Oxpecker gleans ticks from cattle and the Egyptian Plover food particles from the open mouths of cooperative crocodiles, or so it is said. The Secretary-bird—a long-legged hawk of the African plains—makes a specialty of snakes, as does the European Short-toed Eagle, which otherwise preys only on lizards. Snakes and lizards are also the quarry, along with scorpions and tarantulas, of that ramshackle-looking cuckoo of our Southwest, the Roadrunner. Many birds are addicted to snails, the Everglade Kite exclusively so and to one fresh-water genus alone—an extreme of specialization rare among birds and one that is causing the Kite's disappearance from our avifauna as drainage of the Florida marshes eliminates its food supply. Oyster-catchers—shorebirds distributed around the world—are consumers of shellfish; they prise limpets off rocks with their laterally-flattened bills and use these to jab into the gaping shells of oysters, clams and mussels to sever the adductor muscle. Ivory gulls scavenge the shores for whale dung. The prey of bat-falcons is what the name indicates. Geese are grazers and so reliably selective that domesticated varieties turned loose in Southern cotton fields gobble up the pestiferous Johnson grass without damage to the paying crop. Spruce Grouse and Sage Grouse can subsist on the coarse foliage of the plants that give them their name, though only by processing great quantities of the unnutritious fodder. The Lammergeier makes a singular diet of bones, visiting animal carcasses only when they have been cleaned of meat by kites and other vultures. Small bones it ingests whole, the larger it bears aloft and drops on rocks to break them into manageable pieces. This would have been the culprit responsible for the death of Aeschylus in the apochryphal and unworthy tale recounted by Pliny: the noble dramatist, the story goes, had taken to his garden, having been warned that he would die of a house falling on his head, only to suffer this fate when a tortoise dropped by an eagle crashed onto it.

Like other forms of life, birds must ingest not only solids but liquids—and until recently it was a mystery how oceanic birds solved their drinking problem. The solution was finally found in a gland in the nose which, by concentrating and expelling the salt in the sea water they imbibe, adapts it to their internal needs.

In pursuit of their diverse livelihoods, birds have undergone all the modifications of structure that make them of endless interest. While some are small enough to share the flowers and the office of pollinator with insects, others are large enough to fraternize with zebras and gnus and spot distant danger over their heads, to the general advantage. Birds have legs like jointed stilts, legs like horses', legs that have been all but abolished to lighten flying-weight, ample and sturdy legs for running and shorter sturdy legs for swimming, grasping feet, webbed feet, lobed feet, taloned feet, feet with rasped soles for gripping fish, short feet of three toes for sprinting and feet of four attenuated toes for distributing weight on water-plants, feet like hands and feet like snowshoes.

The member most immediately related to the acquisition of food, the bill, has proved especially plastic, in the evolutionist's term; it has assumed the widest variety of forms in response to demands made of it. In this, their primary tool, birds are equipped with every manner of probe, up-curved, down-curved, straight, angled and spoon-shaped. In the Long-billed Curlew it may reach nine inches in length. Five inches in the Andean Sword-billed Hummingbird, it accounts for more than half that bird's total length. The Woodcock's is prehensile at the tip. Bills are nutcrackers: the Cardinal-sized European Haw-finch splits cherry pits in its conical beak, the Hyacinthine Macaw of the Amazonian forest Brazil-nuts between its massive mandibles. (H. M. Tomlinson in *The Sea and the Jungle* tells how one of these spectacular parrots, a solid deep violet in color with yellow-rimmed eyes and mouth, was made captive by a chain attached to its leg and, after experimentally rolling it in its great hooked beak, bit clean through it.) Soft-billed fruit-pigeons and gallinaceous birds depend on the gizzard for nut-cracking, and a Turkey has no trouble dispatching hickory-nuts, swallowed whole, by the dozen. In birds that capture fish by lunging, the bill is a spear for impaling the quarry. In some other fish-eaters, like the mergansers, it is serrated for gripping it. Bills are chisels in woodpeckers. They are knife-edged butcher's hooks in hawks, owls and other predators. In Flamingoes, which feed in shallow waters, they are sieves for straining out plankton.

It is a striking fact of the history of life that animals that pursue similar ways of feeding, however unlike to begin with, come increasingly to resemble one another. Convergent evolution, it is called, and it should gratify the Marxists, who hold that we are all the products, in outlook and behavior, of our means of livelihood. In Australia, for instance, where native placental mammals, which dominate on the other continents, are absent, the marsupials (like our opossum), which have the field to themselves, have evolved into comparable forms, from the equivalent of rats to the equivalent of wolves. Among paired groups of birds that might seem to be closely related but are not are swifts and swallows, auks and penguins and hawks and owls. Two kinds of shorebirds offer striking examples. One, the Pratincoles, which course for insects on the wing, have come to resemble swallows, while the other, the Seedsnipe—seed-eaters of cold South American barrens—to resemble longspurs, seed-eating finches of cold North American barrens.

But this is digressive. The object has been to account for the prevalence of birds around the globe. If their range of diet is part of the explanation, I am tempted to ascribe that, like other parts—their mobility and endurance of cold and heat—to the feather. It is the feather that gives them access to all these foods.

### In Sum: Feathers

What an asset the feather is! I come back to that. In addition to all else it does, it transforms one of the ugliest and most unshapely and repellent objects in nature—a naked bird—into one of the most smoothly and gracefully sculptured and most beautiful.

Nothing excels the feather as an agency of color. In addition to bearing pigments, from which most of the colors of birds derive, it has a structure that lends itself to the projection of others. The blue in a bird's plumage is as ethereal as it appears, having a source comparable to that of the blue of the sky and of ocean waters: the blue portion of the light spectrum is dispersed by the surface cells of the feather as the other portions are absorbed by underlying pigment cells. Green in birds is apt to be a combination of underlying yellow pigment and the blue-glowing cellular structure. Other special modifications of the structure of the barbules affect light as a film of oil on water does to produce iridescence, one color succeeding another with a change in the angle of observation. "In the spring a livelier iris changes on the burnished dove," says Tennyson. I have read explanations of the phenomenon and have not understood them, so that I marvel the more at the shot-silk mail of hummingbirds, sunbirds, trogons, pheasants and many others, which exceeds in brilliance and fire any silk or opal, any other gem, any precious metal.

And as well as enchanting and stunning the eye—or mystifying it by camouflaging coloration—feathers supply many birds with a second voice. The pulsating hum or "bleating" of the Snipe and (probably) shrill twittering of the Woodcock on their courtship flights, the muffled thunder of a Ruffed Grouse's courtship drumming and of its unnerving sudden explosion from the ground, the whistling flight of many birds, especially of some ducks and notably the adult male Golden-eye (called the Bell Duck in German) and the booming of the Nighthawk at the bottom of its dive, are all produced by feathers in different forms.

### Language

Sound-making by feathers in courtship is a form of expression analogous to song. Bird-song itself could be said to bear roughly the same relationship to other forms of avian vocalization as human singing to other forms of human vocalization. These others could be defined as the automatic and the purposed.

Birds' cries of alarm and resentment, their battle cries in the heat of combat, the food calls of their young on the appearance of a parent—all usually harsh ejaculations—are like the "ouch" of a pained human being, his expletive when an action miscarries and his burst of laughter when someone else's does, a woman's scream (probably designed evolutionarily to summon her burly and pugnacious mate), the wailing of an infant.

These are sounds that rise unbidden to the bill or lips, of their own, and are likely to be out before the vocalizer knows it.

Those of the second group are intentional. Among human beings these consist overwhelmingly of words, though *ummms, ahs, ah-ahas* and *hunhs?* can convey considerable meaning. Birds, of course, go only a tiny fraction of the way toward human speech, though some can imitate its sound uncannily well. Some scientists, moreover, would deny that birds make any sounds or do anything else intentionally. They may at least recognize, however, that there is a category of sounds a bird makes when time permits its being conscious of them and that these presuppose a hearer, not ordinarily being voiced unless there is one. Communication calls, they might be termed. "Scolding" notes directed at an intruder are a common example, though it might be argued that they belong in the first group. Another elementary kind is the scattered cheeping in a flock of sparrows or similar notes of other small birds that keep company outside the breeding season and inhabit vegetation in which they could become lost from one another. Such calls keep the flock together. Flight calls, though similarly emitted by birds in a flock, must be of different motive since the members are in plain sight of one another. Such are the per-*chic*-o-rees of Goldfinches, as undulating as their course, the muted squawks punctuating the passage of a stream of Grackles and the honking of migrating geese. One is forced to believe that they spring simply from the need to feel in touch and express affinity. They voice the satisfaction found in the companionship of the flock. Such vociferations are also heard from chickens on their roosts at night, a soft, sleepy queeeeeeeeeeeeeeeeep queeep queeep queeep. It is the very sound of drowsy contentment, only to be known in the bosom of the flock. As I look back on the many summers of our association, I find chickens remarkably communicative. Like parrots in a flock they are constantly gabbling. The boisterous tuk-tuk-tuk-tuk-tuk-AH! with which a hen announces the laying of an egg is notorious. I learn that female Jungle-fowl have the same habit, an expert hypothesizing that its function may be to lure predators from the nest. Maybe. I rather think it analagous to the crowing of cocks. (An advertisement of territorial claims, the expert hazards, while suggesting that the function is not very clear.) Whatever else they may be, both strike me as boasting, statements of an irrepressible professional pride.

The excited, falsetto cheeping of a hen calling her chicks to a trove of food is unmistakable. A rooster, by the way, will call his hens to some morsels in the same way—for your rooster is by no means lacking in gallantry. He is a knight of the barnyard, hardly less, or was in the days when barnyards with chickens still existed and his declamatory Tuk-ah tuk-AH tuk! of warning and defiance of an intruder was as familiar as the barking of dogs. Warning and defiance, although much muted, are also conveyed in the soft, throaty clucking of a broody hen. She may be sitting on eggs laid by others—will be, indeed, if she is a henhouse bird—but if you reach under her to extract them the ordinarily timorous creature will stand, or sit, her ground and deal you savage pecks, drawing blood. The drawled, complacent quaaaaaaaAAAhk quaaahk quaaahk quaaahk (the a's broad) of hens as the peaceful hours pass is probably both an "All's well"—a loud equivalent of the nocturnal queeping—and a conversational "Just let me tell you" or "Take it from me."

I thought I had known and remembered chickens' calls quite well. But—great grief! That was before I saw David G. M. Wood-Gush's *The Behavior of Domestic Fowl.* Nineteen distinct calls are listed for adults. There are two alarm notes. One, a "loud, sustained, raucous scream" warns of an aerial predator and is like the "fear squawk of a hen being held." The other is a warning of a ground predator and is "usually segmented, then ends on a sustained note." Some pretty subtle refinements are recognized, as in number 13: "Rarely emitted. The calls are repeated at intervals. Occurs when a bird is staking a claim to a dustbath." This is the *Staubbad-abwehr* of E. Bäumer—for we have here an international field of study. (The bibliography contains 266 titles.) The cackling of a laying hen is the *Lege-*

*gachern* of Bäumer and my queeping the *Girren.* Twelve chick calls are recognized, beginning with the *Verlassenheits-weinen* of Bäumer, *Le cri d'appel du Poissin isolé* of a French scientist, the *peep* of R. J. Andrews.

Communicativeness is of course less to be wondered at in a social bird than in a more solitary. Jungle-fowl are social and more than ever so after millennia of domestication, but the species has never been considered a brainy one. If, nevertheless, it manages to put so great a variety of messages into sound, how much more subtly must the sharp-witted Corvidae express themselves! Anyone acquainted with Crows at all knows how their cawing varies in pitch, inflection, frequency and duration of the individual caws, from a laconic caaaah to an almost yelping, staccato ca-hahka-hahka-hahka-hahka, delivered by a forward-leaning bird bobbing energetically with each iamb. And other sounds issue from crows, including a rolling, guttural call, like a Raven's, also variously inflected. On the principle that every characteristic of a species serves a purpose (unless the purpose has been rendered obsolete and the characteristic is in process of being lost)—the law of the economy of nature—it may be inferred that each distinct utterance has a significance peculiar to itself. Any attentive countryman, in fact, recognizes the indignant, excited cawing that means an owl discovered. It is said that as many as 300 Crows' calls have been differentiated, that some are recognized by Crows on both sides of the Atlantic and others not, and that there are provincial populations of Crows that miss out on many of the calls of the mainstream members of their species.

Among other wild songbirds, even human beings have been able to interpret as many as a dozen different calls in a single species, meaning variously "Hawk approaching!", "I am ready for mating," "Food is here," "I am taking off," and "Here we are." Some calls, certainly of warning, are understood from species to species. Our chickadees, titmice, wrens and vireos all have their own snake-alarms, and very harsh they are; but one bird proclaiming the foe will summon the neighborhood—and, for that matter, me as well. "Mobbing calls," such as these, according to Peter Marler, speaking on the WGBH-TV program *Why Do Birds Sing?*, "have a very distinctive structure: they resemble one another in a great many species of birds, they all tend to have a very sharp, repetitive, rather harsh tone." There is, however, another type of alarm call that Marler first noticed when studying Chaffinches, "a very thin, high whistle which fades in gently, reaches a maximum intensity, and then fades out again. . . . And it has a sort of ventriloquial property: it's very hard to tell where it comes from." The Chaffinch, he discovered, "and a lot of species used this type of call when there was a hawk hunting overhead."

Marler's hypothesis that songbirds produce two types of alarm calls, one easy to localize, one difficult, received supporting evidence from Masakazu Konishi. On the same program he told how in experiments conducted in a darkened room he found that a tame Barn Owl would aim accurately at the source of a harsh sound, even shifting in mid-flight when it was moved, but found it very difficult to locate the source of a pure tone like a whistle.

It has always been accepted that, whatever might be true of song, birds' calls are innate, being given instinctively without having to be learned. No doubt in general this is true. But the existence of local differences in Crow vocabulary and evidence of dialects among other species would raise doubts about the rule's universality. And then there is the striking power of mimicry of some birds that do not sing and hence do not employ the gift for musical enrichment. The ability of some Parrots—the African Grey and the Amazons only a little less so—and especially of the Hill Mynah to imitate human speech is startling. Anyone meeting such a talking bird who had never heard of one would surely doubt his own senses or credit the supernatural. Since in the wild these birds were not heard to imitate foreign sounds it was supposed that the talent was one that came with captivity. It must, however, be at least latent in the wild and employ a pre-existing apparatus. And if the capacity were present and not used, the law of the economy of nature would stand violated. Now it appears that it is used in the wild—to mimic the sounds of the birds' own kind, to communicate within the social group; the Hill Mynahs and potentially-talking Parrots are all social. The possibility is thus raised that in birds of other groups, though they inherit the basic vocabulary, communication may also be improved through learning.

In what birds can convey to one another, I am disposed to concede more than can be proved. Views, however elementary, were in fact being exchanged, I am prepared to believe, by two female Oropendolas—large, tropical American Orioles— whose dispute over a nesting-site was described by Frank M. Chapman.

> These birds were first observed . . . facing each other on site-twigs about one foot apart. One was addressing the other and so earnestly that, although the birds were of the same size and their voices were not loud, I supposed I was witnessing a courtship scene. The bird addressed with lowered head listened intently. But, behold! when the speech was finished, she "took the floor" and replied with equal vigor while bird No. 1 assumed the listening pose. Developments proved that both were females, and for the first time I learned that this sex had a vocabulary of its own. So day after day the discussion was continued. Both birds were never seen talking at the same time and the bird addressed gave her entire attention to the speaker.

Six days later, after a sharp scrap that "seemed to relieve them," followed by further dignified discussion, each bird began a nest on its own perch.

Len Howard, whose astonishingly close companionship with the wild birds that shared her Sussex cottage and its grounds is the subject of her *Birds as Individuals,* was convinced that birds can "soon learn to understand something of human speech by its tone" and "can communicate with each other by slight inflections of voice and movement." Great Titmice that came to her table and longed to help themselves to butter would fly off at a stern "No" from her but attack the treat confidently when she coaxed them with a "Come on." Explaining that her titmice had different ways of calling for food, she recalls that one

> always perched on my shoulder and looked up into my face with a pleading expression. If I said, "Have none," her expression altered, she looked annoyed, left my shoulder and perched opposite me with a fixed stare. If I said, "Shall I get some?" she instantly flew to the door, her expression eager and expectant.

Some of Miss Howard's experiences raise the question of whether birds do not receive communication by means neither auditory nor visual. For example, a Great Titmouse she called Twist—for she had names for them all—would leave her mate in a distant copse to return to Miss Howard's cottage, where she had been born. But sometimes "she suddenly stood rigid, with a tense expression, and dropping food she was eating tucked between her toes, she hurriedly flew out of the window and across the meadows towards the copse." Miss Howard considered it possible that her sensitive ears, tuned to his voice, could detect it from far away across the meadows through the intervening noise of motorcars and tractors, but other similar cases made her feel that Twist and her mate may have had "some other vibrant or telepathic form of communication." One of the cases involved Curley, a Great Titmouse who had been unable to produce eggs, though she had built herself a nest in a bird-box. One day Miss Howard found an old Partridge's egg and placed it in the nest. Curley's mate, Whiskers, had no way of knowing of this and the pair had not been seen together for two weeks. Yet within one minute of Curley's commencing to brood the egg he came hurrying across the neighboring garden bringing a caterpillar for her— something he had never been seen to do before—and, following her eager reception of it, delivered food every few minutes throughout the morning.

The most notable, not to say astounding, instance I have come upon of seemingly intuitive avian apprehension was afforded by a Lyrebird, that illustrious Australian songster. A male of the ordinarily retiring, secretive species formed the habit of emerging daily from the forest to visit a woman who lived in the mountains not far from Melbourne and, with the ledge of her veranda as a stage, put on for her his species's extraordinary singing and dancing performance. (To this amazing story, first greeted with understandable disbelief by Australian ornithologists but later recounted to the world, with photographs, by the former president of the Royal Zoological Society of Victoria, we shall return later.) The day came when, stricken with illness, the object of the bird's attentions did not put in an appearance—whereupon the visitor built outside her bedroom window one of the display-mounds of his kind so that, on top of it, he was within her field of vision, and there sang to her "as she had never heard him sing before." Quite apart from the bird's having an interest in the matter at all, what is to be explained is how he knew she was ill, how he knew where she was, in a room well removed from the place where he was accustomed to seeing her, and how he knew the mound would bring him within her sight.

# PART TWO

# Birds Through the Year

## _____4
# SUMMER

### Birds at Home

The long days of summer! The season has for us in our school years the amplitude that life itself has. We know, if we are asked, that neither will last forever; yet they seem almost ours for good. There will be time for everything. In hours and days we have a fortune to draw on. If, too, we have birds at heart the happier we, not only then, but in later life. In the future, when the weeks and months press ever more impatiently on each other's heels, rushing us along, birds can take us back to what was, in its reality.

Not everyone has had the enviable lot, as I had, to spend his youthful summers on a farm—not that I always felt the work that went with it to be enviable. But it must be common among Americans to have had summers outside the city and to enjoy memories of a green countryside like mine. The birds we encountered there, if we cared about them then, will thereafter speak of a past when in retrospect the sun stood still in the heavens above a rural landscape. Meadowlarks piercing with keen, aspiring whistles the late June warmth: they are hayfields and the chattering of mowing-machines. I can hear a Red-eyed Vireo voicing its discursive, piecemeal song, seemingly without beginning or end, and for a moment be riding the swaying hayrack, on my back on top of the load, gazing up into the Sugar Maples lining the road. The "warbly chatter" of Barn Swallows, as John Hay calls it, brings back the hayloft at the end of the ride and the gloom, soon to be stifling, beneath the roof; they would be clinging to clay nests affixed to the rafters or shooting through a broken windowpane in a flash of metallic blue and peach. The "Chcr teacher *teacher*

TEACHER TEACHER *TEA!*" of an Ovenbird means a hunt for a newly born calf in the woods; it would be as startling in the sylvan hush as an alarm clock if it did not begin softly. A Green Heron takes me back to the pond as day finally faded, with an explosive *keeunk* of alarm. The Crow-sized form would wing with abrupt strokes over a placid mirror of the sunset sky.

Are birds, for us, above all expressive of summer? If they are to me, it is perhaps because summers were when I was most exposed to birds to begin with, when my mind had least inscribed on it and because it is the season I am in now, as I write.

June is in fact here and a week of it already gone by. The disarming time has come again when the sun is warm as soon as it clears the trees, as it is in the tropics. The earth and its tenants unfold once more under the *Pax Æstiva*. It is a peace not among living creatures, of course, but between them and the climate. If the lamb may not safely lie down with the lion, the rabbit and the fox may both relax with the elements. The heavens are benign, you do not have to shrink from exposure to the out-of-doors. Birds may bring forth new life within only a paper-thin shell. The grass-heads, yellow with pollen, nod heavily, and in the cool shadows the scent of grass is like the taste of fresh green cornstalks, to one who has chewed them and found some almost like sugar-cane. Yarrow and pink clover are coming into bloom and white daisies are everywhere gazing up at the sky. Among the chalk-white flowers of blackberry, little hard, green fruit is forming. The Japanese Honeysuckle is now under a skein of flowers like milk and cream and its heady, sweet perfume has succeeded the lighter fragrance of Multiflora Rose—another naturalized Asian.

It is a quiet countryside, anyone would say. Yet when you stop to listen the chorus of birds far and near is uninterrupted. The clear and loud but rather strained whistle of a Bob-white sounds and with it, as if expelled across the mouth of a cask, the "cuh coo coo coo coo-ah, coo coo coo" that gives the Mourning Dove its name. The delicate, accelerated chiming of

a Field Sparrow's exquisitely pure song contrasts with the Song Sparrow's impulsive snatch of ditty: three spanking notes of a little cymbal and a quick bouncing up and down the scale—a musical cheer. A House Wren chuckles: a high-pitched stutter, then a lower: "Chee chee chee, chu chu chu chu chu." Unlike any of these, which reiterate a more or less set phrasing, a Mockingbird at the top of a tree, virtuoso that he is, pulls phrases from a musical grab-bag, trying each ringing declaration several times, as if to judge of its effect.

All the singers have eggs or young by now. The Phoebes that nest under the eaves of our porch have already brought up their first brood; on the morning of June 5th all five young sallied from the nest within an hour. (As usual, we watched on tenterhooks to see how they would manage and whether the parents would be able to keep them together. Their first flights, though short, were adeptly made, and one when it reached its first tree bobbed its tail just like an adult. But within half an hour of the last departure from the nest all seven birds had disappeared, the fate of the brood not to be known—and that, too, was as usual.) Young Rufous-sided Towhees and a young Brown Thrasher appeared the same day. Once the season for nesting arrives, a drive to press on with it clearly possesses birds. The first young Carolina Wren left the nest on May 18th. One year the first was out on April 29th. (They nest in a box, protected.) By June the second nesting is under way.

The Carolina Wren sings regularly in every month of the year and, as far as I know, is the only Eastern species that does. Even the grimmest day may bring forth its cheerful, full-throated little musical canter. Before the end of January, where we live, one may confidently listen for the first "What cheer" or "Wheeoo wheeoo" of a Cardinal's opening notes. Mild weather even before that will have brought on the vocal flowering of the Tufted Titmouse. The double- or single-note refrain, reiterated without variation, is a modest blossoming, to be sure, but one would miss its undesigning trustfulness. Individual birds of many species may sing a little in the autumn, usually *sotto voce,* some being young trying out their syringial muscles or practising the canticles of their elders. The Mockingbird, after falling silent in August, has a regular second song season in October. Many a frosty morning way down South, and of late way up in Massachusetts as well, is warmed by its exuberant cadenza to summer's closing orchestral movement. With all the exceptions, however, song in birds is pre-eminently a phenomenon of pairing.

Birds have to exert themselves throughout the year; there is little respite for them at any time from hunting and being hunted. However, it is in the breeding season that their capacities are brought most fully into play. They are then, I suppose it could be said, most fully birds. It is at this season, too, that ornithologists are most active—most fully ornithologists. That is only in part because they are then freed from the classroom. In the behavior of their subjects there is at this time more to study. Better yet, tied to a particular spot to which they may be expected regularly to return—the nest—they are easier to study. A blind at the location makes possible observation within feet and photographs difficult to match elsewhere.

The distinctive appeal of birds in summer is to me twofold. The greater is the vigor of their assertion then of life against that negation that ever threatens all of us transients in a brute universe. Birds are deeply engaged in the struggle for self-preservation throughout the year, in what might be called a holding action. In the breeding season they carry the battle to the enemy, wresting from it life for a new generation. In the process, spurred by the exhilaration that springs from asserting one's being against the odds, they have, like men, developed the creative impulse, I believe we are justified in saying. By creative I mean giving outward form to a demanding inner conception, as an end in itself, in pride of authorship —what distinguishes the artist from the utilitarian. I shall return to this presently.

The other special interest birds have for us in the breeding season arises from their being then in the settings to which they are native. These are the places with which they are linked with a special intimacy and dependence and, in a manner of speaking, are integral. The boundless ocean, it is true, must seem to be the home of the pelagic birds. With them you feel that shore-bound domesticity is an abridgement of the life they were born to, an incongruous concession to the necessity of reproducing their kind. Perhaps the sea-birds may fairly be regarded as compounding two dissimilar kinds of creature. One, at the nest, is a heavy, awkward, earthbound waddler, an exotic barnyard fowl. The other is the epitome of grace and freedom in its aerial or aqueous medium. To a degree all birds moving seasonally from one kind of world to another assume a different personality, many a different garb to go with it. But with every species there must be one environment it has primarily evolved to fit, and with most land birds the environment is probably that of the nest. It is to this in particular that they "belong." So if you are settled in an area and feel it to be your home, its breeding birds (if you are interested in birds at all) are bound to be of special concern to you.

The area I have known best is in northern Westchester County, New York, centering in Lake Waccabuc and the three Salems. This, as a boy and in early manhood, I had to myself, ornithologically speaking, though less than fifty miles separated it from the heart of New York City. My introduction to this countryside—then one of farms, woods and quiet lakes— and my introduction to birds took place together, beginning when I was eleven. In the passing years I came to know the one as I did the other, and with all the private joys of the solitary explorer; it was a great privilege. I learned warbler songs as I added to the species I found there as breeding birds. The common population I soon managed to establish: Yellow, Black-and-White and Chestnut-sided Warblers, Redstarts, Ovenbirds, Louisiana Waterthrushes and Maryland Yellow-throats.* But the refinements took me years.

---

* Since then deprived of the "Maryland" in its name by ornithologists, who have taken it on themselves to demote the Maryland Yellow-throat to a local race of a "Yellow-throat," despite the prior existence of a quite different Yellow-throated Warbler. They would now also demote the Baltimore Oriole, making it a race of a "Northern Oriole," thus virtually banishing the historic name.

Bringing more territory into my ken netted the Yellow-breasted Chat, whose extraordinary song, stringing out a grunt, a whistle, a mew, a toot, a rattle, is that of a child trying out various sound-making toys. For the others I had to acquire a sharper and more discriminating ear. Persistence was required, too. I thought I should break my neck before I could see aught but the pale underparts of the fairy-sized, silver voice that lisped a "zwee zee zu zu zee" high in the hemlocks by Lake Waccabuc: a Black-throated Green Warbler with golden cheeks; the spotting of a Blue-crowned Chlorophonia by Lago Izabal could hardly have set me up more. A Parula, sunset-breasted beneath a mantle of grey-blue sky, led me a creeping chase from one apple-tree to another—an agonizing one; each instant I foresaw mischance snatching the unknown little tantalizer away, out of my life. The Blue-winged Warbler turned out to be, in the idiom, not uncommon. Later I found the Golden-winged, then—oh, uplifting rarity!—that hybrid of the two, a Lawrence's Warbler, colored the deep yellow of the one with the black eye-patches and throat of the other. In cavities of dead trees by a remote pond on the shoulder of Waccabuc Mountain I came upon Tree Swallows nesting. The first of the recorded Pileated Woodpeckers returning to the county after generations' absence, red, white and black and big as a Crow, full of the species' wild *élan*, fell to my ecstatic lot to behold. On a grey day in February in the hemlock forest between two lakes I followed a deep, resonant hooting, all on a pitch, to find myself looking awestruck up into a tigerish visage appropriate to a gryphon: a Great Horned Owl's. . . . I drew a map of the area I covered and filled it in with symbols representing different types of vegetative cover. I had come to see breeding birds as part of the texture of the whole, illustrative of the character of the region they inhabit.

That is of course what they are. I think birders would generally agree that of the several lists they may keep of species observed—days' lists, years' lists and a life list are common—the most illuminating is that of birds nesting in a given locale. The Christmas bird-counts, in which nearly 25,000 now enlist, are by way of being a competitive sporting meet. They are an important demonstration of birding zeal and could hardly fail to bring forth valuable information on changing avian numbers and movements, but Christmas is a purely arbitrary and not very significant time for determining birds' whereabouts.

Surveys of breeding species give us more solid information on our avifauna. This is particularly true of organized breeding-bird censuses. These go back half as far in time as the Christmas counts, which began in a small way at the turn of the century. A census report gives the location and dimensions of the tract under study, a description of the topography and vegetation and the number and species of "territorial males"— those whose behavior, including singing, is evidence of their breeding status—together with nests located. To serve its purpose, a tally should be made year after year of the same tract so that trends in inhabitants may be detected. The 38th census in 1974 comprised 152 reports, all printed in *American Birds* and entered in a computer bank at the Patuxent Wildlife Research Center in Laurel, Maryland. Amateurs wishing to contribute to our quantifiable knowledge of birds could well take part in these censuses.

### Flora and Avifauna: The Unrolling Carpet

The absolute determinant of what birds live where is vegetation. Vegetation is food supply. Even the carnivores are dependent for their diet on herbivores. The sea-birds, whose eyes scan vistas barren of the least visible plant, can stray only briefly from the chlorophyl-bearing plankton that supports their prey. Vegetation is also vital, though not to the generality of sea-birds, in providing cover, especially for nesting.

Having said that, one could write volumes on the basically vegetative communities of which birds are a conspicuous and characteristic part. In the contiguous United States alone, the American Geographical Society recognizes 116 broad divisions of "potential natural vegetation"—plant communities as they would exist but for man's intervention. Of that intervention, the less said the less depressing. We have obliterated swamps and marshes teeming with life, reduced the stature and richness of the forest, built upon the shores, poisoned the estuaries and virtually eliminated the prairies. However, by opening up the continuous, great Eastern forest to diversity we created new opportunities for life. Insect- and seed-eating birds of meadow, brush, orchard and farmyard profited. Most of them probably increased greatly in number. However, since World War II the trend must seem to have been sharply the other way to anyone whose memory goes back forty years.

The distribution of birds is of absorbing interest to the ecologist, whose field is the interdependence of plants and animals in an *oikos*, as the Greeks called a dwelling place. (In Latin it became *uicus*, from which, via *uilla*, a farmstead, we have "village.") It is no less so to the artist, to whom the meaning of life is in the achievement of design out of refractory and unruly materials. Either one—and I suppose most of us who are serious about birds combine scientist and artist in varying proportions—can find satisfaction in the observation of a particular *oikos* or countryside, whether the satisfaction of piecing together the parts of an intricate machine or of establishing the many lively elements, great and small, of a masterfully composed landscape drama. There are equally rewards for both, as also for the birder who is a mere acquisitor of records, in travel to other biomes, as the major ecological divisions have come to be called.

Biomes vary most of all, of course, depending on which of the two sovereignties that divide the surface of our planet rules in them, earth or water. In a frontier zone between the opposing regimes, the determinant is how the two interact; the life of a bluff, rocky coast is bound to differ from that of a level one of broad estuaries and tidal flats. For the rest, climate is the main shaper of biomes, except that in those of the ocean the great currents play the larger role. As you cross the United States you can witness life's changing response to changes in the two principal components of climate. It is change in temperature that counts for most if you cross on a north-south meridian, rainfall if on an east-west parallel. Setting aside the northwest Pacific slope, where precipitation is the continent's highest, the western half of our country differs as much from the eastern in its prevailing aridity as the southernmost states from the northernmost in their greater warmth. It is worth a passing mention that our continent, roughly square above Mexico, with north-and-south-running mountains in both east and west and vast plains between them, geologically ancient and quiescent and topographically subdued, for the most part, in the east, young, active and of acute relief in the west, is a model of the work of the earth-shaping forces and their effect on the distribution of the forms of life.

As you move from a land-based to a water-based biome you meet a transformed avifauna. Nearing the coast, as the sky ahead acquires the pale translucence that marks the sea beneath it, you may confidently await the petulant cries of gulls, the shrill creaking of the nervously darting terns and the sight of statuesque herons by the marshes; if in the north those burghers of the rocky citadels in black-and-white attire: Auks, Puffins, Murres and Gannets. In the northern prairies another aquatic world awaits, to the bemusement of the Easterner, who finds its location most improbable. There, in the lakes and sloughs left by the glacier, nest many birds he is likely to think of as coastal: Red-necked and Horned Grebes (both un-recognizable in nuptial finery), Avocets, Willets and Wilson's Phalaropes, and a dozen species of ducks; the northern prairies have been called the continent's duck factory.

If you move up or down our coasts or, alternatively, across the continental biomes you find not so much new avifaunas as progressive modifications in the avifauna. Say that you began a tour at the northern tip of Greenland. Starting with the Ivory Gull you could go southward along the continents' edges from the range of one gull to another with scarcely an hiatus until you took leave of the last Kelp Gull on the Antarctic Peninsula. Or you could proceed eastward to the coast of Europe, through the Mediterranean and Red Seas and along the southern shores of Asia, and again you would have larine stepping stones, only with no break, until you came to the Slaty-backed Gull of Japan or the Buller's of New Zealand.

And all the forty-odd species of gulls would be basically the same bird, all nearly identical in proportions and white with almost always a darker mantle and sometimes a dark head. (Clearly all had a common ancestor not long ago in the time span of evolution, presumably a brown, streaked bird as are all immature gulls today and the Skua in maturity as well.) Your experience with the terns on such travels would be comparable, though they number fewer species.

Turning your steps inland, you will have almost wherever you go in North America a branch of a family in which the gradations are as gradual over as great a series as in the family of gulls and terns: the sparrows. Only look at the field guides! They give birders as much trouble in identification as the Laridae and as much sense of accomplishment when a difficult case falls into place. But the sparrows are only a small part of the show. Crossing the continent with the sun you exchange an array of eastern species for closely related western—the Red-shouldered and Broad-winged Hawks for the Feruginous and Swainson's; the Ruby-throated for half a dozen gem-like Hummingbirds; the Eastern Kingbird for the yellow-bellied Western; the Blue Jay for the peak-crested, dark-fronted Steller's; the Brown Thrasher for the Sage, Bendire's, California, LeConte's and Crissal Thrashers; the Indigo Bunting for the Lazuli; the Rose-breasted Grosbeak and Scarlet Tanager for the Black-headed Grosbeak and Western Tanager, both yellow-bodied. One could go on citing examples. And to these, of course, the West adds more exotic forms: its quails, exquisitely fashioned in predominant blues and greys, which replace the Bob-white; the Band-tailed Pigeon and White-winged Dove; the Road-runner; the White-headed and Lewis's Woodpeckers; the Magpie; the Dipper; the Phainopepla—to name the merest few. Variations within genera and families from one section of the country to another, the consequences of a pristine stock dividing into different species in response to differences in environment, lend an inexhaustible savor to long trips and can make bird guides as seductive as mail-order catalogues to a farm boy or girl.

The tendency is for Eastern forms to split up into several in the West, where topography and climate are more varied and compartmented. (The wood-warblers are a notable exception; the East is richer in these than the West.) All the same, a summer trip from the Deep South up into northern Maine and Quebec offers plentiful change along the way. Such a trip, which, with time for birding, would have made me breathless with anticipation in my boyhood, will take you through four of the seven life zones into which C. Hart Merriam of the Department of Agriculture divided North America. Basically longitudinal, these stretch across the continent from coast to coast, except the Tropical Zone, which reaches the United States only in extreme southern Florida. There, from Lake Okeechobee southward, are Sawgrass plains, Coconut Palms, Mangroves, broad-leaved evergreens, Sand Pine and Slash Pine and, for key birds, the Roseate Spoonbill, Reddish Egret, Noddy and Sooty Terns, Everglade Kite, Caracara, White-crowned Pigeon and Mangrove Cuckoo.

The next three of Merriam's zones to the north account for all the contiguous forty-eight states except for bits and pieces. Each of the three was divided by their formulator into a humid eastern and arid western half. The conception of life zones, while a revolutionary one when Merriam proposed them after a team of scientists under his leadership had explored the continent's flora and fauna, is today, it is true, treated rather disparagingly by the professional. For one thing, life zones have been around a long time—over eighty years. Biomes are much more up to date. But life zones relate the parts of the continent to one another, which biomes, each an entity in itself, do not. They are still very much with us as a key to distribution.

If I had my way, the local life zone would be posted at rest areas on federal highways, which would also be planted with trees typical of the zone. In the Deep South, which is to say the Southeastern coastal plain, these would include Live and Laurel Oaks, Longleaf Pines, Water Tupelo, Bald Cypress and Southern Magnolia. "AUSTRORIPARIAN, OR EASTERN LOWER

AUSTRAL, ZONE," the sign would state. And it would add: "Look for the Black Vulture, little Ground Dove, Chuck-will's-widow, Brown-headed Nuthatch, Boat-tailed Grackle and Painted Bunting."

Then, on highways to the north and west, where they reach the Piedmont or lower Chesapeake Bay, signs would announce the Carolinian, or eastern Upper Austral, Zone. The planting would be of Oaks (especially White and Post), Hickories, Flowering Dogwood, American Holly, Tuliptree, Black Tupelo, Shortleaf Yellow and Virginia Pines. Characteristic birds listed would be the Turkey Vulture, Acadian Flycatcher, Tufted Titmouse, Carolina Wren, Prothonotary and Kentucky Warblers and Cardinal.

The next zone comes with New York and New England. It is the Alleghenian, or eastern Transition, and it is special in that most of the American writers who first made us conscious of nature grew up and lived in it. Here are staples in the lore of trees: Sugar Maple, Beech, White and Red Oaks, Hemlock and White Pine. Here are birds that are household names: Bob-white, the Cuckoos, Eastern Kingbird, Great Crested and Least Flycatchers, House Wren, Brown Thrasher, Catbird, Veery, Baltimore Oriole, Bobolink, Indigo Bunting and Chipping Sparrow. Also the Golden-winged and Chestnut-sided Warblers. Here a caveat should be entered. Most of the birds cited as characteristic of a zone breed also in the zone to the north or to the south or in both; but where they are all together, you are in the zone of which they are said to be characteristic.

The Transition Zone is, I think, well named. Below it, you feel that the ruling influences have their seat of power in the tropics, above it that they have theirs in the arctic. Put another way, below the Transition, summer is normal and winter the exception, north of it, the converse. Beginning with the Canadian Zone, which succeeds the Transition—the Alleghenian—in northern New England and northern Wisconsin and Michigan, the avifauna is one that most Americans know, if at all, only as migrants: Goshawk, Spruce Grouse, the Three-toed Woodpeckers, Grey Jay, Red-breasted Nuthatch, Winter Wren, Hermit and Olive-backed Thrushes, the Kinglets, Junco, Siskin, the Crossbills and the majority of the warblers. In the northern part of the zone, the Spruces, Balsam Fir, the Big White Birch and Quaking Aspen are the mainstays of a forest that crosses Canada from sea to sea; there is no division here between an eastern humid and western arid half. Some would say it crosses Eurasia, too, making up a single boreal forest, or *taiga*, though with somewhat different but allied trees on the two continents. In the one as in the other, I am sure, the sense of the North is ever present among the dark conifers laced with the palest of deciduous trees. . . . Beyond the Canadian Zone the forest runs out in increasingly scattered and diminished stands separated by muskeg, scrub-growth and lichen-covered rocks: the Hudsonian Zone, home, if only for the short summer, of the Rough-legged Hawk, Great Grey Owl, Northern Shrike, Pine Grosbeak, Redpoll, Grey-cheeked Thrush and Tree Sparrow, all but the last two Eurasian as well as North American. The farther north we go (and I believe I am repeating myself here) the higher is the proportion of species common to the two hemispheres. When we put the last trees behind us and enter the Arctic Zone of tundra and briefly-flowering uplands, the Ptarmigan, Gyrfalcon, Snowy Owl, Lapland Longspur, Snow Bunting and most of the numerous water-birds we find nesting there we should also find across the ocean.

Because life zones are expressions of temperature, they follow protected waterways northward. The Carolinian, for example, in addition to extending out the coast of Connecticut and Long Island, ascends the Hudson and Connecticut Rivers deep into the Alleghenian. More strikingly, Canadian Zone forest snakes northward with the Yukon and its tributaries through the Hudsonian Zone and most of Alaska to Arctic tundra. Conversely, the northern zones go south down the mountains, on which temperature drops, on the average, three or four degrees with each thousand-foot gain in altitude. The spruce-fir forest of the Canadian Zone makes its way southward three-quarters of the way down through Maine at sea-level. Thereafter it crowns elevations above 2,500 feet along the Allegheny Front in Pennsylvania, above 3,500 in West Virginia and above 4,500 in North Carolina. In the higher Western mountains its southward projections are much larger. In Arizona it stands above 9,000 feet and in southern Mexico, on mighty volcanoes, above 12,000. In both places it is topped by belts of Hudsonian Zone rising to islands of Arctic.

In the southern Appalachians, from woods of Spanish and Water Oaks, Sweetgums and Tuliptrees, where the heat of noon silences the White-breasted Nuthatches, Carolina Chickadees, Yellow-throated and Hooded Warblers and Wood Thrushes, you may in an hour or two gain cloud-dewed forests of northern hardwoods and fragrant stands of balsam and spruce cool as a mountain spring and hear the tiny tin trumpet of the Red-breasted Nuthatch, the clear little skidding refrain of the Canada Warbler, the high, pitch-pipe notes of the Black-capped Chickadee, the minute Winter Wren's cadenced, twittering air, too swift for the human ear to follow, the Veery's downward looping scales that thrill the soul. The compression of zones in the range makes for heightened contrast. It makes, too, for that quality of delectability a model has in bringing what is vast into the compass of the embraceable—what delights a child in a miniature train or dolls' house. But if mountains that span a mere three life zones arouse the imagination on that account, how must it be in the Sierra Nevada of California, which encompasses twice as many?

The Sierras rise in the south from a steppe of Needlegrass and Speargrass and a desert of Creosote Bush and Joshua-trees: Lower Sonoran—Lower Austral—Zone vegetation. The basal quarter or third of the range is Upper Sonoran—Upper Austral— which you can tell from the Coulter and Digger Pines and Live Oaks, chaparral, Pinyon Pines and Juniper. The Transition Zone, climbing to 9,000 feet, brings great trees like White Fir and Douglas Fir, Ponderosa and Sugar Pines. Above it, the Canadian Zone forest is dominated by Red Fir. This is as high up the zonal ladder as the Appalachians go. Of what is above, Ezra Bowen of Time-Life Books writes in *The High Sierra,*

"There is an aura of suspense in the Sierra at the upper altitudes where the ground turns to rock and plants are few. This is the beginning of the high Sierra, the edge of another world—the Hudsonian Zone. . . . The nights are always chilly. Plants have three months in which to grow." Whitebark, Foxtail and Lodgepole Pines are typical trees. But, "as the tree climbs the mountain it shrinks, stoops and finally prostrates itself before harsh winds and heavy snow." The Hudsonian ends here, trees yielding to bare rock, lingering snow and an alpine tundra of low-growing grasses, sedges, lichens and little flowering plants of brave and captivating blossoms. Each stage of the ascent has its suit of birds, from the Roadrunner, black and yellow Scott's Oriole and giant Cactus Wren at the bottom to the little Grey-crowned Rosy-finch that is the special feature of the Arctic Zone, above 13,000 feet.

On the heights of the Rockies of Colorado and Wyoming, the Rosy-finch—here the Brown-headed—has the White-tailed Ptarmigan for a companion. As Bryce S. Walker, also of Time-Life Books, writes in *The Great Divide,* "A species of grouse lives at every level in the Rockies, and an old mountain hand can tell his elevation by them. Sage hens [Grouse] nest in the low hills and sage plains, as their name implies. . . . Ruffed Grouse inhabit the foothills among the Gambel oaks. . . . High up, in the conifer groves, live the spruce grouse, with dappled black and brown plumage. Blue grouse are a subalpine species. . . . Above the tree line there lives another grouse, the white-tailed ptarmigan." Scant cover offers up there, and the brown-backed Ptarmigan, which when it crouches becomes one with the sere plants and earth of summer, does in winter what the Varying Hare and Weasel do in snow country: alone among birds it turns white.

But birds differ in the degree of their conformity to zones. In the Sierra Nevada the Barn Owl inhabits the Lower Sonoran and fades out in the Upper, while the little Saw-whet confines itself to the Transition and the Great Grey Owl of circumpolar northlands to the Canadian. But the Great Horned, from the mesquite of Lower Sonoran arroyos breeds on up through the next three zones and into the Hudsonian. The hurried, slurred song of the Purple Finch tells you that you are in the Transition Zone, but the modest "chip chip chip . . ." of the Chipping Sparrow is heard from the foot of the range up to timberline.

Why these differences? To say that some birds are more adaptable than others merely restates the problem. Aggressiveness and vitality doubtless have much to do with it, but, again, in saying so we are only putting the question back another step: what makes for *them*? Leaving man out of it, intelligence appears to be an unreliable factor. The brainiest creatures other than man himself, the great apes, have succeeded in only the most special and limited environments. Yet the not-very-brainy Cougar ranges from swamps and deserts up high mountains and from Alaska to Patagonia. Superior wits have doubtless contributed to the near world-wide distribution of the Corvidae outside the polar regions, but the pigeons, which no one has ever thought very bright, have done almost as well. Neither the Great Horned Owl nor the Chipping Sparrow—those zone-straddlers—are noted for their mental gifts, nor are the Sharp-shinned Hawk, Kestrel or Robin, which breed from about treeline south through nearly all the continental United States.

Competition or lack of it obviously enters into the explanation. Few birds vie for the barrens and close-cropped grasslands that the Horned Lark makes its home and that man's destructive agriculture has greatly extended; and this species, with the decorated face of a tiny sacred bull, nests from the shores of the Arctic Ocean down through nearly all North America, except the southeastern states, to northern South America as well as around the top of the world (as the Shore Lark) and down into North Africa and Asia Minor. By contrast, a far-northern neighbor of the Horned Lark's, the handsome, black-fronted Harris's Sparrow, our largest sparrow, nests only in a strip of the Hudsonian Zone at treeline from Hudson's Bay part way to Alaska. But pushing out in any direction but north *Zonotrichia querula* would have to contend increasingly with other Sparrows having similar wants, including other *Zonotrichias*—the White-crowned and White-throated Sparrows.

Contrast, however, the black-masked Maryland Yellow-throat, which thrives over most of North America below the latitude of Hudson Bay, with the yellow-masked, black-throated Bachman's Warbler, which is bound so closely to a particular habitat—rather deep swampy woods in the Southeast —that with its shrinkage the species has become the most diffi-cult to find of all our Warblers. The noted case of the Kirtland's Warbler is even more extreme and certainly more puzzling. Only an open growth of young Jack Pines suits it; as the pines mature it must find other such stands, which come about only as an outcome of fires. In north central Michigan, to which it is now confined, fire prevention has been so successful that tracts must be deliberately burned to provide for the species. Presumably if deprived of this peculiar and comparatively sterile habitat it would simply accept extinction.

While the Bachman's and Kirtland's Warblers, with nothing to fear from man himself, have been receding toward possible disappearance, two birds in the face of strong human opposi-tion have fanned out globally in the past century, exploiting man's own works to do so. The European Starling and House Sparrow, from beach-heads to which man assisted them, have made most of the human world their domain, like the Norway Rat and House Mouse, and to the detriment of native birds, whose nesting cavities they aggressively commandeer. Another successful avian immigrant to our country mentioned earlier, and one that so far we have had no reason to regret, made it across the Atlantic on its own, albeit assisted by the trade wind that blows from Africa to northern South America. Though its coming was inadvertent, the Cattle Egret has, since its landing in the Guianas, pushed northward in increasing numbers to reach Newfoundland, Saskatchewan, Washington and British Columbia. In a fourth case of recent dramatic avian expansion the moving force was some dynamics within the species itself, perhaps a population explosion resulting from a diminution of natural enemies. Beginning in the 1930's, the Collared Turtle Dove began to expand northwestward from its breeding areas in the Balkans. It has since crossed Europe to occupy the

British Isles, southern Scandinavia and the Baltic states. The same kind of dynamics has doubtless contributed to the expansion northward in recent years of a number of American species formerly of the Carolinian Zone: the Great Egret, Little Blue Heron, Cardinal, Mockingbird and Turkey Vulture have spread all the way to Canada. In each of these cases a bird has pressed forward to colonize new and unfamiliar realms, the Starling and House Sparrow with belligerent assertiveness.

In the past it was common to write about animals in human terms. Today it is the other way around. We are more apt to look into ourselves for manifestations of our animal heritage. And possibly if we understood more of the reasons why birds differ so in adaptability and drive we should gain some clues to the causes of similar differences in the human race—for it does seem that some human stocks, or social groups, and individuals do better than others at meeting new and challenging situations and are more aggressive. Of course there may well be no analogy here between birds and men. Whether there is when we come to the next level of bird distribution is an issue in hot contention.

At the level we have been considering, there is the division of the world among species by biomes. Below it, there is the division of biomes among individuals of the same species—the staking out of the private properties of breeding pairs.

### Birds and Territory

To speak of birds as territorialists is—for me—to think of the Kingbird.

When asked as a boy what my favorite bird was, I answered unhesitatingly, the Kingbird. It is said, and I believe with warrant, that much can be told about a person if he can be pinned down as to what his favorite animal is. His true being may not stand revealed in the choice but in the way he would like to think of himself. The Kingbird's qualities were those I particularly admired, and still admire. The species could be considered, I suppose, among our more successful, though it is one of those that seem to me to have decreased markedly in the past generation (from pesticides, I should imagine). While here and there it nests in the forest roof where some trees rise well above their fellows, which must have been its original habitat, its strong preference is for a generous reach of open country set with trees and patches of weeds and if possible supplied with water. Given something of the sort it is not concerned with zones. Together the Eastern and Western species blanket the 48 states in their breeding ranges, which in sum extend from southern Canada to Argentina. But the Kingbird is not merely a summer inhabitant of a significant part of the earth's land area; for its size—about two ounces—it makes its presence felt in the preserve it marks out for its own more than any other creature less than ten times its size could—as far as I know—except a Sharp-shinned Hawk, which is not only larger but far better armed.

Smaller than a Robin, it is conspicuously patterned, sooty above to near black on the head and tail, and snowy beneath. An ordinarily concealed fiery crown and a striking white terminal band to its tail are its special insignia. *Tyrannus tyrannus*, the king of the kings, shows itself without constraint, scarcely bothering even to conceal its nest. Energy simmers in it; its "tseet! tseet!" could almost be the sound of steam released through a whistle valve. Frequently this energy brims over, lifting it from its perch and sending it skimming off over the tops of the vegetation of its estate. At such times and others the Kingbird often adopts a style of flight unique among birds of my acquaintance. The beats are so shallow and fast that, as Richard H. Pough says in *Audubon Bird Guide*, the wings appear to be quivering. Flying slowly, it is unmistakably holding itself back, as a cat will pull its punches when playfully cuffing its kitten or, less endearingly, a mouse. This practice, to one who knows the bird, is almost as expressive of its mettle as the speed it can unleash when it is of a mind to.

A Kingbird has its favorite perches, and they are those from which it can command the scene. Flying insects and inadmissible trespassers are the objects of its watch. Either will bring on its charge. The flycatchers are all of necessity accomplished in aerial evolutions, expert darters and twisters. The Kingbird is extremely fast as well. On a short course, at least, it can keep on the tail of a Chimney Swift. "Savage and fearless," Edward Howe Forbush wrote of it. (The brief essays on the species included in Forbush's monumental *Birds of Massachusetts and the Other New England States* are, all in all, probably still unexcelled—half a century later.) It may harry almost any bird from the neighborhood of its nest; I have seen one burst into a flock of Starlings and, striking right and left, prevent any of them from alighting in the hallowed tree. But the smaller the interloper, the safer it is. The larger—crows and hawks especially—are assaulted with a moral outrage that a half mile chase of the ducking, swerving quarry may not placate. A Buteo seeking escape in the soaring ascent at which it excels may be pursued to a height at which its assailant almost disappears from view below, its battle cries, like the jingling of steel pellets, softened by distance. The female may join in the initial attack; she is, indeed, a regular participant in the defense of the domain, at which, I understand, the pair arrives in the spring already conjoined.

Contrary to the rule propounded above, there is one smallish bird that the Little Chief, as it was called by some Indian tribes, throws itself against with unbridled belligerence. Because this is one adversary that can match its speed both in a straightaway and in maneuver and equals it in pugnacity, contests between the two unreel such sprints, ups and downs and zig-zag dashes through the trees as the eye can hardly follow. The other bird is another Kingbird.

The Kingbird is a supreme territorialist in a class of vertebrates among which territorialism is in general a key element of behavior in a crucial season of the year.

Except among colonial-nesting species it is common among breeding birds for a pair to claim a nesting and foraging preserve from which it seeks to expel others of the species. In most cases this is a matter of the male's defending it against other males. The Kingbird is highly unusual in its fits of intolerance of other species. Red-winged Blackbirds, Grackles, Mocking-

birds and some others attack Crows on their territories, but the object is to expel not a rival territorialist but a predator on eggs and young. Colonial birds share their often wide-ranging hunting-areas but are likely to guard jealously the immediate environs of the nest. These environs, however, may extend no farther than the reach of a sitting bird's bill. As might be expected, sea-birds that nest in close proximity from necessity owing to the limited availability of nesting grounds seem to be much touchier about property rights, especially where failure in vigilance may result in loss of nesting material to a snatchy neighbor, than swallows and weaver-finches—those apartment-dwellers—that nest together more from choice.

A territory is customarily selected by the male. He will probably have arrived from the south ahead of his destined mate. If a permanent resident of the area he may have been in occupation of the territory through the winter. A Mockingbird will have been; the vigorous October song season of the species indicates that that is when territories are being staked out. (Female Mockingbirds are reported to have territories of their own over the winter, and one Mocker to a territory at that season is certainly my experience.) Arriving on the scene, the female evidently chooses among the opportunities on the basis of both the charms of the suitor's person and address and the qualities of his territory as her inspection will have discovered them—and happy the female of any species to whom sentiment and practicality speak with one voice! This territory the male will have picked and defended against any challengers or, perhaps, have won from the possessor as a challenger himself. It may be one he held the year before.

The establishment of exclusive territories must be advantageous for a species; otherwise evolution would not have made it as widespread as it is. What it does is space out the occupants and give them *lebensraum*. Without rather clearly defined territories, breeding pairs might be brought into close juxtaposition. Friction between them, squabbling over nesting sites, mates and sources of food could be incessant. The parties, their capacities already strained by the demands of the season, might be critically distracted if not bodily injured. The territorial system also disperses the population of a species, preventing bunching up in favorable locales. The species may gain in adaptability and dominion, too, from its members' being forced into marginal environments, as the younger sons of a landed aristocracy may be forced to emigrate to new lands.

That territorialism should reduce conflict is, however, not self-evident. Why does it not simply substitute conflict over territory for conflict over other issues? To begin with, it does. Battles over territory may be so intense, it appears, as to cause the rupturing of a combatant's heart or aorta from stress. Even when these have been fought to a conclusion and the countryside is divided up, there is apt to be continuing territorial conflict. You may see Mockingbirds in such conflict, prancing before each other, face to face, erect, tails up, throughout the nesting season. Such sparrings are conspicuous among Robins, too. But mostly it is along the demarcation lines of territories where sovereignties are less clearly defined and the birds' passions less engaged that these stand-offs take place, not in the heart of a territory. That this is so is because of an ingredient of the territorial instinct without which the whole system might collapse into just the kind of continual warfare that would seem implicit in it. The possessor of a territory has a profound psychological advantage over an intruder. He has on his side, it would seem, a sense of rectitude and a reservoir of emotional strength. We have all seen how the most wretched cur at the home of its master will challenge the trespasser with righteous and vociferous wrath. It is on its territory. On a public road even a more formidable animal may slink away from a stranger, lacking moral conviction. With our own species, in which territory may be either individual (giving rise to the legal conception of a man's home as his castle) or collective (embodied in the idea of patriotism or nationalism), it is proverbial that a people fights with peculiar tenacity and courage in its own country.

The strength of the territorial psychology in birds was brought out by the English ornithologist David Lack in an experiment with European Robins, a species in which territory is defended the year around. (Referring to Christmas cards that show four or more Robins happily sharing a holly branch, Lack observes that "Should the depicted incident occur in nature, furious conflicts would arise." Lack's book on *The Life of the Robin* is a model study of an avian species.) A male trapped by him was left in a cage where caught. When its territory was invaded by another male, identified by Lack as Double Blue because of the bands he had placed on its leg, the rightful tenant "at once postured violently and uttered a vigorous song-phrase from inside the trap, and Double Blue, who was one of the fiercest of all the robins, promptly retreated to his own territory, . . . I now caught the first male and moved him into a trap in the territory of Double Blue. The formerly timid Double Blue now came raging over the trap, posturing violently at the first male inside, while the latter, formerly so brave, made himself as scarce as possible, and did not attempt to fight or posture back." The psychological advantage a bird gains by being on its own territory is brought out even more forcibly in Frederick B. Kirkman's observations on the mutual behavior of young gulls and alien adults: "Outside the nest the chick is a hunted creature, pecked by every adult it passes and fortunate if it escapes with its life. Yet, inside the nest it opens its stubby wings, raises a small shrill voice, charges heroically, and the adult beats a retreat."

Joint possession of a territory, like the shared occupation of a home by human beings, doubtless strengthens the bonds of a mated pair. Border confrontations and tussles between neighboring males may well also stimulate both to the more active performance of their connubial roles. But that, it seems to me, is only the beginning. With the territorial imperative, as Robert Ardrey calls it, there was, I cannot help feeling, introduced a new element in life almost comparable in ultimate psychological potential to the introduction of sexual reproduction, of which it came about as an outgrowth and remains a partner. In the Kingbird's ardor for its small plot of the vast earth may, I believe, be discerned a germ of lofty human achievement.

Into the defense of its holdings the Kingbird throws itself with a combativeness that is unmistakably exhilarating to it. This is no mere functional protection of the nesting area from injurious invasion. That is evident from the zealous territorialist's enthusiastic pursuit of birds offering not the least threat, preferably big birds. When hawks are lacking, a wholly innocuous heron will do. What counts is the sport of the thing, the demonstration of prowess. It is the heady wine of victory. You can tell that from the jaunty bearing of the small warrior when it returns from a high-climbing pursuit in a series of glissandos to fetch up on its tree-top perch. "Tsee-ee-ee-ee-ee-ee-ee!" it cries, tail spread, wings trembling and flaming crown doubtless displayed.

Up to now, while I have not disguised the subjectivity of my approach to birds, I have tried to remain within the bounds of objectively ascertainable fact. Here I depart for a space. As I see it, the possession of a territory must give the possessor a view of the universe from a quite different plane.

Where otherwise it would be a mere visitor to its surroundings, a bearer of the brunt of physical forces, driven by hunger within and harried by others similarly driven, it now becomes a proprietor, a power in the scheme of things. As pride is stimulated, the sense of self is strengthened. In the hierarchy of the Army, the difference between being a private and being a corporal is all the difference in the world, as I can testify. The corporal acts with the authority that comes down to him through the chain of command from the President, who derives it from the governed—and *vox populi, vox dei.* And I suggest that it is with a sense however dim of a comparable moral authority that the Kingbird surveys his domain. He is a communicant of the Universal. Observe him as evening nears. He needs then no intruder upon his fiefdom to set him off, no "releaser," as the behaviorists term it. As the sun approaches its setting he launches forth, beating a steady course, repeatedly sounding his sharp and challenging cry. Then at intervals come his acrobatics. He throws himself into a flurry of twists, turns, feints inextricable to the eye and accompanied by an excited acceleration of his tsee-ing. This is the Kingbird's dance, his war dance, akin to the war dance of the Indians. Thus he dispatches the enemies of the rightful order —he, the warrior, the elect. Higher he goes, breaking his even pace every moment with that tangle of gyrations. He is enraptured, ecstatic. And higher still he may go, his underside gleaming silver in the sunlight that has now left the earth. He is possessed by spirit, like the Indians celebrating the powers that rule. He is at one with the greatness of things.

At length he must return to earth to abide the morrow, and let me emulate him. The New World flycatchers, the Tyrannidae, of which the Eastern Kingbird is the titular head in scientific nomenclature, belong to the great modern order of Passeriformes, as do about half the existing species of birds. It is these we have approximately in mind when we speak of song-birds. Technically, however, the song-birds are contained in the suborder Oscines, which excludes the New World flycatchers. The former have a more complex arrangement of membranes and of the muscles controlling them in the syrinx, or voice-box, located where the windpipe branches to the two lungs. Where the Kingbird delivers its manifesto in a dramatic aerial pantomime, Oscines in general employ song for theirs. I am speaking now not of performances to win a mate; the Kingbird has its courtship flight, too, as have many and diverse birds. What I have in mind is a performance that, however purposeful in origin, is carried on as an end in itself as I believe flight often is in many birds and—though here I am getting ahead of myself—song as well.

The Willet, *the* summer sandpiper of our east coast, and a big and conspicuous one, breeding also by ponds in the northern plains, puts on an aerial show analagous, I believe, to the Kingbird's. A "ceremonial flight," William Vogt calls it, as one might the Kingbird's. (Bill Vogt, an ecologist whom I first met when, at Jones Beach, Long Island, Louis Halle and I recovered an injured teal and returned it to the sanctuary he was running, became one of the first to try to rouse the world to the potentially catastrophic population explosion.) As the Kingbird's must be, the Willet's performance, Vogt's observations in the *Proceedings* of the Linnaean Society show, is basically a territorial demonstration, but—well, let the reader judge for himself:

> The male, rapidly and loudly calling *pill-will-willet* over and over again, would rise into the air and, with wings arched stiffly downward and moving in short, quick beats, fly in circles, . . . would mount higher and higher, often until he nearly vanished. At times he would drop thirty or forty feet only to zoom upward again with a vigor and lightness it was difficult not to call ecstatic. The tips of the wings flicker like tongues of black and white flame. . . . Against an intense blue sky, or piled cumulus clouds, this display is as stirring a performance as I have ever seen in the bird world. . . . After flying about in

circles of varying diameters and for varying amounts of time, the male would begin to descend often almost vertically, often with wings barely moving as it rode the wind head on, and with long legs drooping. The *pill-will-willet*-ing usually continued, unabated, until the male had dropped near to the ground. . . .

If the flight of birds awakens a poetry in us, their song goes to our hearts. It seems to me, conscientiously as I try to re-sist the idea, to bespeak a certain affinity of sentience between them and us transcending miraculously the biological gulf dividing their kind from ours. If that gulf is immense, the prime begetter of song in birds is a stimulus by no means alien to us—or so some ethologists contend. We, too, in their view, are responsive to the territorial voice. "Man, I shall attempt to demonstrate in this inquiry, is as much a territorial animal as is a mockingbird singing in the clear California night," Robert Ardrey asserts at the start of *The Territorial Imperative*, in which he makes an effective statement of his thesis. "If we defend the title to our land or the sovereignty of our country, we do it for reasons no different, no less innate, than do lower animals," he writes. "The dog barking at you from behind his master's fence acts for a motive indistinguish-able from that of his master when the fence was built."

The contention has been strenuously disputed. I suspect that many persons simply find it unthinkable that a commit-ment to personal and tribal demesnes should be embedded in the nature of man. Minimizing man's animal inheritance, such persons are temperamentally inclined to view our species as capable of indefinite self-reformation and social progress to-ward utopia—a utopia necessarily based on the full sub-ordination of nature. (If a man is to order himself and his world, no interference by another authority can be brooked.) Others are of a different temperament. They—we—see nature as an organic whole, man included, and believe that while its tissues are elastic, the farther they are stretched the more likely their recoil becomes and the more devastating when it is released. And in the marvel of nature's ultimately mysterious arrangements there is as much satisfaction to be found, I think, as from any projection of a fully rationalized and all-victorious human society.

According to Professor Edward O. Wilson of Harvard, one of the founders of sociobiology, writing in *Harvard Magazine* for April 1975, territoriality among monkeys and apes "occurs widely, but [is] variable in pattern," in early man "probably occurred [but the] pattern [is] unknown," and among existing hunter-gatherer societies is "general, especially marked in rich gathering areas." It would appear to be in our blood, and I cannot see that it has been much diluted, if any.

To me, territoriality in man, while provocative of some of his worst excesses, has given rise in him to great achievements. Human cultures, as I interpret history, have a territorial base. By that I mean not only that all peoples of cultural attainments have inhabited a geographically defined area but that a sense of their identity with that area, in all the cases we know about, has lain deep in the collective psyche. I suspect, even, that a sense of their identity as a people derives from a sense of their identification with their country. Of this we have probably been witnessing the most impressive illustration ever in the determination of the Jews to repossess Palestine, after two millennia. ("If I forget thee, Jerusalem. . . .") Men have died in the tens of millions for the fatherland, the homeland: *Dulce et decorum est pro patria mori.* The sense of our territory's being ours makes us the Creator's surrogate in its rule. We see this symbolized in the divine right of kings, from which our conception of sovereignty is derived. We invoke the Creator's powers, or, if pagans, the powers of the deities of hill and river and forest. We share in the divine role and assume, if palely, divine attributes. We, too, engage in creation. Carving in bone, sculpturing, inventing songs and dances, we go on to enact dramas, design temples, paint murals, compose symphonies and write novels.

And birds conduct rituals of courtship, demonstrate histrionically on the wing, perform pantomimes of display, in some cases create architecturally and—above all—sing.

## The Ritual of Courtship

While singing seems an expression of birds' nature and harmonious with it, one is impressed on the whole by how awkward the requirements of reproduction have been for the Class Aves. A low-keyed accommodation to sex, as to a function to be taken in stride, which the Class Mammalia appears in general to have managed (though it may be my ignorance that gives me that impression), has been too much for birds as it has for civilized man. The reasons in the two cases are rather the opposite, however. Man's difficulties arise from the intensity of his desire coupled with the possibility of indulging it at any time; he has the leisure for it and both human sexes are physically ready for sexual intercourse from day to day the year around. In birds the desire is intense enough, by all the signs, certainly in the males, but it strikes seasonally. It explodes then within creatures that for the balance of the year answer to totally different concerns and excitations, and its satisfaction has consequences that transform their routine. Except when the gonads are enlarged for breeding, birds are essentially sexless, even more so than pre-adolescent human beings. At those times it would be as unreasonable to expect a male bird to act with gallantry toward a female as to be surprised if a nine-year-old boy comports himself less than romantically toward girls.

Birds go through a highly compressed puberty, with all its dislocations, every year. When it comes, they cannot waste time; the testes have grown by as much as 200 or 300 times and the ovaries between ten and 50 times, and flying machines so finely honed cannot afford to carry the excess weight around longer than necessary. Yet serious impediments to fruitful union must be overcome. In many species the sexes are so like in appearance as to have difficulty telling each other apart. Even gregarious birds are ordinarily somewhat wary of one another, keeping at least out of lunging distance. Moreover, a physical preparedness for coition does not imply a psychological. As well as rival males having to be repelled, females have to be won over, while males themselves may not be self-starters. Finally, many species of birds share a breeding range with one or more others of similar appearance, and cross-breeding must be prevented if vital energies are not to be squandered on the production of sterile eggs or offspring.

The answers to these needs have been found in courtship rituals and song—and quite different ones among similar species. The heading off of the female pigeon by her bowing suitor, who puffs out the burnished feathers of his neck as he traipses in front of her and protests his ardor with a smothered "coo, coo, ruckata coo!" and the crouching of the male House Sparrow as, with flattened body and head back between the shoulders he hops stiffly before the object of his desires: these spectacles are familiar to most of us from public parks. Others are well known to those who grew up on farms: the quick promenade of the clucking cock in an arc before the hen, head and outside wing lowered, his even showier hackles distended; the ostentation of the male Red-winged Blackbird in an alder who leans toward the brown-streaked female, fluffed out, half extending his wings and perhaps vibrating them the better to display his expanded epaulettes, scarlet against his raven suiting, while out he pours a liquid gurgle rising to a high-pitched "reee!" of challenge.

Sexual union, it would appear, comes more naturally when it is led up to by stylized, thus unequivocal, and stimulating theatricals. Then, too, where male and female are indistinguishable to the eye, a ceremonial overture by a male to a stranger invites a clarifying response. Michael Fedak says that "It's not uncommon to see an Emperor Penguin waddle up to another bird at the rookery and get bowled over when his amorous advances are mistakenly directed toward another male." A male Adélie Penguin's gambit, Robert Cushman Murphy writes, is "bowing and making the gesture of placing a pebble (real or imaginary) at the feet of a neighbor." He adds that "If the latter pays no attention to the approach, it is at best an unreceptive female; if it fights, it is probably a male. . . . If, however, the second bird responds appropriately, it is a female nearing the oestrus condition." She "may reply in kind. On the other hand, she may peck the suitor cruelly, to all of which he tamely submits, hunching himself up and shutting his eyes. After a brief display of such fractious temperament, the hen usually becomes appeased, whereupon the abused male rises to his feet, edges up to her in his prettiest manner, and utters soft guttural sounds as preliminary love-making. Both birds then assume the 'ecstatic' attitude, swaying their necks from side to side with crossed beaks and both uttering shrill cries."

The crossing or scissoring of beaks among courting sea-birds may be analogous in origin to human hand-shakes, if it is true that the latter came about from two warriors' gripping each other's sword hands to immobilize them, symbolically if in no other way. Hostile and courting behavior seem closely linked, at least to the extent that the same demonstration—song, notably—that warns off another male advertises to a female the swain's receptivity and desire. Among some species in which males and females look alike, the former customarily establish the sex of a newcomer simply by attacking. If the one attacked does not fight back and flees only half-heartedly, perhaps by appeasing signs, it indicates it is a female. How reliable the method may be is open to question, however. The Mockingbird whose territory is the surroundings of our house has so far this spring had two visitors, one in mid February, the other on May 1st, and, while he is unusually pacific toward other birds at the feeding-station, he pursued both with such vigor as scarcely to give them a chance to reveal themselves as potential mates—if they were.

A theory developed by various ethologists, Niko Tinbergen observes in *The Animal in Its World*, "briefly . . . states that courtship originated as, and often still is, the outcome of a conflict between sexual attraction and agonistic tendencies"— *agonistic* meaning combative, from the Greek word for a contest. Tinbergen has found the theory confirmed in the gulls, of which his studies are famous. The movements that male and female gulls go through, he says, are identical with or extremely similar to those of two males in a hostile encounter. Pair-formation, he explains, begins on a "pairing territory [where] males are on the lookout for passing or approaching birds—males and females—to which they respond by the Oblique-cum-Long Call." Oblique is Tinbergen's term for the position of a half-elevated gun-barrel the challenging male assumes. "Whereas other males avoid such 'singing' males, unmated females are attracted to them and alight near them. . . . The sequence after alighting consists of one or two threat postures, followed by an appeasement posture. . . . A striking difference in the performance of these displays between agonistic encounters and pair formation situations is that in the latter the birds often stand or run parallel to each other, whereas in a hostile clash the two opponents often face each other." One appeasement posture is "the Hunched," but a more general is "the Facing Away." In the latter one suspects that the significance lies in the removal of the powerful and generally bright-colored gull bill as a threat, just as an appeasing wolf turns its jaws aside and presents its vulnerable throat and a bison turns aside its horns, presenting its flank. This seems to be borne out by the Facing Away in Black-headed Gulls, which, like some others, wear a dark and probably provocative mask in breeding plumage, "for by pointing the bill down even the upper rim of the mask is completely hidden from view. This effect is further safeguarded by raising the white feathers of the nape."

Among many unrelated species of birds it is courtship practice for the male to proffer food to the female, who customarily receives it in the dependency pose of a begging nestling. (Human females have also been known, at this stage of affairs, to adopt a child-like behavior or speech, inducing a sense of protective maleness in the suitor.) Undoubtedly this helps attune the partners to their respective sexual roles. So, surely, do courtship dances. These have many and startling forms, the females in general taking equal part where the sexes are alike in appearance.

None of the dances is more astonishing than those of cranes and grebes. The former bow and pirouette to one another, skip, hop and jump; one pictures a quadrille of solemn senior dignitaries, stilt-shanked and knobby-kneed, incredibly agile for their years. Our own Sandhill Cranes have been seen to leap fifteen or twenty feet into the air. "Occasionally whole flocks on the wintering grounds, or on the resting grounds while migrating, will go through these antics together," Oliver L. Austin, Jr., writes. "They may be an outlet of emotion, or perhaps just a playful release of energy." Grebes, ordinarily restrained birds, dance upright on the water. A pair of European Great Crested Grebes face each other in the so-called penguin dance, each with a piece of pond weed—nesting material—in its bill. Our Western Grebes, heads and long, arched necks in the position of a striking snake's or attacking swan's, go skittering across the surface of the water side by side in a performance that not only has to be seen to be believed but even when seen is hardly believable. In the Fulvous Tree-duck of our southern coastal areas, pairs also run upon the surface in a post-copulatory dance, side by side, each partner with off wing raised. In most species of grebes both sexes, drab in the off-season, not only acquire nuptial ornamentation—head plumes or bright colors of head and neck, or both—but display to each other. In gulls, terns and alcids, it is common for both sexes to assume a more striking pattern in spring as it is among their relatives the shorebirds to acquire bolder, bright hues. In general, however, only one sex takes on showier dress for breeding. We could say only males were it not for the Phalaropes, Painted Snipe and Button- or Bustard-quail. Among these the brighter colors adorn the females, who do the courting and leave the incubation of the eggs and care of the young to the male, in a reversal of roles hard to account for.

Where one sex stands to profit disproportionately from its commerce with the other or have special need of the other's favor, its courtship garb is likely to be particularly highly developed or its courtship behavior aggressive, or both. (The human species is no exception. While in most societies both sexes attire themselves fancily for amatory conquests, in the century following the accession of Queen Victoria to the throne, when middle-class *mores* held males to monogamy and the respectable status and economic security offered by husbands were indispensable to females, men generally contented themselves with sober dress while women decked themselves out extravagantly, to the misfortune of birds, whose plumes and even whole skins they flaunted.) Among avian species, the males that most exceed the females in ornament are likely to be the confirmed bachelors that mate with as many partners as they can and bear no responsibility for the rearing of the young. Such are the lordlings of those families in which an apparel of splendor second to none in nature is sported. One feels uncomfortable for the drab objects of the display, the females that suffer not only the contrast with their overpoweringly brilliant consorts but all the household duties as well. But only contemplate those males: hummingbirds in fiery gorget and suit of burnished mail; birds of paradise with patches of feathering like glass, quills like twisted enameled wires, plumes like mist and pennoned plumes sweeping back from the head, all in colors of the richest variety, displayed against velvet blacks and browns in expandable and erectable mantles, breastplates and false wings—such plumage as led Europeans on seeing the first skins brought back by mariners to believe them truly the garb of birds celestial in abode; pheasants clad in scarlet and molten gold, in overlapping capes of metallic scales, silver, emerald and cobalt, each edged in black, or one of a score of other habiliments beggaring imagination. By heavens! To be courted by such a creature must be for the plain henbirds like a visitation from a god. Juno herself was not above appearing with a Peacock as her intimate. And let us reflect that it was the plain hen-birds that largely brought into being the gorgeous caparison of their lovers—for it is not to be imagined that the sublime artistry birds exhibit is something in which they have had no say, as it was ordained that rubies glow red and opals be opalescent. The choice was theirs. It was not that, created beautiful, they made show of what they were given. On the contrary. Ernst Mayr (whom I had the distinction of showing some of my special avian province in Westchester County when he was a young man newly come to the United States) has spoken on this matter with the authority that is his in his *Animal Species and Evolution:* "A shift into a new niche or adaptive zone is, almost without exception, initiated by a change in behavior. The other adaptations to the new niche, particularly the structural ones, are acquired secondarily." The stunning visual attributes of birds today must have had their start in the display by the ancestors of those birds of what little they had. Then, by the process of natural selection, their plumage grew more varied and brilliant in hue, acquired iridescence, combined colors in more daring and arresting patterns, developed novel forms—aigrettes, hackles, ruffs—was seconded by gaudy wattles. Males so fashioned as to overawe rivals and attract mates tended to pass their endowments on to subsequent generations. It was those rivals—other males—and the females that determined at every stage in the slow and gradual process what embellishments would be adopted. Each avian species is the author of its own heraldry.

As a rule, the more a bird has to display, the greater the pains he is at to display it. The Peacock, as Welty engagingly puts it, "spreads his fan-like tail-coverts and approaches the female obliquely with the drab rear-side of his fan exposed to her. At just the right distance, he suddenly swings himself around and dazzles her with every one of the hundred or more shimmering 'eyes' vibrating and every quill rattling. To climax the performance, he screams with demonic ardor and then settles back to let his theatrics sink in." Birds of paradise may even hang upside down and turn backward somersaults to show their finery to most striking effect. They are, as E. Thomas Gilliard, an American ornithologist, writes in *Birds of Paradise and Bower Birds:*

famous . . . for their strange and beautiful dance movements which frequently make the males appear startling and grotesque and more ornament-like than bird-like.

Some species dance in trees, charging and then posturing stiffly with their long lace-like cascades of plumage; some hang in shimmering, pendulous masses beneath limbs. Other species dance on vertical shafts in columns of sky light which they let in through the roof of the forest by laboriously stripping away the leaves. Other males dance on low vines or on the ground, alternately freezing then spinning with their circular feather skirting extended ballerina-like.

The birds of paradise described by Gilliard are among the diverse species in which the male, to win whatever females come his way, puts on his displays at a regular station, or court. One of them is the Argus Pheasant of Malaysia, largest of the family after the Peacock and believed by some to be the origin of the legendary Phoenix. With its elongated "argus-eyed" secondary wing-quills and tail it forms great fans, and of such lovely shades of brown and grey, so subtly marked with black tracings that you would suppose the hen a creature of the most cultivated aesthetic sensibilities. At the opposite extreme are the little manakins, of a tropical American family somewhat resembling the kinglets but bright as enameled brooches. In these the males are given to joint performances, to which they are drawn by a characteristic call—not just the two stars but additional males, to look on. Paul Slud, writing in *The Auk*, has described a dance of one of the species, the Long-tailed Manakin:

> Perched crosswise a foot or two apart, facing in the same direction, the two birds alternately rise straight into the air for a foot or two. Each fluttering rise is preceded by a lowering of the head, and at the top of the rise the bird hangs suspended for an appreciable pause, as though attached to a rubber band. The red crown of the bowed head appears unusually large and bright, the sky-blue back loosely fluffed, the long tail arches and hangs in a graceful curve, and the bright orange legs hang too. A guttural *miaow raow* punctuates each rise. . . . As the

tempo mounts, the crest of the risings falls lower and lower and the pitch of the accelerating *miaow raow*'s rises higher and higher until the former degenerate into seemingly uncontrolled flutters and the latter into unintelligible buzzy sounds. . . . As though a switch were pulled, the orgiastic frenzy ends suddenly, and the birds cock their heads innocently in calm possession of faculties restored. . . .

In some birds, numbers of males spend their time on communal displaying grounds, called arenas or "leks," in which each has acquired a court in contest with other males through artifices of intimidation and actual fighting. One is that singular sandpiper the Ruff, which breeds across northern Eurasia and occasionally turns up on our shores. In the nuptial season, along with red or yellow facial wattles, the male Ruffs grow extravagant feather collars and showy tufts from the crown fitting them, it would seem, for a box at the opera. The colors, as *Audubon Magazine* observes, "may be black, white, purple, orange, yellow, or almost any shade between. The pattern may be spotted, speckled, or solid, and the ruff may contrast in hue with the tufts." Continuing, it remarks that

> showing absolutely no interest in nesting or rearing young, the males dance in meadow and marsh for almost two months. A half-dozen or so males display on each lek, which is merely a slight rise in the ground often worn by years of use as a mating site. . . .
>
> Competition for the courts triggers furious battles between the ruffs, which leap into the air, pecking, kicking, slashing with wings, and seizing one another with long, pointed bills. Strangely, despite the violence, the battle is as bloodless as it is turbulent, for the territorial combat of ruffs is so highly ritualized that exhaustion rather than death or injury signals defeat. . . .
>
> As the reeves [the females] enter the lek, the ruffs compete for their attention with swelling plumage and drag-

ging wings. They turn about, charge one another, or freeze with ruffs and tufts raised.

Recalling that in these postures they reminded the British ornithologist C. R. Stonor of a bed of flowers, Gilliard presents a touching picture of the finale:

> The female wanders through the cluster and pecks at the neck feathers of the bird she prefers. Mating occurs immediately—whereupon the rejected males collapse on their courts as if in a fainting spell.

Other arena birds are the Black Grouse of the Old World and three of its North American relatives—the Sharp-tailed, Sage and Pinnated Grouses (the last called the Prairie Chicken). Among all these, competition brings out much dancing, strutting, bowing and other dramatics and the display of erectable feathers and, in the American Grouses, of inflatable colored neck sacs, from which issue cooing or booming sounds. In the Sage Grouse, several hundred cocks may resort to an arena as much as half a mile long. For the female, opportunity offers to indulge in two of her sex's favorite pastimes—going shopping and enticing males—in a single operation. Promenading through the arena, she makes her choice or accepts the advances of one of the dominant males. In either case, the liaison does not last beyond coition.

The foot-stamping, bowing and strutting of the Sage Grouse are imitated by the Blackfoot Indians, even the Grouse's spread tail in the costume of the dancers, according to Welty, who goes on to cite other examples of the imitation of birds' dancing by primitive peoples, back to the introduction of a Crane Dance at Delos by Theseus. His view is that with both birds and men the dances may serve not only to prepare the actors for love or combat but also—as Austin suggested in the case of the cranes—to release excess energy. Discharging overloaded circuits would be another way of putting it. Impulses that Nature instills in us have a way of proving excessive. They build up faster than our internal machinery or external circumstances will permit us to give expression to them. (Pinnated Grouse cocks begin performing in their arenas months before the hens arrive.) Nevertheless, they demand an outlet—and thus is the basis laid for what I should call the creative.

That reflection leads naturally to those court-performers that, in the words of G. Evelyn Hutchinson, "exhibit behavior of a kind which in its complexity and refinement is unique in the nonhuman part of the animal kingdom," or, as Austin declares, "have developed skills as architects and decorators found nowhere else in the animal kingdom below man": the bowerbirds, a family closely related to the birds of paradise and less closely to the crows and jays. Some bowerbirds are brilliantly colored. Those that gave the family its name make up for what they lack in personal adornment by the elaborateness of the theatres they construct for their performances and the striking decorations with which they embellish them. The Stagemaker Bowerbird (cited in an earlier chapter for smashing snails on an anvil-stone) lays out a green, as it were. Clearing a space, it covers it with leaves it cuts with its serrated bill, disposing them paler side up (repositioning them that way, moreover, if an experimenter turns them over) and replacing them with fresh specimens as they wilt. Others create "the most beautiful structures built by birds," as an early investigator, A. L. Goodwin, put it, interweaving sticks to form cradle-like corridors up to three feet long, huts like thatch-roofed cottages with yards enclosed by hedges, tents with a sapling as a center-pole from four to nine feet in height, some of them the work of years. One can understand how the first naturalist to encounter a bowerbird's court, a century ago, was led by its scale and intricacy, its garden of plucked flowers and its other bright appurtenances to believe he was seeing a product of human inventiveness.

Does any other animal than man go to such lengths to win a mate? Male bowerbirds strew their courts with the fruits of their collecting zeal. Where others of their sex display spectacular feathering, they pick up and show off to the female their most striking possessions. The German ornithologist Heinz Sielmann found 500 bleached kangaroo bones and 300 pale yellow snail shells before one of the tunnel-like arbors of the Great Bowerbird of Australia. One courtier of the species had a very special *objet d'art* to hold up to the female: a tin mug. To the predilection of some of the tribe for whitened bones, man has ministered by introducing sheep and rabbits into Australia. A. J. Marshall of the University of London relates that one observer counted 1,320 bones in the edifice of a Spotted Bowerbird in Victoria, adding that European settlement has also enriched the species' collections with broken glass, brass cartridge-cases, screws, bolts, other pieces of metal and wire, scissors, knives, spoons and thimbles. He tells of a knowing owner of a motorcar who, finding the keys missing, repaired to the nearest Spotted Bowerbird's court, half a mile away, and there retrieved them. A Bushman dignitary's prized glass eye, having disappeared from its overnight repository—a cup of water—was found in a similar site, "staring vacantly up from among the bones and shells on the display-ground."

Marshall considers the Spotted Bowerbird "probably the most gifted mocking-bird known." Certainly the vocalizations of some bowerbirds are among the most astonishing features of this fascinating family. Gilliard writes of the Archbold's Bowerbird of New Guinea:

> The frantic male . . . performed and "talked" in the most extraordinary manner, almost seeming to be communicating in a complex avian language with the female. . . . At the climax of activity . . . the male . . . began emitting loud cat-like *meows* and explosive sounds like the drumming of grouse—also rapping, ticking sounds and windy creaking noises too numerous and varied to describe. It also emitted calls of other birds, and "other" birds seemed to be everywhere in a forest which at other times is noteworthy for its relative silence.

The male Satin Bowerbird of Australia is of particular interest as a collector because of his partiality to blue objects—flowers, scraps of cloth and paper, bits of glass, bags of bluing—which match his startlingly blue eyes and the sheen of his black plumage, and his secondary preference for yellowish green objects, which approximate the color of the female's plumage and eyes. The instinct would indicate that the objects of display are in fact to be accounted an extension of the bird's person. What is most remarkable about the Satin Bowerbird is that he daubs his bower with a paste he obtains by masticating colored plant substances and charcoal mixed with saliva, applying it with a spongy pellet of fibrous bark and replacing it as the rain washes it off. The Regent's Bowerbird is another painter, taking "a small piece of greenish material held between the mandibles" and wiping it "all over the sticks with a pecking action." The witness of the performance found the upper ends of the sticks "coated with a wet mixture of saliva and macerated pea-green vegetable material." To find another instance of such a capacity one has to come all the way up the animal kingdom to the Chimpanzee—and Chimps paint only in association with man.

There is something almost eerie about the bowerbirds. They seem to require one to re-examine one's notions about Nature in nearly as radical a fashion as a demonstration of the reality of fairies would. Read Karl von Frisch in *Animal Architecture* on the Orange-crested Gardener, a bowerbird whose displays Sielmann was able to observe and film in the mountain forests of New Guinea after weeks of searching and patient waiting:

> The dome-shaped roof of the hut, made of densely inter-woven twigs, . . . was built around the stem of a sapling for support. The front of this stem, or center column, was covered with a thick layer of very dark green moss. It is the habit of the orange-crested gardener to place the treasures of his collection on the dark moss in the manner of a jeweler exhibiting his wares on a ground of dark velvet for better effect, and here the bird had much work to do after each heavy rainstorm. He insisted on perfect order and regularity. To the left there would be a collection of glittering blue beetles; to the right, the shiny fragments of broken snail shells; both groups were separated

from each other by a line of yellow flowers. All this was meticulously arranged and stuck into the moss at carefully chosen intervals.

In Sielmann's own words:

> Every time the bird returns from one of his collecting forays he studies the overall color effect. He seems to wonder how he could improve on it and at once sets out to do so. He picks up a flower in his beak, places it into the mosaic, and retreats to an optimum viewing distance. He behaves exactly like a painter critically reviewing his own canvas. He paints with flowers; this is the only way I can put it. A yellow orchid does not seem to him to be in the right place. He moves it slightly to the left and puts it between some blue flowers. With his head on one side he then contemplates the general effect once more, and seems satisfied.

In the course of many weeks of Sielmann's observation, only two females were seen to appear at the bower. When one did, however, the eager proprietor drew her attention to the display by retreating to the hut and emitting a rattling cry. Having given her a chance to feast her eyes on the art collection, the wooer executed a circular dance, running in one side of the bower, around behind the decorated center-column, then back out from the other side, displaying his red crest. The end came when the initially frightened female joined her suitor in "a *pas de deux* in which they almost touched, until, quite suddenly, they disappeared into the hut." . . . *Cut.*

Most male birds do not devote as much of their energies to courtship as the polygamists. Fairly strenuous rites may, however, be expected of them. Exhibition flights are common. They may be either for visual effect, as in the Lapwing and many hawks, or for sound as well. The Snipe's is accompanied by a high-pitched, throbbing bleat or whistle, produced by modified feathers in the tail, that of the promiscuous Woodcock, as it spirals skyward of an evening, by an accelerating twittering, which may issue from its narrowed outer primaries. The Night-hawk at the end of its steep dive opens its wings to produce a muffled boom. Two of its African relatives—the Pennant-winged and Standard-winged Nightjars—sport a pair of inner primary feathers over twice the bird's own length during the season of courtship to render their exhibition flights the more spectacular. (In the latter species the elongated feathers are thin-stemmed racquets.) In some species there are headlong chases of the female by the male. The Kingbird is one. Another is the Chimney Swift, in which the flight ends high above the earth in a singularly poetical consummation when, as Roger Tory Peterson writes, the pair "lock in a copulatory embrace and fall a thousand feet, their wings flailing the air like a pin-wheel."

But in the majority of existing species of birds an essential prelude to pairing is song.

### The Musicians

"Birds are the most instinctively musical of all creatures," Charles Hartshorne declares in his *Born to Sing*. Not all are musical, of course, by any means. But those in the great major-ity do sing, if we allow the term to cover the wails, hoots, screams and trumpetings that serve a purpose similar to that of more euphonious recitals, certainly if we accept as song such analogues as the drumming and booming of grouse, the sounds produced in the courtship flight of many birds, the tattoo of woodpeckers. ("We have a stupid woodpecker who pecks on the gutter surrounding our roof, making a hell of a racket," a friend of mine writes. Not stupid but astute: sheet metal pro-vides for better tympany than wood.) Song in all its forms is an adjunct of sex and a device for promoting the successful repro-duction of the species, whether by repelling a territorial in-vader, winning a mate or strengthening the matrimonial bond. To stress the practicality of that which has the power to charm and enchant us is not to deny it other qualities, however. Music among human beings is doubtless also utilitarian in origin. If the fugues of Bach and sonatas of Beethoven transcend all things earthly, their roots are nonetheless in the simple dance rhythms that prepared our ancestors for hunting, warfare and amatory pairing. Birds' song may be and generally (but not always) is linked to the condition of the male gonads; but if my observation has been valid, the human impulse to sing is at its zenith in adolescence and thereafter diminishes as vital powers do so—which is not to say that spontaneous human singing is merely mechanical. Love has inspired a large share of the masterpieces of the arts and provided their theme, but as Karl von Frisch observes in connection with the bowerbirds' displays, "Do not human males, too, court women only under the influence of their sex hormones?"

Can the vocalizing of birds, however, even the most accomplished to our ears, be considered music, in the human sense? In answering this question in the affirmative, Hartshorne—a professor of philosophy and lifelong student of avian song— remarks that "The basic elements of music are rhythm, tones (pitch-definite sounds as contrasted to noises), harmony and melody." The more advanced songs of birds certainly possess all. A Hermit Thrush's song recorded and then played at one-quarter speed sounds to me quite like a human composition, and one that Antonin Dvorak—who, by the way, called birds "the true masters"—could have readily incorporated with the Indian themes in his symphony *From the New World*. To be sure, the Hermit Thrush is an exceptional singer, to say the least, achieving, in the opinion of P. Szoke, a specialist in avian song, "the highest summit in the evolution of animal music so far known to us." Hartshorne observes that its song "approximates a complete pentatonic scale, with all the harmonic intervals in play," and quotes an encomium written by S. P. Cheney in 1891.

> After striking the first low, long, and firm tone, startling the listener with an electric thrill, [he] bounds upwards by thirds, fourths and fifths, and sometimes a whole octave, gurgling out his triplets with every upward movement. Occasionally, on reaching the height, the song

bursts like a rocket, and the air is full of silver tones. A second flight, and the key changes with a fresh, wild, enchanting effect. Start from what point he may, it always proves the right one. . . . It is like listening to the opening of a grand overture.

To quote Hartshorne further:

> Compared with human music, there seems but one radical inferiority in the best bird songs . . . : their ultra-simplicity as shown above all in the extremely brief temporal span of the motifs, or musical units. A bird, it seems, cannot follow a fully definite music pattern occupying much more than fifteen seconds (so far as species known to me are concerned), and only a few manage patterns of even six seconds' duration. . . . The average for all singing birds is probably a unit of less than three seconds.

Vocalizing mammals, he finds, with one exception—the Humpback Whale—do little if any better than the more competent birds. Birds' songs of long duration, which may continue for several minutes, like a Mockingbird's, "always consist of elements each lasting a few seconds at most, and with no fixed order of sequence."

Here I am reminded of a lecture given by Hartshorne in Washington, D.C., in which he played a recording of a rambling, uncertain, not very dulcet singer, identifying it as a local bird and asking the audience to name it. He added that four species were eligible as choices. The rendering sounded to me like that of a very inferior Mockingbird and I guessed a Catbird. I was wrong. A Brown Thrasher and then a Mockingbird were proposed and both were wrong. "That uses up three of the four possibilities," the lecturer declared. Two more guesses were obviously wide of the mark. Then a voice hesitantly suggested a bird that had not occurred to me—a Starling. And that was what it was: a captive young Starling that had been exposed to a Mockingbird's singing and been "imprinted" by it.

"There are only four continuous singers among birds in this part of the country," Dr. Hartshorne concluded, "and no discontinuous singer could be made to sing continuously."

The Starling is, of course, a fair mimic. Were it not one, it would not have been introduced into America when it was. The perpetrator of the crime had in mind establishing here all the birds mentioned in Shakespeare, and in *King Henry IV, Part One*, occurs the fateful line, "I'll have a starling shall be taught to speak/Nothing but 'Mortimer'. . . ."

Probably nothing makes it more difficult to put ourselves in a wild animal's place than the narrowness of its awareness-span. We proceed in the light of what has gone before—minutes before, hours before, days, weeks, months, years before, not to mention our expectations of the future and foreknowledge of our inevitable death. But for our fellow beings the light is a beam of a width measurable in seconds. They live in the present to a degree probably unimaginable to us. That is not to say that they lack memory. Birds can be acutely sensitive to and retentive of associations. My Crows remember my food call over periods of months. Food-storing European Jays can find their caches in conditions that might well defeat us. Probably most migrant birds can come unerringly back to a nesting site from hundreds or thousands of miles away, exhibiting a precision that, whatever its navigational aids, must depend on stored visual images for the final zeroing in. But memory of this kind would seem to be like an electronic memory-bank in which specific data are instantly retrievable but are otherwise out of sight and mind. What flashes the retrieval signal is the recurrence of circumstances in which the information was previously implanted. It is recognition, not purposed recall. We may have a clue to the process in the sudden, swooning reality with which a certain scent or melody will bring back a scene or experience of long ago with a reality impossible to recover by a conventional act of remembering. Birds do conduct operations requiring sustained application; the building of an artfully contrived nest may take many days. And doubtless the nest-builders can tell by how far the finished structure conforms to standards. But that does not mean that they work with a visualization of the finished structure in mind. Probably they see no more than a step ahead, and progress from one to the other, as we assemble a contrivance guided not by a mental image of the completed whole but by successive directions in the placement of one part after another.

The conception of avian consciousness as confined to a time-span of at most fifteen seconds is, however, subject to an important qualification. Birds' nervous systems function at high speed. Twelve seconds for a bird may well be the equivalent of a full two minutes for us. Or so we are justified in believing by the evidence that birds can detect as many as ten different notes in what is to us a single sound. A Winter Wren's song played at a speed at which the human ear can grasp its intricacy and richness takes almost thirty seconds. This conforms with the impression we have, from observation, of the tempo of a bird's reactions. Our own would certainly not permit us to whisk at twenty-five miles an hour through a maze of tree branches or follow the twists and turns of a winged quarry with an effect of simultaneity as a bird-hawk or jaeger will. The two or three years of an average small bird's existence may contain as much living as do twenty or thirty of ours. Writing further of the Hermit Thrush, Hartshorne reports that "The most recent study, and the most thorough of all, by Szoke's slow-down method, shows that a song of this species, less than 2 seconds in length, may have 45-100 or more notes and 25-50 or more pitch changes, not a few being sounded simultaneously, as in the Wood Thrush." There are passages in a Wood Thrush's song played at quarter speed that one would swear, if not assured otherwise, were delivered by two birds singing simultaneously.

Charles Hartshorne's *Born to Sing*, subtitled *An Interpretation and World Survey of Bird Song*, is a work based on more than fifty years' study. The extent of my quotation from it can leave no doubt of my admiration of it; it has greatly improved my understanding of the subject and stimulated my imagination. Consequently, I am keenly aware of being honored in having an observation of mine cited in it, one I had made after a stay in Java. I had spoken of the tiny Mountain Tailorbird as "striving in tones of unutterable sweetness and rarity to reach and exceed the upper ceiling of audibility, lost to all other concerns in the mists of its forest home on the high slope of a volcano." Hartshorne has found that the enchanting singer employs at least six patterns of between four and eleven notes each, none apparently ever immediately reiterated, three closing with a falling pitch, three with a rising, so that "the suspense created by the 'gothic' upward trend . . . is adequately balanced." Having recorded it, he found that "playing the song at quarter speed brings out the structures."

That is one reason for recording songs. Hartshorne indicates another in telling us that while the Mountain Tailorbird's voice is high-pitched, "slow playing reveals perfect tones." If we are to discriminate fully the tonal qualities as well as the structure of phrasing of which birds are capable, we have to hear their songs at something approaching our own tempo. It may be that we hear them then as birds themselves hear them. Birds do tend to sing in a high register. In tests reported in *The Auk,* Arthur R. Brand found that on the average 59 passerine species sang at a frequency of about 4,280 vibrations per second, or "about an octave and a half higher than the highest note an operatic coloratura soprano can reach." The range was from a low of 1,100 in the Starling to a high of 10,225 in the Blackpoll Warbler, "over an octave above the highest note on a piano."

"By singing, a territorial bird communicates several things at once," William L. Thompson and Kenneth A. Shiovitz, two professors of biology in Michigan write in *Natural History:* "avian equivalents of 'I am a male indigo bunting,' 'I am in breeding condition,' 'This is my territory,' 'I am tough,' and 'Get out!'" Or so it registers on another male. A female would receive the message not in the last two senses but as "I am attractive" and "Come hither!" (Having responded favorably she may still decide against the singer. "Song may guide the female to a territory," the authors observe, "but the intuitive choice to remain there probably depends upon the overall potential for successful breeding within the territory.") But are not the same messages that the Indigo Bunting puts across conveyed in much simpler songs, say, by the Henslow's Sparrow's brief, reiterated *flee*-sik . . . *flee*-sik or by the Ring-necked Pheasant's klaxon crow? For contrast, consider the Wood Thrush. In tones touching those of flute, carillon and piano, this instrumentalist sounds first the three notes of an E-minor chord, next the three of a C natural, then proceeds through a variety of harmonic structures, sometimes sounding a vibrato on a tiny cymbal, to achieve—for us—heart-melting effects. Why have we this rhapsody?

The farther we go toward an answer the more we must speculate.

It is self-evident that great variety among songs is needed where many species are found in close proximity in country affording good cover. Otherwise the males and females of one species would constantly be responding to those of another in a futile expenditure of energy which nature would not tolerate. Certainly birds' songs *are* well differentiated. Even the human ear has little trouble separating them, even in the tropical rainforest, where, conditions being most favorable for passerines, the greatest number of singers is present—and variety of song also greatest. In many instances species difficult or impossible to differentiate by sight are readily separable by song, among them the Willow, Alder, Acadian and Least Flycatchers, the Eastern and Western Meadowlarks (which ornithology divided into two species chiefly on the basis of their quite unlike songs) and the Black-capped and Carolina Chickadees. It is difficult to learn and easy to forget which wood-warbler songs go with which species, but I can think of few birds' songs that are difficult to tell apart.

Birds themselves are found not to react to the songs of other species than their own. Of their work with the Indigo Bunting, Thompson and Shiovitz report that:

> When the territory owner began to sing, we played a recording of a lazuli bunting or a painted bunting. Male

indigos did not respond to the songs of either of these species, even when a dummy of a male indigo was placed next to the tape recorder. The playing of an indigo bunting song, however, usually brought an immediate response. . . . We were able to create experimental songs composed of new figures by playing a normal indigo song backwards. When this is done, the detailed forms of the figures are changed without altering frequency ranges or gross temporal features. If species recognition were limited to normal feature types alone, the new backward figures should elicit no positive response from male indigos. In fact, however, they gave almost a full response to the backward song.

Stephen T. Emlen at Cornell University got the same results even after rearranging the order of the Indigo Bunting's notes at random and altering the timing and pitch.

If conservation of energy among birds calls for variation among the songs of different species, it calls also for variation among songs of individuals of the same species. The Indigo Bunting species is better off for males' knowing whether a song they hear is that of a settled neighbor or of an intruding stranger who must be dealt with. The species gains, too, from the female's being able to identify her mate by his song; only confusion could result from wives' being continually drawn to the wrong male. "Tape-playback experiments with several species of birds," Thompson and Shiovitz note, "have demonstrated that male birds respond more vigorously to a stranger's song than to either their own or a neighbor's."

It seems to me, however, that birds' songs have gone much farther than the requirements of species- and individual-recognition. Many birds are incomparably superior vocalists to the buntings, whose songs seem to meet those requirements adequately. There is—to get back to it—the Wood Thrush and there are its relatives. And among these are, of course, the Nightingale and the solitaires, the Townsend's Solitaire of our West and "the dark slaty blue Clarin (*Myadestes unicolor*) of southeastern Mexico," which, Frank M. Chapman writes in *My Tropical Air Castle*, "may, in my opinion, claim first place among American song-birds." There is also the Mockingbird. Even a Southerner has to admit that the Mockingbird is not the musician the thrushes are. In making the difference clear, Hartshorne cannot be improved on:

> A highly imitative species must be one with no very strong fondness for any one musical form; and hence it must have a rather loose sense of overall musical form. . . A Mockingbird takes a phrase out of the variable sequence of the Wood Thrush, simplifies even this phrase (in all cases which I have heard), and either repeats it immediately two or more times (which is quite contrary to Wood Thrush practice and musical spirit) or passes immediately to something different and musically rather irrelevant. In either case he misses the main musical point of the song, which is the eliciting of exquisitely harmonic contrasts between the successive phrases in the sequence, these phrases being both deeply contrasting and musically related.

All true. And yet what a vocalist! Song wells up out of him as from a fountain. It jets in spurts of silver and gold—sometimes, let it be confessed, in less sovereign metals; he is too ardent and impetuous a singer never to lapse from a fine discrimination. He does repeat his phrases, to be sure, before passing on to others of his astonishing repertoire. It is because he must hear and relish them; they are too rejoicing of the ear not to be savored. The Hermit and Wood Thrushes are reflective. They are deep ones, you would say, listening to them: creatures of the spirit. And so you would of their cousin, the third of "the leading trio of North American song-birds," in Chapman's view, the Veery, of the downward spiraling trills: a voice to summon up in the soul all that responds to the eerie, profound and elusive presence of the forest, mysterious and tantalizing. The Mockingbird is ebullience. The joy of singing carries him off his feet, literally. He rises from his chimney, telephone-pole or tree-top on spread wings in stylized, slow-motion flight. Does he really feel joy? To doubt it seems to me not so much proper scientific caution as contrariety. I know of nothing vocal in nature more expressive of zest in the performance. Such gusto! His mimicry seems testimony to it. As if even his rich vocabulary were inadequate to his responsiveness to life, he tosses at us the calls and songs of Flicker and Cardinal, Carolina Wren and Phoebe; all are pelf for his fancy.

To applaud the Mockingbird's exuberance is not, however, to deny his singing the quality we should call poetic. Listen to him in the moonlight of a scented June night:

> Co-*lee*-to co-*lee*-to co-*lee*-to
> Coo-lee coo-lee *coo*-lee
> *Pee*-chew *pee*-chew *pee*-chew
> Peach-eater peach-eater. Tulip tulip tulip!

Out it pours, warm, urgent, mellifluous, into the hushed receptacle of the wan darkness. It is the very voice of Midsummer Night's witchery, of lyricism, you would say.

Of the two most famous singers of the bird world (if I may call the Mockingbird one), the other is a nocturnal performer, too. Its name tells us that: Nightingale—*niht-galan* in Old English, literally night-singer. "When at last it is full dark, . . . with light only from the stars, he begins to sing and, according to our best observation, sings all night steadily," Louis J. Halle writes in *The Storm Petrel* in a most discerning tribute.

Lyly's *jug jug jug jug terheu* is the bare bones of the matter, the skeleton which is clothed with different flesh at each performance.

All possible tones are available, high and low, harsh, reedy, smooth, piercing. Challenging or fainting. Often cacks and clicks. To one who knows the Mockingbird this is equaled, and the Yellow-breasted Chat also astonishes this way. What is unequaled is the phrasing; the combination of rhythm and nuance; the rapid repetition, but with a development, a crescendo or deepening of tone or a lifting, all proceeding rapidly (or sometimes slowly), then culminating in a terminal flourish of grace notes. Period. Begin again with a new motif, new nuance, new development, all over again, swell out . . . and stop abruptly with a new flourish. Invent endlessly, never quite repeating yourself.

But there can be enough even of the Nightingale's song.

> When I am surfeited I find no attraction in it. It does not seem particularly musical. Let a few hours pass, however, and then the burst of song is like the Gates of Heaven opening.

Halle writes of hearing "the Nightingales in their neighboring territories obviously competing in song, each driven to improvise creatively on the basis of aesthetic standards that we can recognize—with diminuendos, crescendos, accelerandos, ritardandos. . . . The territorial theory, which I do not question, tells me why the Nightingale sings at all. It does not tell me why it sings beautifully."

Here, before we go farther, we might take note that the division of birds into Oscines—song-birds—and non-Oscines is not a division between those that sing beautifully and those that do not. Many plovers and sandpipers have far more musical voices than grackles, cowbirds, nuthatches and many sparrows, while Cedar Waxwings are silent but for a low, beedy call. Some of the most mellifluous of all singers are non-Oscines. One is a large nightjar (hence a relative of the Whip-poor-will's) of the South American tropics, the Giant Potoo, known locally as the Poor-Me-One (Poor me all alone), whose human voice is popularly ascribed to an anteater or sloth. Its "soft but loud, sad, flute-like note . . . made the goose-flesh rise all over me," Chapman wrote in *My Tropical Air Castle* on first hearing it. "In form it is a very simple song of six full notes slowly descending the scale, each an interval apart. But notes of such richness of tone, so suggestive of sorrow, that in all the world of birds or man I have heard none sweeter or sadder. So strongly does this song express human emotion that one thinks of it as a woman's voice—a deep, mellow contralto calling in hopeless grief."

On Barro Colorado in the Canal Zone, where he wrote of the Potoo, Chapman also heard tinamous. A South American family of some two-score species, superficially partridge-like distant relatives of the Ostrich and Rhea, the tinamous are among the most early-evolved of existing birds, if taxonomists are right. Yet the voice of one, W. H. Hudson wrote, is "perhaps the sweetest on the pampas," while Chapman avows that "if one may judge by the effect of their calls on the sympathetic listener, [they] are among the great songsters of the tropics," adding, however, that "nothing I can write will give even a faint conception of the singular beauty and appealing quality of their notes." Of the small Pileated Tinamou, an inhabitant of the forest border and bushy second growths, he writes, "To be impressed by the voice of this bird one should be near enough to the singer to feel the pathos of its exquisitely pure, vibrant trilling as, uttered with an impassioned increase in rapidity, phrase after phrase rises in volume and then suddenly dies away. The bird may be at your very feet but always it remains invisible."

The most famous vocalist of the non-Oscines (one belonging to the Passeriformes, however) is the Lyrebird, of which there are two species dwelling in the densely forested mountains of Australia's southeastern seaboard. It is a shy, elusive, soberly-colored creature. That we have a close-up description of its recital is owing to the all but incredible departure from the ways of its kind by a male Superb Lyrebird who adopted a woman living on a mountainside twenty-four miles from Melbourne. "James" performed daily for her on the ledge of her veranda, later on the platform she had built there, just outside her window. The Australian zoologist Ambrose Pratt in his *The Lore of the Lyrebird* tells of a performance he witnessed —for it developed that the bird, far from being frightened off by the presence of others, "positively enjoyed displaying himself before a crowd," so long as Mrs. Wilkinson herself was present.

"Hullo, Boy!" Mrs. Wilkinson greeted the bird when he appeared on the platform. And, "Hullo, Boy!" he responded. After keenly examining the waiting spectators, James groomed himself. In his proportions he suggested a Guinea-fowl to Pratt, but one with "a beautiful head . . . with a dusky brown crest" set on "a long and amazingly flexible neck" and with "a sweeping tail nearly twice the length of his body." After twenty minutes he slowly advanced to the edge of the window and again gauged his audience with "quick, intense glances" of his "large and prominent eyes, extremely bright and intelligent." Then

unexpectedly he opened wide his beak and emitted a low chuckle that speedily swelled in volume until the air resounded with the full-throated cachinnations of a kukuburra. As the last note died away, . . . [he] suddenly erected his wonderful tail fanshape above his back and head. The magnificent spectacle held us spellbound. . . . Not only were the gorgeous lyre-shaped plumes displayed to their most exquisite advantage, but the light under-colouring of the finer wire-like accompanying feathers provided a matchless contrast with the more sombre colouring above, as their tips drooped like a silver curtain over the bird's head, completely screening it from our view. Hiding behind his beautiful curtain, "James" gave us the most marvellous concert it had ever been my good fortune to hear. In swift succession he imitated precisely and perfectly the calls and songs of at least twenty of the most famous songsters of the Australian forest . . . also the sounds made by a hydraulic ram and the tooting of motor-horns. . . .

Tiring at length of mimicry, he began to dance to a weird lilting music of his very own. Advancing and retreating (always facing his audience), with regular steps and rhythmic swaying movements of the body, he wove a strange pattern on the platform with his feet, which he crossed at periodic intervals in the manner of human dancers, until the climax of the *pas seul*—three swift steps accomplished within the space of two clanging beats of his tune, then a sudden dramatic pause of silence, and a slow lowering of his splendid tail.

Quitting the veranda then to forage in the garden, James was, after much entreaty by Mrs. Wilkinson at her guests' behest, prevailed upon to return to the platform, "where he gave another short but wonderful performance." The hen Lyrebird, Pratt reports, offers an "apparently insatiable audience" for her mate's performances.

We saw in an earlier section how James constructed a special mound to bring his display within her view when Mrs. Wilkinson lay ill. His response was such as to take one equally aback when his friend collected a store of grubs and beetles, much relished by Lyrebirds, and spread them on the platform in anticipation of his appearance. Regarding the feast "spellbound" for a moment, James then with "every possible sign of indignation" swept the platform clear of the dainties with his powerful claws and volplaned off. Feeling it ridiculous to suppose that the bird had been offended, Mrs. Wilkinson repeated the experiment a week later, and with the same result, except that this time he remained absent for several days.

Previously, after performing every day on the veranda ledge during an initial mating season, the Lyrebird had disappeared. Then, upon completing a moult, he had returned, to the elation of his anxious friend, and greatly surprised her with a notably enlarged repertoire. That takes us back to a question we had reached with Halle's observation about the competitiveness of his Nightingales' singing. Male birds do indeed each have cause for striving to outdo their fellows. All sing to demonstrate their prowess. But how much leeway in his singing does a bird's nature permit him? How nearly is the character of the song predetermined and fixed? Is its song one that it masters, or is it one it acquires with its instincts?

The answer would seem to be: both—to a degree and depending on the species. Many captive young birds have been hand-reared in isolation to find the answer. In well-known experiments individual Chaffinches so reared came out with songs typical of the species in length and number of notes characteristically organized but of poor tonal qualities and lacking refinement. (Oddly enough, two young males brought up in each other's exclusive company did markedly better. They also came to sing almost identically, each having turned to the other for the model it needed.) Recent experiments in California by the English botanist-ornithologist Peter Marler were reported on the fascinating television program *Why Do Birds Sing?* produced by WGBH of Boston, enabling the listener to hear the results for himself. Marler had noticed that White-crowned Sparrows at Sunset Beach and those at Berkeley sang in different dialects. As the program narrator told it:

> Marler raised newly hatched birds, each from a particular dialect group, . . . in isolation in soundproof chambers. The first group of birds, growing up without hearing any adult song at all, sang when they were adults a strange, greatly over-simplified version of the normal song. . . . A second group of birds were played adult song with the dialect of the group they came from, in this case the Berkeley dialect. When they became adults they reproduced it perfectly. . . . And, indeed, even if it wasn't from the area they'd been born in, as long as the adult song was the right species, the birds copied the dialect.

In other words, Berkeley-born birds learned the Sunset Beach dialect when adult song in that dialect was played to them—provided that it was played during a critical period before the subject was seven weeks old. On the other hand, young White-crowned Sparrows brought up on a recording of the Song Sparrow's song ignored it and in maturity sang as poorly as those brought up on no adult song at all.

Song Sparrows themselves, raised in isolation, are said to have turned out to sing indistinguishably from their wild relatives. And so, it has been reported, have birds of a number of other species, including even such an accomplished performer as the European Blackbird.

I find it easier to believe of the Song Sparrow's ditty than I should of many birds' songs that it is predetermined. It is a pleasing and cheerful but rather mechanical-sounding production. Even so, I am struck by the great range of individual variation in the singing of the species and by the repertoire of some males of as many as a dozen songs. As for the Blackbird, I confess to an unscientific satisfaction in reading in a recent publication by Masakuzu Konishi and Fernando Nottlebaum, two former students of Marler's, that "in the Blackbird, contrary to the previous conclusion . . . audiospectrographic analysis showed that nestling-isolates could not arrange the component sounds to produce normal wild-type songs without exposure to wild blackbirds." To me, the analysis casts doubt on reports of other competent singers that inherit finished songs. I find more plausible the suggestion of R. A. Hinde of Cambridge in his *Bird Vocalizations*, that one way of relating all the findings with respect to the source of birds' songs is to suppose that a bird is born with "a crude 'model' or 'template' of the species-characteristic song, which is improved by experiences of that song. On this view, sounds which approximate to the model are reinforcing and are also effective in eliciting singing."

If a bird is to improve the song inherent in it, an imitative ability must prove very useful, and probably most song-birds have one. To this I should add, again, a bird would not have the ability if it did not use it. Life in the wild cannot afford luxuries, and mimicry of sounds is not a faculty come by casually. Across the whole breadth of the animal kingdom it has been attained to only by parrots, Passeriformes and man. Not even man's closest relatives, the great apes, possess it; it is one more odd way in which man and birds form a confraternity. And, as Hinde says, "some species [of birds], like parrots and mynahs, seem able to imitate almost any kind of sound they hear." An African Grey Parrot is said to have had one hundred sounds at its command and an Amazon between fifty and one hundred words, while the fidelity to human speech achieved by the Hill Mynah, greater even than that of the best parrots, is demonstrated by comparison of audiospectrographs of the original and the imitation. So far as is known, however, it is only in the company of man that these birds imitate alien sounds, and nowhere does their native song benefit from imitation, for they have none. In captivity as in the wild, their mimicry is reserved for the sounds made by those to whom they are socially close, their own kind or their human associates.

Probably all birds that can imitate do so to improve their vocabularies, but all the truly singing birds among them presumably imitate to the advantage of their musicianship. How important mimicry must be in that respect is attested by those birds that have been reared apart from their kind but exposed to the singing of another species and have acquired its song—unlike the White-crowned Sparrows exposed to the Song Sparrow's lay. Hartshorne tells of two such, one a Western Meadowlark that learned the song of the Baltimore Oriole, the other a Malabar Whistling Thrush that mastered a song of the human species, *For Me and My Gal*. Welty speaks of a Bullfinch reared by Canaries that not only learned the Canary song but passed it on to his sons, as they to theirs to the fourth generation. Another Bullfinch he cites was trained to whistle *God Save the King*, following which a Canary in an adjoining room learned the song from the Bullfinch and with such commitment that if the latter "paused over long between the third and fourth phrases the Canary would pick up the tune and finish it."

Most song-imitating birds in the wild confine their imitation to songs of their own species, but there are, of course, exceptions, some famous, that embellish their native songs with those of others. Of these, probably none surpasses the Lyrebirds in range of imitation or fidelity, though A. J. Marshall considers the Spotted Bowerbird supreme in the field. This Australian species, he reports, gives a remarkably faithful reproduction not only of the calls of many other birds but of the barking of dogs and the noise of cattle breaking through scrub, of a maul striking a splitter's wedge and of Emus crashing through twanging fence-wires. It also "mimics a Whistling Eagle so faithfully that a hen and chicks fly for cover." While uttering the notes of other birds in its bower display, it evidently also uses mimicry for distraction when eggs or young are menaced.

Since imitating a variety of songs and other sounds must be more taxing than imitating few, the question arises as to why birds do it. A clue is suggested by the fact that all our four Eastern continuous singers—Mockingbird, Brown Thrasher, Catbird and Starling—are mimics. The significance of this comes out in the light of an astute observation of Hartshorne's: that monotony dulls and Oscines (and Menuridae, the Lyrebirds) avoid it in their singing. "The interestingness of the song, for performer and avian listener, is of its essence. Repetition carried so far as to inhibit attention and cause the activity to lapse into an automatism for the singer and a negligible stimulus for the listener (mate or rival) is scarcely compatible with the status of song in the bird's life." The inhibition against a burdensome repetition notoriously does not operate on the Whip-poor-will, which thinks nothing of loudly reiterating its name thirty times without pause. (For a rough way of counting seconds, you have only to imitate its singing.) But the nightjars branched off the avian family tree much earlier than the Passerines and are doing well to sing at all. As a nocturnal vocalist, moreover, the Whip-poor-will holds forth when the attention of hearers, even if abused, has fewer other claims on it.

Birds resort to several means of avoiding a deadening monotony. The simplest, to which simple singers like most of the sparrows and wood-warblers are given, is spacing the renditions so that each makes a renewed call upon an audience. Hartshorne has found that with singers that repeat a set ditty, intervening periods of silence will be at least two and a half times the length of the song. I should think that in general they would be much longer. Another device employed is the working of variations in a simple song, altering tempo, pitch or organization—or all three, as in the case of an outstanding example, the Pine woods (or Bachman's) Sparrow. This Southeastern species, like the Field Sparrow, makes me wonder if a sheer celestial quality of tone cannot be counted an offset to monotony—and if the objection be made that I am assigning a human value to a quality of song, I should ask why, if it has no avian values, *aves* developed it. In his *Handbook*—bible of my boyhood—Frank M. Chapman says of the Pinewoods Sparrow's song, "It is very simple—I write it, *che-e-e-e-de, de, de; che-e-chee-o, chee-o, chee-o, chee-o*—but it possesses all the exquisite tenderness and pathos of the melody of the Hermit Thrush; indeed, in purity of tone and in execution I should consider the Sparrow the superior songster."

A species may also possess a repertory of several simple songs enabling it when one threatens to become tiresome to switch to another. One Carolina Wren, recorded in audiospectrograph, had twenty-four. Our own male recently gave me an illustration of the working of its psyche in respect of their use. Near dusk of a winter's day it repaired to the inner sanctum of its territory, the work-area beneath our second-story porch where it was accustomed to spend the night with its mate. Startled to find me there, it did what I had never heard one do before. It ejaculated one song, then without a break another: "Trick or, trick or, trick or treat! Seebelo, seebelo, seebelo!" It was the spontaneous, ultimate response of the agitated, indignant territorialist. Once thereafter, however, on a September 18th, I heard one try song after song, sounding almost like a Mockingbird.

The Cardinal is another repertory singer but has much more variety among its selections. Its performance is of a rather high order for a bird that in other respects seems quite wooden. In a typical song sounding like "Teeu . . . teeu . . . teeu . . . Secret secret secret," the vocalist might be releasing drops of pure tonality to hear them splatter in succession below. Or: "What cheer! T'wheet t'wheet wheet wheet wheet wheet," it may sing for five minutes, with the Cardinal deliberateness, then, after a break, "Tseet—Wheeto wheeto, cheeu cheeu cheeu cheeu cheeu" for another round. But I have not succeeded in keeping track of the variation. It is among birds with a repertory of songs and a capacity for varying them that the highest development of discriminating avian musicianship is achieved, though in songs much more complex than the Cardinal's, as outstandingly among the thrushes.

In another category are tireless vocalists like the Red-eyed and Yellow-throated Vireos that sing in snatches, seeming to draw at random from a collection of phrases and never repeating a phrase in succession. It is significant that the Red-eye, with a wider stock than the Yellow-throat and double the number of notes in its phrases, pauses only about half as long as the latter between utterances. One, timed by Louise de Kiriline Lawrence, sang 14,027 phrases between sunup and noon. The spacing out of the Yellow-throat's leisurely two- and three-note remarks (as they sound to be) bears out Hartshorne's anti-monotony principle.

As tireless as the foregoing but more voluble and varied in expression is a group of birds that may be called the continuous singers. These are the bravura carolers that pour out a stream of differing phrases, not hesitating to repeat in quick succession, but singing with an effect of inventiveness and improvisation and in some of exceptional ardor. The stars of the group, as far as my experience goes, are the Lyrebird (which I know from a recording), the Mockingbird and the Grey Drongo. This last, when I heard it many years ago in the vicinity of the hill-station of Kaliurang in Central Java, struck me as the greatest virtuoso of any bird I had ever heard. I had at first believed the torrential upwellings to be issuing from two birds singing simultaneously, and maybe more. The drongos, a family perhaps related to the crows and jays, are mimics like the Lyrebird and Mockingbird (and like the latter vital and belligerent). Continuous singers probably have to be, if they are to possess the musical resources to supply so unflagging a recital without losing the listener's interest. In the cases at least of the Mockingbird, Brown Thrasher and Catbird (which is said to be capable of 170 different vocal phrases), the objects of mimicry are no doubt chiefly individuals of their own kind. That would account for the exceptional performance of the famous Mockingbird recorded, by Cornell University, in Massachusetts, where the species was then still rare; lacking models among his own kind, he imitated 30 other species. Even alien songs rendered by Mockingbirds may be suspected of having usually been borrowed from other Mockers.

The expenditure of energy demanded by continuous singing makes us wonder how a bird, a species, is repaid for it. Is the sustained and passionate overflow more effective in repelling rivals, attracting mates and stimulating connubial interests than the intermitting singing of, say, the thrushes? It may be, but I doubt that that is the whole explanation. And consider the thrushes. Why should it be of advantage to them to have evolved such artistry of expression?—and whatever its source, the artistry is there. In the Nightingale, as Halle puts it in *The Storm Petrel*, it is "elaborate, inventive and as beautiful in its way as a sonata by Mozart."

The answer that comes to me is that a bird finds fulfillment in its singing and that (we may reasonably believe) the more demanding the song the higher the degree of fulfillment it finds. In this view, the sense of fulfillment is the reward nature holds out to living organisms for enduring the pains and trials of existence. It is the spur to their exerting themselves, the means of obtaining their commitment to life. It is what makes the system work. Who knows but that plants achieve, in whatever dim counterpart to consciousness, a sense of fulfillment in the making and storing of sugars and in the maturing of fruit from the flowers they put out?

I am not sure whether the idea will be received as fanciful or as self-evident. The satisfaction of hunger and of the progenitive or sexual impulse may be counted the primal fulfillments. But the fulfilling sense of knowing that I am I begins to dawn, I suspect, rather early in vertebrate evolution, and it, too, is a stimulus to the struggle for existence. The turtle and the lizard that climb up a log for a place in the sun may do so figuratively as well as literally. The sense of self-realization enters, I believe, into the motive of birds' singing, at least into that for which the vocalist suspends other activity to give himself up to it: "It is I who am being heard!" That self-assertion is a prime element in the crowing of cocks, for example, would seem to be unmistakable.

Man is not alone in the animal kingdom, I feel sure, in being able to find experience rewarding in itself. When you take a dog for a walk you know it does so; it is frantic with excitement at the prospect of novelty and relief from tedium—non-experience. I have seen behavior in birds that, likewise, could be described only as adventurous. Many of the Kingbird's chases I should characterize as such, as I should also those energetic pursuits by superlative predators—falcons and jaegers—of quarry they have no intention of capturing. Other cases of aerial contests I have seen come to my mind as further instances. In one, high over Montauk, Long Island, a Crow and a Sharp-shinned Hawk were the principals. The Crow would mount above the fierce little Accipiter and dive on it. The latter, easily eluding the attack, would then turn upon its assailant, chivy him briefly as he fled, then veer off. Thereupon the Crow, winging hard, would regain a superior position and dive again to the attack. These passages were repeated three or four times—simply, I had the impression, for what is called the hell of it, on both sides. The Sharp-shin, in any event, was not to be troubled either to tackle the Crow seriously or to put on the burst of speed that would have left the latter far behind. For the Crow there must have been the titillation of playing with fire, though its much larger size probably insured its safety. Playing with fire, again in safety, was evidently the inspiration of another game of the sort. A Red-tailed Hawk was flying high across some fields in Martha's Vineyard with a flock of some fifty Starlings above it. My first thought was that in maintaining this position the Starlings were moved by caution. But not only did the heavy Red-tail pose no threat to them, but they were accompanying it, not fleeing it. While I watched I was startled to see the flock pour in a stream down directly past the hawk, exactly like liquid from a jug. They then reassembled in their former position and, after accompanying the hawk farther, repeated the maneuver. I was reminded of a matador's provocations of a bull. The Red-tail, incidentally, would not be baited or allow its dignity to be ruffled.

Man, it could be argued—if it would not be putting the cart before the horse—has come to where he has because the fulfillments he requires are so far-reaching. Only think what, in his quest for the ultimate in these, he has made of the simple hungers. A savage appetite for a haunch of venison has become a gourmet's delight in the subtleties of French and Chinese cuisines, and the unadorned gratification of coition has given rise to the romantic ecstasies of *Romeo and Juliet*, of *Tristan und Isolde*. It may be that the great apes, second only to man in intelligence, have made so little of their opportunities on earth because, like some human tribes and many, if not most, human individuals, they lack the need for exotic fulfillments. Their psychic wants are few. Strange thirsts have not disturbed them, only to be slaked by the conquest of new worlds. And what stranger thirst could there be than that for the fulfillment afforded by the appreciation of beauty and the creation of beauty, such as has been given to man?

To man and, I am inclined to believe, in some degree to the *avant garde* of birds. I can hardly conceive that birds could bring forth madrigals so musical to man and yet be devoid of aesthetic impulses themselves, of an ear for beauty of sound. It may be admitted that birds in general sing in accordance with a predisposition that is handed down to them and that leaves only a limited latitude for creative initiative on the individual's part. Yet even stereotyped songs, it would appear, must be mastered by practice. The ability to mimic would not be as widespread as it seems to be among the Oscines, moreover, unless something were left up to the individual in the determination of song. Finally, there is the practice of duetting, which to me argues for birds knowing what they are doing when they sing and exercising some choice in the matter.

As T. Hooker and Barbara L. Hooker explain in *Bird Vocalizations*, "In some tropical parts of the world, . . . where the seasons are not so strictly demarcated, many of the indigenous birds pair for life and hold the same territories for long periods. Instead of the male singing alone, both members of the pair sing, either more or less together or antiphonally, each making a distinct contribution to produce the duet. This duetting continues throughout the year, though the intensity of singing is much increased when the birds are nesting." Each partner may sing between one and four or five notes at a time. Listeners to the WGBH-TV program from which I have quoted had a chance to hear the duetting of a pair of Himalayan Jay-thrushes in captivity, recorded stereophonically by Frederic Vencl. The song was a rapid, varied, tumultuous outpouring. Slowing it down disclosed that each bird supplied practically every other note. This made the tight fit of the fast recital played at normal speed almost incredible; you simply could not see how each bird could come in on cue every time in the split second allowed it. And, as the narrator explained, "Different pairs devise different songs, so that each bird of a pair can keep track of its partner."

William H. Thorpe in his recent *Duetting and Antiphonal Song in Birds* writes, "There are 32 or more families in which duetting . . . is known to occur," the habit being "general or highly developed in nine of these," while "there are something on the order of 120 species which have been noted as duettists and of these nearly a hundred are tropical." Vocalization of all kinds is of course pronounced in the tropics, where, in the luxuriant vegetation birds must depend more than elsewhere on auditory means of making themselves understood. Thorpe estimated that duetting between Bou-bou Shrikes might take place when the partners are as much as 200 meters apart.

The Bou-bou Shrike is pre-eminent among the duettists. Dark, glossy blue-black above and white beneath, it ranges all across Africa below the Sahara. Its singing, says Thorpe, combines "pure, flute-like notes" (the "bous" of the name), which have a "deep, ringing quality," with a "snarling noise." Significantly, the "duet patterns are worked out, so to speak, experimentally between the two members of a pair." Thorpe "more than once heard what appeared to be counter duetting between two or more adjacent pairs, the pairs alternating precisely but not uniting their duets." Writing of audiospectrographs of Bou-bou Shrikes singing, he observes that their "complexity and organization . . . illustrates the extraordinary quickness and restraint shown by the birds—quickness in taking the cue and restraint in not intervening when another bird was having his say." He adds that this restraint is very noticeable in a graph in which the female pauses long enough between her first and second notes to permit the male "to get in his five A-sharps." The graphs were made of wild-caught birds in captivity, of which Thorpe writes: "The results of having all these birds together without sight of each other were very remarkable. The response-singing started up apace in the first three weeks and an astonishing variety of duets, trios and quartets were produced. . . . The quartets, although brief, were far more elaborate in structure than anything I have heard in the field." By the end of the three weeks, however, the birds had largely reverted to their usual singing.

In short, it would appear that birds' singing is by no means limited to the equivalent of putting on a phonograph record the individual has been given to play. But the point to which I have been coming is that while the young bird is in fact born incorporating a record that will determine the basic character of its song, the record is not handed down to it from on high. Even in such part as the Blackbird's roundelay is prescribed by inheritance it is entirely, one hundred per cent, the composition of *Turdus merula*, the Blackbird species. Blackbirds and Blackbirds alone have created this song, adding to and modifying its essential elements in the course of thousands of generations. As with the finery of male birds, the criterion of selection has been the effect on other Blackbirds, male and female. If the song a male had in him were such as to lend him stature in their eyes, the odds favored its being passed on to coming generations and becoming characteristic of the species. So they favored also the transmittal of a creative ability to render the instinctively-acquired song more effective through innovation: "Perched high on the tall old apple tree, this odd-looking, battle-scarred Blackbird sang by the hour [Len Howard recalls], . . . composing his own melodies, embellishing them, turning them all ways and experimenting in different tone effects, tempos and pitches." And the presumption is that the process of natural selection is still at work. The Blackbird song may be expected in the course of more thousands of generations to gain in the admiration it arouses among Blackbirds and, it is likely, among any human beings around to hear it. The growing fulfillment that in the course of evolution the Oscines may be supposed to have been finding in song, engaging them more closely with life, may have contributed to making them the outstanding successes they are, like man.

### The Variety of Nests

An old saw has it that birds are spared the need of developing intelligence in being able to deal with problems by flying away from them. Like most saws, even old ones, it is not without teeth. But it does not apply to nesting birds. The problem of raising young from eggs cannot be flown away from. To meet it requires an enormous compromise with what birds are in other respects—free spirits, itinerant and unfettered. Maintaining the species cannot be easy for mammals either. In all but the best defended of them the mortality among the dependent young is undoubtedly great. But mammals have an immense advantage. The female, of course, is able to carry her young in her body until they reach the stage at which young birds hatch from eggs; and eggs, laid anywhere from eleven or twelve days to nine weeks previously, have had to be incubated all that time by one parent or both. The most primitive, marsupial mammals do lay eggs, it is true, and perhaps in the course of evolution some birds may come to retain their eggs in their bodies until they hatch, as some snakes have come to do, giving birth to active young. It is a theoretical possibility for birds that are primarily swimmers or runners and can maintain their populations by rearing only one or two young at a time. One group of birds has mastered a function considered the distinctive feature of mammals. While they have not, certainly, acquired mammary glands, the pigeons and doves (between which there is no difference, by the way) do secrete a genuine milk, said to resemble rabbit's milk chemically. Composed of sloughed-off cells from the lining of the crop in both sexes, it is pumped up for the young, who probe the parent's mouth for it. (Pigeons and doves are also unique among birds in drinking like horses and cows, with mouths immersed, drawing the water up instead of taking a mouthful and tipping their heads back to let it flow down.) But as for viviparous birth, it is manifestly out of the question for a flying bird to go about day after day containing three or four mature eggs, let alone the dozen that ducks and gallinaceous fowl may lay in a clutch. Even if it were not, about half the Class Aves would still have to build nests as cradles for the young.

The degree of competence of young birds on hatching varies enormously as among the different Orders. A farmer can raise newly hatched chickens and ducks merely by insuring mild temperatures and spending a few minutes a day putting out food where they can find it. Nurturing newly hatched songbirds takes most of one's time and patience and is then likely to fail. In general, birds that are most at home on the ground or on or in the water—penguins, procellarines, loons and grebes, gallinaceous birds, cranes, rails and coots, ducks, geese and swans, alcids and shorebirds—lay relatively large eggs (relative to their own size) from which the young hatch open-eyed, clothed in down and mostly able to get to their feet almost at once and toddle, scamper or paddle about. Those that are at home perching, or more in the air than on the surface—herons, the pelican-frigatebird-gannet-cormorant tribe, hawks, falcons and vultures, storks, pigeons and doves, cuckoos, owls, swifts and hummingbirds, parrots, kingfishers, woodpeckers and, of course, the great Order of Passeriformes—lay relatively small eggs from which the young hatch naked, blind, prostrate and able for days to do little more than lift a wobbly head, open-mouthed, for food. Young of the first sort are called precocial (from the Latin for "pre-cooked") and are mostly adorable, young of the latter altricial (from a Latin word for "nourisher") and are uniformly repulsive. If we expected evolution to work toward the adorable and competent in young we should be disappointed. All the more recently-derived Orders of birds (as well as some of the earlier, too, to be sure) have altricial young. There must be advantages that outweigh this juvenile help-lessness (Nature can presumably overlook juvenile repulsive-ness), and there are.

What birds of the more modern orders have done is to trade infant competence for speed of development. Though the typical passerine bird emerges from the shell rather less ac-complished than a grub and not much bigger, it is flying about, as large as its parents, in two weeks. The whole process, from the laying of the egg, has taken only a month. That must be about 50 per cent faster than in even the smallest precocial species—and, other things being equal, the smaller the bird, in general, the shorter the period of incubation and maturation. (It is interesting that the longest incubation is that of the fowl-like Megapodes, the young of which, on digging their way out of the mound of decaying vegetation or warm mineral grit in which the eggs are incubated, using their large feet— their *mega podes*—are able to fend for themselves completely and to fly within twenty-four hours.) Only a prodigious rate of metabolism and the consumption of comparatively huge quantities of protein-rich food can sustain the rate of growth of the young Passeriformes. And only the tireless pursuit of insects by, usually, both parents can supply such consumption. Even birds whose own diet is of fruit or seeds generally feed their young on insects.

Among the larger birds of the older Orders that have altri-cial young, however, the rate of growth is anything but speedy. A European Stork is not capable of flight until it is about 70 days old and even after three months out of the egg a young Condor is still less than two-thirds the weight of an adult. So, for these birds to have thrived, there must be another compensatory advantage in altricial young. (The Condor does sufficiently well in the absence of man to maintain the species with only one egg per pair every other year.) We have not far to look for it. In most situations it is obviously safer to have eggs and young off the ground, in trees or on cliffs. (Ground-nesting sea-birds show an overwhelming preference for nesting on islands, safe from ground-prowling predators—until man comes, and brings with him his rats, dogs and cats.) And if young birds are to be raised on high, it does not do to have them promenading about. In their case, helplessness must prove the better part of restlessness.

To the advantages of height, however, birds of recent orders have added protective features in the design of the cradle far beyond what we should have thought them capable of. As birds have evolved, so has the nest. The larva-like infant oriole in its woven pouch at the end of a nodding branchlet is safer than the bright-eyed duckling able to swim and scare up food for itself before it is a day old. The nest, in which the eggs and then the young may be brooded in the heat of the parent's body and shielded from rain and excessive sun, secure to a degree by concealment or inaccessibility, neutralizes the mammalian advantage of the womb. In a manner of speaking it is a womb, albeit an external one which, while it cannot accompany the mother, does not encumber her either. One problem afflicting many nests has not been solved, however. Mites and lice infesting them prey on the young and may even cause the death of a second or third brood reared in the same nest.

Birds with precocial young need little in the way of a nest; a bare ledge or slight depression in the beach or under concealing vegetation suffices for most, though shearwaters and petrels nest in burrows and some ducks in cavities in trees. (Young procellarines are apt to stay in the nest until so fat they outweigh the adults and then until they convert the fat to feathers, but ducklings tumble out to the ground immediately.) Fairy Terns, which in habits as in appearance live up to their name, lay their single egg quite simply on the branch of a tree, and to this the hatchling is expected to cling from the start. Grebes, however, construct floating platforms of pond weeds. Many of the duck-goose-swan Order build nests by pulling together such sticks, stalks and grasses as are within reach and use their own down for lining—and for insulating softness the lining of an eider's nest has no superior, as the high price it brings in commerce indicates. Correspondingly, the nightjars, with semi-altricial young, lay their eggs directly on the leaves of the forest floor or on gravel in the open. Like other vulnerable ground-nesters, they depend for safety on camouflage coloring; their eggs and young, which are downy (unlike other altricial young) vanish in the forest litter as they do themselves. Like many others, too, they feign a broken wing to lead a predator away from the eggs or young. But some, at least, of the nightjars—the Whip-poor-will and Chuck-will's-widow—are said to have the added, almost unique ability to move their eggs or young to a new site if the nest is disturbed. If this is true, it would seem most likely to be through the agency of their enormous mouths—those bristle-flanged, capacious insect-scoops.

Withal, it remains true that nest-building as an art, if it may be so termed, is the accomplishment of the newer sorts of birds. (The nests on which the earlier-evolving herons, storks, hawks, doves and others raise their ungainly offspring are little more than platforms or heaps of sticks.) To appreciate what an accomplishment it is, one has only to imagine turning one's massive brain to duplicating an oriole's reticule, even a sparrow's little bowl of grasses, with only a pair of pointed chopsticks held in one hand to work with. And as astonishing as the intricacy of craftsmanship displayed in birds' nests is the diversity of forms they take and the variety of locations exploited by the nest-builders. These testify, surely, to the range and intensity of dangers that have to be met. But they testify also to the resourcefulness of Nature or, again, if you like, of birds themselves. It has been they, after all, who have come up with the inventions, however unconsciously and even inadvertently. And, while among even vertebrate animals, if I may quote again from the Nobel laureate Karl von Frisch, "building activities are ruled by inherited instincts to a greater extent than many people believe, . . . among certain highly developed birds and mammals, the factor of individual achievement is added, and an animal's own experience may lead to exceptional individual solutions."

Which are the master builders? Of the cup-shaped nests, which are probably the commonest form, it would be hard to find a superior in delicacy of workmanship or dissimulation to those built by the smallest of birds for their two pea-sized white eggs. Hummingbirds' nests are of fine plant materials bound together and anchored in place by spider webs. Softly lined with plant down, they are so deep that the female sits in them with head and tail erect. Being characteristically plated with lichens, they blend into the supporting branch or twigs without a seam.

Hummingbirds have achieved a large measure of security in their version of the cup-nest by means of disguise. Other birds have developed it in other directions to the same end. In the New World orioles the rigid, thick-walled structure has been fined down and deepened into a woven bag which is suspended from a terminal branch, out of reach of most predators. The most remarkable builders of the family, as well as its largest members, are the oropendolas, tropical American birds with faces tapering to a point in impressive bills. Colonial, the oropendolas weave nests in the form of heelless stockings, several feet long, with a bulge in the toe enclosing the nest proper. Scores hang in the top of a single tree. Chapman, keeping twelve females and a male under observation in a 24-power glass, wrote in his journal that "the females are using some fibre and all work furiously. . . . They thrust over and pull under without apparent study and without waiting. Each one seems to know exactly what she wants to do and goes at it like a master workman absorbed in her task." (Male oropendolas are greatly outnumbered by females, take several mates in a season, and otherwise serve chiefly as sentinels to warn of danger.) Yet some other females, as he wrote, "show but little interest in their work and seem at a loss to know how to use the material they have collected." The "wide variation in the nesting ability," he added, anticipating von Frisch, "is probably in part individual, but it is doubtless also a measure of the extent to which their instinct has been developed by experience."

Other birds have made the cup-nest safer by doming it over, leaving only a hole of minimal size for entrance and egress. Among them are our Marsh-wrens, of which the males have the singular habit of building extra nests which will never be used, working on them even while the female is completing the one she intends to lay the eggs in. It seems to be a matter of sheer excess zeal for construction, perhaps a nascent creativity. Or it may be that false nests detract enemies from the real one. Of nests of this kind, none is more admirable than that of the penduline titmice, an Eastern Hemisphere group, except for the Verdin of our West. Built by the male with the object of winning over a female, the nest is woven of plant fibres with vegetable fluff worked into the mesh to produce a flask so strong, as von Frisch recounts, that in Eastern Europe children use the nests as slippers. Added security is gained by swinging the nest from the end of a branchlet.

Another bird that builds—and with comparable excellence— to attract a mate is the Cassin's Weaver-finch or Malimbe, a glossy black bird with a red hood. Its nest is sleeve-like, entered from below, with the globular nesting-chamber at the shoulder. According to von Frisch, if the male's creation "is approved of by a female, she takes over decorating the interior with grass and other soft materials." If not, the suitor may take it apart and rebuild it in the hope of better success!

The weaver-finches are an African group of which some members have pushed up into and across Eurasia. One of these, the House Sparrow, makes one think of the pushy, plebeian forebear of a cultivated family. Where the House Sparrow builds a bulky, rough, domed nest (when not nesting in a box), its most highly evolved relatives, among them the Cassin's Malimbe, weave containers of superlative workmanship and produce the most spectacular of all avian architecture. In these species, as in the oropendolas, the males are successively polygamous, taking a new mate when one has settled in a nest with a family on the way. But in their case, in contrast to the oropendolas', it is the males that do the nest-building. Depending on the species, the products are coconut-shaped, with a portal on the side or at the bottom, or are like the Cassin's in being entered through a sleeve-like tube. Tough grasses and even tougher strips of palm frond, peeled away for the purpose, are used in their construction, being twisted and wound around the twigs of a tree and, as the nest progresses, formed into loops through which the strands are passed; weaver-finches actually tie knots. The group as a whole is gregarious, like the oropendolas. On the outskirts of villages in Africa and southern Asia, a tree bearing up to a hundred weaver-finch nests, like baskets of human fabrication put up to dry, is no uncommon sight. The Social Weavers of Africa, buff-colored little birds with black throats, are famous for their communal nests. Selecting a sturdy limb of a tree, they construct an apartment-house that from a distance resembles a broad haystack or thatched cottage and is large enough to be either—several yards across. Beneath, it is seen to be perforated. Each trim little hole leads up a tunnel to a tidy nesting-chamber, of which the occupant, cozy and dry, may listen to the rain beating down on the dome's canopy of coarse grasses above. The black Buffalo Weaver, also of Africa, constructs communal nests, too, but interweaves twigs of thorn-scrub in them to confront marauders with the equivalent of a barbed-wire entanglement.

If it is hard to understand how the weaver-finches acquired their skills, it is certainly no easier to account for the Tailor-bird's. Distributed through southern Asia, this inconspicuous little Old World warbler is actually capable of sewing. Its stitchwork is of the kind physicians call suturing. By means of it, employing a thread of fibre, insect silk or spider web or, if available, one of human origin, it joins the edges of a large leaf or of two leaves to create a receptacle for its nest. By what combination of billwork and footwork it manages to curl a leaf around on itself or hold two leaves in juxtaposition, I do not know. Having succeeded in this, however, it punctures the facing edges in sets of opposing holes, inserts its thread through a pair, draws the leaf edges together and, if necessary, knots the thread at the ends.

The flask design of the penduline titmice and weaver-finches lends itself not only to carpet-baggery and basketry but to pottery. The nests of Cliff Swallows, which now establish their colonies mostly beneath the eaves or on the sides of barns, are clustered, horizontal bottles of hardened mud. As a potter, however, no bird can equal the Rufous Ovenbird, a southerly member of a family spread through Latin America, the Furnariidae. (Our unrelated Ovenbird is a wood-warbler.) Resembling a shorter-tailed, unspotted thrasher, this remarkable mason builds a semi-spherical shelter like a Dutch oven or kiln on the limb of a tree, a fence-post or even a house-roof. The joint work of male and female, it is composed of pellets of clay with straw or dung for a binder. It is a regular house, a foot long and nearly as high and incorporates a baffle that separates a small foyer from the grass-lined nesting-chamber. Not only artful, it is also durable enough to last for several seasons after the builders have used it once and vacated it and may be occupied by other cavity-nesting birds. One wonders whether the architects of classic Greece, who built so nobly on the column-and-lintel principle, might not have gone on to anticipate the Romans and design the dome had they had the example of the Rufous Ovenbird.

Other birds, rather than building a container, hollow one out of existing material. Living wood is not too resistant for the chisel-billed woodpeckers to hew deep into; and the cavities in which they rear their young are likely to serve other avian tenants, from titmice, wrens and Bluebirds to Kestrels and owlets. Kingfishers, Bank Swallows and Eurasian bee-eaters of metallic hues tunnel into banks of earth, scooping out a nesting chamber well within. In Australia, Africa and South America a variety of birds excavate nests in the towering, clay-walled cities built by termites and occupy them, apparently, in a mutual truce with the swarming inmates.

As startling in their way as any are the nests the swifts have evolved. In all of them, a mucilaginous saliva is used as cement. Most of the family collect bits of windblown leaf, grass, plant fluff or feathers in flight and glue them together to create shallow cups on the inside surface of hollow trees or rock crevices. Our Chimney Swift, which has almost wholly come over to the man-made equivalent of hollow trees, breaks twigs from dead limbs in passing and bonds them in a wickerwork container. Among Cave Swiftlets of the genus Collocalia, of southern Asia and Australia, saliva becomes a building material in itself and in two species is the sole constituent of the nest, in which the eggs are deposited like large pearls on a small oyster-shell. These are, of course, the nests relished in soup by the Chinese. No less singular, really almost incredible, are the nesting habits of the tiny Palm Swift, a smaller version of our Chimney Swift but with a tail deeply forked instead of short and spiny-tipped, which breeds from Africa eastward to the Pacific. By way of a nest it cements a slightly concave pad of down and feathers together on a palm leaf. Anyone seeing such a receptacle would wonder what on earth kept the eggs in it. They are glued in. The adults incubate them clinging vertically to the pad; and clinging to it in similar wise from the moment of hatching, the young grow to flying-age.

From the meagre cradles that serve their relatives, the Swallow-tailed (or Scissor-tailed) Swifts of Central and northern South America have gone to the opposite extreme, albeit with no lessened reliance on the family fixative. A hollow stalactite of felt, open at the bottom end, as much as two feet long or even longer, pendent from the underside of rock ledges or of the limbs of trees; such is their idea of a swiftery. The nest itself is the floor of a bulge in the sleeve at the top, as in many of the weaver-finches'. The product of extraordinary labors, it must offer as snug a nursery as is imaginable.

I spoke at the start of the resourcefulness of Nature, or of birds. The case may well be rested with the Megapodes. This family of gallinaceous birds of Australia and the islands to the north, through the Philippines, utilize external heat to incubate their eggs, exploiting no less than three kinds—solar, geothermal and oxidational. In all the young are able to look out for themselves from birth; there is no parent-offspring bond whatever. The Maleo Fowl of Celebes buries its eggs in beach-sand, choosing beaches of dark, lava sand, which absorbs heat better than the pale sands. "On Savu in the Solomons," the Australian ornithologist Harold J. Frith writes in *The Mallee Fowl*, "there are two sandy areas through which volcanic steam percolates; jungle fowl nest there in great numbers, simply digging a small hole in the heated sand and covering over the eggs laid in it." (These "jungle fowl" are of course not to be confused with the ancestors of domestic fowl.) The Malaus of Niuafo'ou, in the Tongas, enter the caldera of a volcano to bury their eggs in volcanic ash near a heat vent. According to Donald G. Weir in the *Wilson Bulletin*, the female digs out a burrow three to five feet long in which a dozen eggs may be laid, though "almost certainly not the work of a single female." Weir believes the incubation period to be of three months—a very long one indeed—and "the young can fly at hatching."

Scrub-fowl—Megapodes of the southwest Pacific Islands—rely on the heat generated by decaying vegetation to hatch their eggs. Forest litter is used. This the birds scratch together with vigorous backward kicks from over a wide area. A large mound is thus formed, and in anticipation of the explanation of what is meant by "large" the reader should brace himself. One measured by Frith was fifteen feet wide, ten feet high and sixty feet long. (Not surprisingly, such mounds were taken by early white explorers to be burial places of the human natives.) As fermentation in the mound proceeds, the temperature is checked frequently by the nesting pair. When it reaches about 95 degrees the female digs a hole several feet deep in the top, lays an egg and covers it over. The process is repeated every day or two until half a dozen or so eggs have been laid.

Continually thereafter the parents dig down to the eggs to test the repository for temperature, which they evidently do by taking bits into their mouths. If too cool, they add more of the fallen leaves; if too hot, they leave off some. This continues for two months, until the young dig themselves out and, with no visible sign of recognition between them and their parents should they chance to meet, flutter off with only instinct for guidance. In the larger Bush Turkey of eastern Australia, all the responsibilities of the mound are borne by the male.

A grouse-like Megapode of arid southern Australia must toil more to bring young into the world than any other living creature. The Mallee Fowl, as Frith writes in his book of that name, while they "usually begin to build a mound on the remains of an old one, four months of intermittent work is needed before the mound is ready to receive eggs, and when the eggs are laid the birds must continue to tend and work on the mound until the eggs are hatched. The incubation period is six or seven months [for the entire laying of between 15 and 24 eggs, not for each egg]. Altogether the birds are directly occupied with nesting for eleven months of the year."

The Mallee Fowl's mound rises less than three feet above the ground, but it is assembled in a pit about three feet deep and ten in diameter, to dig which the birds must remove something like 470 cubic feet of earth. The mound-building is timed to allow the spring rains to soak the compost. If the rains are late, the operation is delayed, and if the drought continues, says Frith, the mound is abandoned for the year. The male does most of the work, including the nearly daily testings for temperature. To hold this steady, ventilation is likely to be required at the beginning. Later, while fermentation slows down and the internal heat slackens off, heat from the sun increases. The layer of sand with which the bird covers the mound at the start is augmented for insulation. As the sun grows still stronger, the mound is opened to the fresh air of morning, nearly down to the eggs, and the ingredients spread out, allowing them to cool—whereafter they are heaped up again. The declining sun of autumn calls for a reversal. The mound is opened as before but this time in the heat of noon to warm the material, which is spread out in the sun and repeatedly turned before being reassembled. Of the male's stewardship, Frith declares, "Whatever he did it always resulted in a return of the temperature to 92°." And he has this to report, too, that "as the birds grow older they learn how to build better and more reliable incubators." That is another way of saying that more than blind instinct is involved.

These are fantastic operations for a bird to carry out. They would have to offer some advantage over ordinary incubation to compensate for their cumbersomeness. And it would appear that they permit the production of more offspring more advanced in development at hatching than any alternative. To bring forth young as far along toward maturity as the Megapodes', eggs have to be large. Megapodes' eggs are several times as large as those of domestic fowl of similar size; in a year of high production, according to Frith, a Mallee Fowl hen may lay eggs weighing in the aggregate three times her own weight. She would obviously be quite incapable of covering them. Other birds with eggs proportionately as large incubate only one or two at a time. As for what compensates the Megapodes as individuals for their fidelity to their exacting duties, when they can have no comprehension of their purpose, I should argue again that it is a matter of a sense of fulfillment. That is to say, as far as their psychical equipment permits, they feel completed and enhanced in the construction and management of the mound as a potter in the creation of the pot, which is to him an end in itself, independent of its destined employment. As possibly supporting this view, I cite a delightful piece of information Frith passes on to us. In his studies of the Mallee Fowl, he and a colleague made a mound of their own, emulating the procedures of the species, and in this, he writes, "we were helped by the male bird, who each evening, when we had gone, inspected our work and made any adjustments he judged necessary, to the digging or the heaping of the organic matter." All the same, it is well to bear in mind from the example of the Megapodes' advanced technology, which no avian intelligence could possibly work out, how far the directives of inheritance may serve birds. It helps us resist the temptation to ascribe cleverness to them. I am prone to this when I try to find their nests.

Not all birds, of course, have the problem of concealing their nests. Oropendolas and weaver-finches have nests that, difficult to reach, are not less so to enter. Sea-birds that nest on high rocks or barren islands mostly have neither the need nor the opportunity to dissimulate what they are about, nor have swifts and swallows that nest on the face of cliffs. The same might be said of eagles, whose nests in tree-tops or on lofty ledges, bulky to begin with and likely to be augmented year after year, have been known to reach ten feet in diameter and twenty in height—not likely to be overlooked. But for most birds, especially the smaller, concealment of the nest is vital. And uncannily good at it they are, too. Your respect for them grows as you match wits with them. Unless your time and patience are ample, your best bet in locating nests is to wait until autumn has removed the sheltering foliage. "How on earth could I have missed it?" you ask yourself of the Wood Thrush's cup of twigs and grasses stuck about with strips of paper in a crotch of a sapling you passed repeatedly within ten feet. When we built our present house I set out a number of densely-growing shrubs to provide cover for nesting birds. But what in time became apparent was that a shrub that stood apart was unacceptable. The reason was not hard to divine. However well camouflaged a nest in such a site, its discovery would be simple once the comings and goings of the parents had been remarked. Birds that hide their nests choose a location that they can approach and quit without themselves being observed.

They can count on being watched—by four-footed carnivores and by snakes, which, able to flow along almost imperceptibly, to put off eating and give the quest all the time it takes, in many cases to climb adeptly, are extremely dangerous enemies. The most dangerous we have, being the best climbers and only too common, are the Black Rat-snakes. When it comes to reptiles getting young birds, I am afraid I am not for letting nature take its course, and continually during the summer I am responding to birds' alarm cries, hiking another snake up into a barrel on a hoe and removing it to where I hope it will do less harm. In a recent summer, in answer to a great hue and cry, I pulled one out of a boxwood at the corner of the house where it had already frightened some newly fledged Catbirds out of their nest. Replacing them did no good; they were out of the nest again at once and, I fear, all perished. On top of that, the parents associated me with the rapine—birds are nature's greatest associators—and for the rest of the summer, whenever I appeared, warned the neighborhood of the approach of evil with their nasal *waaaaaanh* I took it hard. Apart from that mewing protest note and the nearly uniform grey color, of a shade common in cats, there is nothing in the least feline about the Catbird. Lightly setting down and elevating its tail in an easy gesture to regard you appraisingly, singing reflectively, as if half to itself, somewhat chortingly, refined in all its manners, it is a bird I find singularly lovable. . . . And here is another reason I am less than assiduous in seeking out birds' nests; I hate not only to agitate the owners but to be seen as an enemy.

If mammals and snakes are ever on the alert for a bird's nest, birds have predators sharper-eyed than they: other birds. They are those that rob nests either habitually or as occasion offers— crows, jays, grackles—and, surest nest-finders of all, those that seek to supplant that nesting pair's progeny with their own.

Of the seventy-five or so known social parasites, as birds that lay their eggs in other birds' nests are often called, more than half are Old World cuckoos. The cowbirds of the New World, the African wydahs (a subfamily of the weaver-finches) and honey-guides, also of Africa, make up nearly all the remainder. The common European Cuckoo is the most thoroughly adapted to the role. While our Brown-headed Cowbird has been known to parasitize some 200 species—no mean number—the total for the Cuckoo is about 300. But the high degree of the Cuckoo's specialization is attested more in the character of its eggs. Small birds making the most promising victims, and its usual ones, the species has evolved an egg no larger than a House Sparrow's, though the Cuckoo is four times the Sparrow's size. Even more remarkably the species has subdivided into different strains, each laying eggs closely resembling those of its chosen victim, one medium blue to match the Redstart's, one ivory with black scrawlings to match the Meadow Bunting's, one green with red dotting to match the Brambling's. That natural selection has favored the development of this diverse mimicry indicates that Cuckoos habitually lay their eggs in the nests of the species that reared them and that a female Cuckoo's inheritance from her mother alone determines what colors will be applied by the pigment glands to the eggs as they pass through her uterus; given time, evolution thinks of everything.

What is also indicated is that the Cuckoo's victims tend to recognize a foreign egg if dissimilar to theirs and take countermeasures. This is corroborated not only by observation, which shows that some will abandon a nest in which a Cuckoo's egg has been laid, eject the egg or build over it, despite the resemblance of the egg to their own—some of the Cowbird's victims will respond similarly, too—but by the negative example of the Hedge Sparrow. In their book *Birds Fighting*, in which many small birds are shown vigorously attacking dummy Cuckoos placed near their nests, Stuart Smith and Eric Hosking observe that that species "fails completely to react aggressively against the Cuckoo" and "Cuckoos using the Hedge Sparrow as a fosterer have not developed a mimicking egg to match the pale blue eggs of the Hedge Sparrow." Evolution, which will perform near miracles when necessary, will refuse to budge when not.

The Cowbird nestling usually crowds the young of the foster parents out of the nest, but in this respect, too, the Cuckoo is more highly evolved as an interloper. Its young is especially designed to dispose of competition. During its first four days of life, while still blind and otherwise helpless, it is possessed by the urge to maneuver under any object in the nest, hoist it onto its slightly concave back, and holding it in place between its upraised stubs of wings, push backwards up the side of the nest with it and dump it over the edge, taking care not to go with it. The performance, I am told, is an eerie one to watch.

I began this subject—the concealment of nests—by warning myself of the temptation to attribute cleverness to birds. To withhold the tribute from the social parasites is especially difficult. Only consider their problem: to get their egg into a suitable foster home when the homemaker has begun to lay but only just begun; if the legitimate eggs have a significant head start, it will be the interloper's young that succumb. The Cuckoo manages to pull this off as many as fifteen times in succession, laying her eggs at about 48-hour intervals, selecting not only the right species to impose on but a nest containing the first egg and it alone. (This she holds in her beak while laying her own, flying off with it afterwards to drop it or eat it.) It can only mean keeping tabs on a great many nests indeed. If I am impressed by this mental jugglery, so was Frank M. Chapman by that of the Giant Cowbird of the genus Cassidix, which victimizes exclusively its relatives the oropendolas and their smaller cousins the caciques. Of the "brazen" entry of one of these into an oropendola colony, he wrote in *My Tropical Air Castle:* "Her first visit is made not long after the nests are started, evidently just to see how affairs are progressing. Although it is clear that she is then merely making a reconnaissance, she is at once recognized as an enemy. No alarm-note is sounded, but all the Oropendolas join forces in driving out a common foe. . . . Cassidix, however, goes when she gets ready. If her tour of observation is not completed she flies from limb to limb. If she is driven from the sandbox tree she circles and at once returns. When, finally, she has acquired all the information she desires she takes leave. . . ." Though evidently flying a long way off, she returns in due course. "Coming from afar she perches near the top of the sandbox and surveys the colony. By some uncanny instinct she selects her nest and then by short stages makes her way toward it." Though attacked by the oropendolas, "she dodges, twists and turns, fights back if necessary, until she actually forces her way into the desired nest and presumably accomplishes her purpose." But how, Chapman asked, "does she possibly time her visits so that she will reach the right place at the right time?" He said he "always thought of her as possessing a notebook in which she had entered data concerning all the Oropendola colonies within her local range."

I had not read Chapman's *My Tropical Air Castle* since it had come out early in my sophomore year in college, and in looking through it I came on a passage bearing on a notion that I had realized I had been groping for nearly all the while I had been thinking about the breeding behavior of birds. It comes in the chapter on oropendolas.

> One day, at noon, when the vigilance of the males may have been relaxed, the expected happened. Death, in the form of an Eagle Hawk, fell from the sky, struck an Oropendola at work on the foundations of her nest, bore her to a nearby limb, and, later, to the forest. This event caused tremendous excitement among the Oropendolas, their united cries of alarm producing the effect of a loud chorus. They all left the tree and for the remainder of the day the colony was completely disorganized.
>
> The following day the effects of this catastrophe were still evident in the nervousness of the birds and the frequency with which the alarm-call was uttered.

My notion has to do with the quality of awareness in animals. Awareness is the basis of intelligence. To the degree that a living creature is aware of itself in its surroundings it is aware also of its having a choice in its response to those surroundings. The architecture of termites may be the most remarkable in the animal kingdom below that of man. But the architecture of some crystals is marvellous, too, though only the result of the action of atoms as dictated by their structure. And the building of termites, I suspect, is of much the same order; they flow through the corridors of their cities performing their assigned tasks like blood corpuscles, which also have exacting functions. But there is in birds a dawning consciousness. Certainly the extent of it varies among them by species, even by individual, and by occasion. It is there, however. The response to tragedy and danger of Chapman's oropendolas is closer to that of human beings—among whom, also, the extent of consciousness varies—than to that of ants.

But that is not the end of the matter. The higher the degree of an animal's consciousness, the more it knows what it is doing, the weaker instinct's control and assistance will be. Consciousness is the enemy of instinct. It brings a falter in obedience to instinct's command. It is freedom versus confinement, doubt versus certainty—in more strictly human terms, independence of mind versus convention and habit. No doubt there are both perils and rewards in relying on either. If natural selection—and/or social selection among men—tends to raise life to higher levels of consciousness, as it certainly has done among some forms of life, it doubtless operates in the other direction as well, to arrest the tendency toward the acuter consciousness, harbinger of dilemmas. My point is that in judging the performance of birds as exhibitionists, musicians and architects, as in the rough and tumble of existence generally, we should bear in mind that however unevenly among them, partial and fitful its gleam, the light of awareness illumines their world. They are, as individuals, to some extent on their own.

Seasonal monogamy is the commonest pairing arrangement among birds, the bond being dissolved with the end of family responsibilities and the reversion of the parents to sexual neutrality. Where pairs that separate on migration reunite the following spring, it is probably most often the nesting site, to which both are drawn back, that reunites them. But many migrants form enduring bonds, as among gulls, terns and other sea-birds. Canada Geese (in which families remain together from one breeding season to the next) and Royal Albatrosses are reported to mate for life and may be far from alone in this. Birds occupying the same territory throughout the year, ranging in size from titmice to ravens and eagles, may keep the same mate indefinitely. The year-around singing of permanently resident wrens, like the Carolina and Cactus, and that of many tropical birds, presumably has as a purpose the sustaining of the pair bond.

## The Beginning Ebb

The hours, the days and weeks of summer that appear inexhaustible in prospect at school's close in our early youth do hasten finally to an end; and they prove the more fleeting as we grow older. We have hardly settled down to the enjoyment of a countryside resounding with song before the chorus begins to taper off. Birds continue to sing while the eggs are being incubated and then while the nestlings are being fed, whether or not the males share in those duties. (They are more likely to share in the latter than in the former.) Species that rear a second brood, like the Robin, Phoebe, House Wren and Mourning Dove (which may attempt three or four) have an added reason for a prolonged song season. This is especially so of the House Wren, in which the male, as in the Barn Swallow, goes on to woo a second mate while the first takes care of his initial offspring. By the middle of July birds have become desultory in their singing. Parental duties are largely over except in the Cedar Waxwing and Goldfinch, which start late (I have found a female of the latter brooding eggs on September 10th) and the Mourning Dove, which may nest into October.

In northern Europe, where the hours of daylight grow and contract so much during the year, the longest day, usually June 21st, is called Midsummer Day; Midsummer Night, which is half crepuscular, is reputedly a time of magic. By other criteria, however, that is putting the zenith of summer very early. I must say, though, that regularly at just that time of year, flocks of six or eight Grackles come by our house winging purposefully southeastward, headed toward the coast, the sight dismaying me as a forerunner of the autumn migration—already, with the last of the spring transients having passed through less than three weeks before! Where we live the mean mid point of summer, by temperature, comes during the third week of July, and that is roughly true of the 48 contiguous states as a whole, striking an average—for there are local differences. By then the cicadas by day and the katydids by night have been sounding their brash refrains for a week or more. The calling of field-crickets and tree-crickets is in full swing. The Blackberry crop is at its zenith, Elderberries are ripening, Flowering Dogwood fruit fully formed. Queen-Anne's-lace and Chicory give the roadsides the white and blue of chinaware. Goldenrod is coming into bloom and with it Joe-Pye-weed, which bears its big hemispheres of raspberry froth on stalks seven to ten feet tall. Summer fullness has been reached and the season is rounding the corner. One becomes aware of the days' being a little less long, the katydids even calling up the feeling of chilly nights to come when their voices will be reduced to a few persisting drawls.

Now there come spells of silence in the brightest weather when Nature turns pensive, like a man in middle years receiving the first clear intimations of his mortality. The foliage, which has reached its maximum growth, is showing the depredations of insects and looking a little toneless. We are told that already, against the needs of spring, the leaves are beginning to return to storage the nitrogenous compounds required in the manufacture of the plant's food. Some leaves of Shining Sumac and Black Tupelo are actually turning scarlet. All through July one has the sense of a gradual running down. The heat itself is a depressant. At the shore, the least rewarding time of year arrives. All but isolated or protected beaches harboring colonies of terns are given over to the human swarms. Glare vibrates between the sun-filled sky and the shimmering mirror of the ocean. The birdworld, it is true, is seldom static, perhaps without movement only for two or three weeks at the height of the nesting season. July brings the northward drift of the white herons—Great and Snowy Egrets and immature Little Blues. Breeding finished in the heronries, up from the South they come, reaching as far as the Great Lakes and New England, some bringing a token of cypress swamps and marshes framed by moss-hung Live Oaks even to spruce-rimmed Canadian lakes on which the Loon calls from out of the solitudes of the Far North.

Early August is sometimes considered a nadir of the year for ornithophiles. The familiar birds, it is true, tend to be subdued. They are doubtless feeling the nervous and physical strains of nesting and, it is said, are put out of sorts by the moult now beginning for them. Still, it is surprising how many species may be heard singing from time to time through the first half of the month, the Yellow-billed Cuckoo perhaps more than ever, like a girl with a hand over her mouth gulping help! help! help! Not only does our Carolina Wren continue challenging his neighbor to singing duels, but so does our Yellow-throated Vireo. On July 23rd another male of his species turned up and the two sang at each other at close range, alternating their phrases, like the wrens, and fairly bawling. The August days pass and our resident male persists with his provocations. Sometimes he is answered and the duel is on, or a week may go by without result. Then the taunt will be taken up from a distance. This goes on into September. I do not know whether the answerer is always the same male or a different one that happens to be passing through. But with no mate to be sought or territory to be defended for nesting, our singer seems to me a small avian knight offering a standing challenge to all comers, for the honor to be won. So taken up is he with this pursuit that we fear he will overstay his season; but on September 18th he is heard for the last time.

By then it has been almost two months since the throaty, gurgling twitters of the Purple Martins on the way to one of their roosts in the afternoon will have foretold the pull of the skyroads to the south on the avian multitudes, and on tidal flats and the broad, open shores of fresh-water shallows the precursors of the coming shorebird flocks will have appeared.

# 5

# AUTUMN

### Arrival of the Season for Birds and Birders

In the central Atlantic states, autumn begins in the middle of April. That is when dandelions and little early white mustards will have made their first seed—their versions of the ripe pumpkins and red apples of October. After another month almost all the other first spring flowers will have done likewise. As the days and weeks roll on, more and more plants will have passed through the springtime of flowering and matured their crop. In marking the onset of autumn by the setting of fruit we go wrong, I grant, in one respect. For any given plant the stage is reached earliest in the south and progressively later the farther north we go, at least for the first half of the year. Thus we should have autumn moving up from the south, whereas one can scarcely think of it otherwise than as moving down from the north. If maples in the Carolinas are tasseled with strings of winged seeds even before the flowers have burst their buds in New England, the reverse is true of the reddening of the leaves, when the trees' work is done for the season. All the same, fruiting is autumnal to me, whenever it comes, and not it alone. All those things that mark an annual fulfillment and presage a decline mean the afternoon of the year. Autumn is mortality. *An overcast sky with darker clouds beneath it, like shadows cast upon it, and now and again, fitfully, an east wind, with the foliage of the trees bending to it as if in lamentation. The east wind is the ghost-filled wind. A sombre, solemn autumnal day with a feeling of departure about it.*

But that was a day in October—I am ahead of myself—and

if there is autumn in spring, there is equally spring in autumn. Wild Sunflowers and Goldenrod light up whole fields early in September. Blue spires of Pickerelweed blossoms rise from the tidal flats of our estuary, on which Jewelweed blooms abundantly, the little pouting, orange trumpets evenly distributed on the shrub-sized but delicate plants of bluey foliage, looking misted. Here, too, are Marshmallows with white porcelain cups of flowers blood-stained at the bottom and Virgin's Bower, its flowers like white crosses bursting with white stamens and so thick the vines appear lathered over. If summer is the three warmest months of the year and winter the three coldest, then autumn, intervening between the two, begins about September 5th. But the woods then are almost as green as ever. Only in the high mountains of the West, as a rule, has there been a frost.

Autumn began for us last year on August 18th when the dogwood berries were getting red: a young Blackburnian Warbler appeared at the bird-bath. Three days later it was back, or another like it, with a female Blackburnian, a female Canada and a Tennessee. (The little visitors are comical in their ablutionary impulses. They flit nervously to the water and bounce off as if scalded.) The 24th brought an extraordinary flurry. At one time a Blackburnian, a Canada, a Hooded and a Blue-winged Warbler were all bathing in a row.

The Canada lingered longest, a beautiful male, suede grey above with necklace of black slash marks against a glowing yellow breast. Like the others, he could have no idea of what he was flying all the way to Peru or Ecuador to escape, may never have known a cold day. Or am I being parochial? Perhaps by his lights he was going back to where he belonged, in a South American rain-forest, after a long and perilous excursion to raise his young in the comparative security (no monkeys or lizards and few snakes) of the Canadian Zone woods. There is, indeed, probably validity in the view that our wood-warblers, orioles and tanagers, as is certainly the case with hummingbirds, are tropical species that come north to breed, taking advantage of the annual spring-time opening up of the vast, underpopulated (or under-avianated) lands vacated by the snows—in human terms as if the settlement of the New World from Europe were a yearly occurrence. By contrast, our thrushes, sparrows, crows and jays, pipits and larks, might be considered northerners that retreat southward before the rigors of winter. However it may be, that this sunbeam mite of birdity, this Canada Warbler, should twice yearly journey from one to another of two such mutually exotic homes 4,000 miles apart—*four thousand miles, please*—is to me utterly fantastic and would remain so, long as I might keep my mind fixed on its reality.

The small forerunners of the migration were a call to quit the leafy ark of our woods, in which it is easy to spend most of summer and be spared the charging columns of motorcars—the rank and vile—that must be contended with to go anywhere else. Autumn is not only the season of the year's ebb, of shortening days in which crickets stridulate with little pause to make the most of them before the Silence comes. It is, as well, that of the opening out of the world. The humid, incubating heat is lifted by freshening breezes, the longer nights are close no more, and even before the foliage thins one is more conscious of the loftier, deeper sky down which the birds are beginning to wing. It is a time of movement, and one thinks more of those far distances to which the blue space curves and of the shores, which the seas and winds are now beginning to repossess, bringing the birds that ride upon them.

One who goes afield with interests the reader shares with me (else he would not be a reader of so many pages about them) faces a fundamental question of purpose. Is he to enjoy the totality of nature, immersing himself in it and absorbing as best he can all that comes within his ken, taking what birds may come, as part of a larger whole? Or is he to go out for birds as a huntsman extraneous to the scene in quest of the greatest variety and of the rare—of the aberrant outside its normal range? The pursuit of big lists has become so popular a sport as to have made the *Reader's Digest*. From an article published originally in *National Wildlife*, it appears that while days' lists are important, the heavyweight crown goes to him who in the course of a calendar year sees the greatest number of the 645 species, more or less, that breed in North America above the Rio Grande and of the strays that irregularly visit the continent. These bring the total to 794, according to the checklist of the American Birding Association, which maintains records of outstanding lists and sightings. (The waters up to 100 miles off shore are included, but not the Bahamas or Greenland.) The title for a year's maximum so far is held by Joseph W. Taylor, a retired executive of Bausch and Lomb, who went all the way to the end of the Aleutian Islands for his 700th species, an Asian Grey-spotted Flycatcher.

Reviewing for *Atlantic Naturalist* a recent book on the adventures of racking up over 600 species of North American birds, Carl W. Carlson, a veteran birder, wrote that "there is little or no evidence [in it] of any love of birds, or even any real interest in them." One is bothered also by another aspect of listing. When the object is to come over one's fellows with a big and star-studded score, it is easy to give oneself the benefit of the doubt in deciding that a rarity is what it seems. As Witmer Stone remarked forty years ago of a certain kind of observer in *Bird Studies at Old Cape May:* "Unfortunately he is inclined to make identifications in the nonchalant manner that he is led to think constitutes him an ornithologist while the Christmas and other censuses, into which the spirit of rivalry enters, puts a further premium upon unintentionally careless identification."

The collecting impulse is of course a strong one, and a collector is what the lister is. One told me he might almost as well have become a philatelist or numismatist. Doubtless it is true of others, too, that what counts is collecting, the object coming second. But it is not true of all. For many, only birds will do—and if there were no birds it would have to be living beings of comparable diversity to be sought outdoors and from city parks to wild shores and mountaintops. It may be said for the lister that he does not leave a trail of blood and spent cartridges as his predecessors, the garnerers of bird carcasses, did, beginning with Jean Jacques Audubon, as the legions of gunners still do. There is no less of anything because of his forays. A seven- or eight-power binocular and a 30- or 40-power spotting scope comprise his entire equipment. It is an endearing quality of his that he seeks no tangible spoils. If listing adds little to our knowledge of birds other than of their distribution and where to look for them—their habitat—it does call for a skill on the part of the conscientious only to be achieved with time and application, and plenty of both. The identification of birds in the field when it comes to the fine distinctions is difficult, and for the inexperienced all but impossible. The skill, moreover, like the musician's, requires continuing exercise; disused, it quickly rusts. And there is this, too, to be said for listing, that it gets one off one's backside and out of the house. The thrill of seeing a Swallow-tailed Kite above the watershed of the Potomac (as if Nature had stepped out of its wonted path to hint of ultimate fulfillment for the questing heart), the understanding response of one's fellows (to whose own finds one responds in kind), the gratification that the recording of the occurrence in the bulletin of the state ornithological society affords: such are the harmless trophies of this hunt, and the anticipation of reaping them is a spur to rising before first light. Then, too, the bird-chaser (as he was called when I was one) is a person whose rightful satisfaction is a large and growing acquaintanceship with the Class Aves.

To improve one's own, if one is not already among the cognoscenti, there is nothing like going out with those who are. They are to be found in bird societies. The National Audubon, for one, conducts tours of up to three or four weeks' duration to outlying areas of the United States and most other rewarding parts of the world. For ordinary life, when we can get off for only a day or two at a time, local bird clubs organize excursions in the neighborhood. Though I have done most of my exploring alone I have full respect for the well-led party. There is not only all that may be learned from the expert. While a dozen observers may be more alarming to birds than one (though I am not sure how much more), my impression is that few birds escape detection within range of a dozen pairs of alert eyes.

Last fall I went out on three Sundays during the first half of September with parties of the Audubon Naturalist Society of Washington. The trips of the 1st and 15th were to inland areas, one a turf farm with standing water in places, the other a fish hatchery with a score of ponds, full and empty, scattered over a hundred acres. At the start of the first I was rather amused by the leader's calling out, with reference to a smart-looking, thrush-sized bird on a bare branch, dark above with a yellowish cast to its white underparts: "Does anybody need a Crested Flycatcher?" But the major objective was shorebirds. And we were not let down. They were feeding in the short grass of the turf farm; and the leader, as a good leader should, pointed out the diagnostic features of the species.

Killdeer: "Two rings around the neck."

Greater Yellowlegs: "Bill slightly upturned. Dark slash marks on the breast."

Semipalmated Sandpiper: "Greyish where the Least is brown. Don't let the Peeps throw you. Black legs; the Least has yellow."

Western Sandpiper: "Tell it from the Least by the reddish brown on the shoulders and the long, droopy bill."

Solitary Sandpiper: "White eye-ring, greyish, given to teetering."

None of these characteristics was perceptible except through a spotting scope. Neither were the dark lines down the head of the long-billed Common Snipe that obligingly showed itself.

Two weeks later at the fish hatchery we added some other species: Least Sandpiper, the third of the common Peeps (but neither of its uncommon cousins, the Baird's and White-rumped, which several members of the party "needed"), Lesser Yellowlegs and Semipalmated Plover. The Least, Semipalmated and Western Sandpipers, all less than six inches long without bills, could almost have had feet still wet from Barrenlands tundra, yet here were meeting a projection of the tropics. Along the river that supplied the hatchery with water, eight Great

Egrets perched in the Tuliptrees, while humped upon bare branches, as in an allegory of the spirits of light and darkness, were fifteen Black Vultures, both as they might be seen above a tributary of the Amazon. We dwellers in the middle latitudes alternate between the Equator in July and the arctic in January; but in our birds we may have both at once. No other season brings the mixtures that autumn does.

## Autumn and the Shorebirds

Most of our sandpipers and plovers—shorebirds, or, as the British call them, waders—are northern breeders, some nesting as close to the Pole as there is land to nest on. One of each, however, is a common summer bird throughout almost, if not quite, all the forty-eight states. To the many Americans who in successive generations have left the farm for the city, these two birds and their plaintive cries must evoke, forever after, those youthful years that are looked back on with, if not regret, at least nostalgia. One is the Spotted Sandpiper that takes off ahead of you from the edge of stream or lake, flying with down-bowed, almost vibrating wings, to fetch up farther along, pumping its rear end as if it could not stop. (Where the Solitary Sandpiper and the two Yellowlegs—Yellowlegses?—teeter rather stiffly from the hips, the little Spotted keeps up a rhythmic pulsation of its rear half.) The other is a statelier bird, the nattily-attired Killdeer, banded or striped in white and chocolate on wings, head, neck and tail-tip and, as it flies off, conspicuously rufous rearward. Early in the past century the pioneer American ornithologist Alexander Wilson wrote of it that "this restless and noisy bird is known to almost every inhabitant of the United States." As the inhabitants spread out, converting the forest and long-grass prairie to ploughed land and cattle range—and golf courses—the Killdeer went with them; it may even, like the Nighthawk, nest on flat-topped, graveled roofs. The Crow, Mourning Dove, Meadowlark, Redwinged Blackbird and Killdeer: these would impress a traveler versed in all parts of our country as our truly national birds, ubiquitous and unlikely to be overlooked. The Killdeer is restless, as Wilson said, but "noisy" is uncalled for. Most shore-birds are vociferous, but the calls even of those with slightly husky voices—and most are clearer than a child's treble—are sweet and touching, and part of their charm. And no group of birds is more charming. Unfortunately, there is no satisfactory name for them; some, like the Killdeer and the Mountain Plover of the West—a bird at home even amid sagebrush and cactus—are found far from shores and even any water to wade in.

Autumn and spring, the shorebirds repay the cost of a trip to the coast, where in some places they may be concentrated in thousands. Some you will find on the outer beach, prob-ing assiduously for marine organisms in the wake of the re-treating waves, but chiefly they gravitate to the shores of the lagoons behind the barrier dunes, the tidal flats and the short-grass marshes, where small crustaceans, mollusks, worms and insects are most plentiful. What is it about them? Why are they lovable? You feel to begin with that you could cuddle their compact, shapely, quick little bodies in your hands. There is a precision of definition in everything about them, a deftness and delicacy of form and movement. How animated they are! And how eager! Quickly and nervously they stab the mud or sand, and each prize seized appears to whet anticipation of another; the little searcher spins and darts its bill again to right and left into the ground. On the wing they do not simply fly; they race—or all but the largest appear to, whipping the air with tapering, pointed pinions. Birds of the open as they are, they have to meet the danger from falcons where often no cover offers. They must be fast, and not only that. Pere-grines, Merlins and Gyrfalcons are winged meteors, unmatch-able in a straightaway as they streak earthward in their air-scorching stoop; only a consummate dodger may hope to escape. Shorebirds zigzag in flight with a swiftness in change of direction too quick for the eye. Whole flocks wheel with un-canny unity. One banking around you, all of rakish forms dark against the blue, will in a split instant, as it wheels away, putting you on the outside of the curve, be transformed into white—then two seconds later back into dark.

Here is the dichotomy of shorebirds. Speed demons on the wing, they drop to earth in a dainty flutter and with a run of a few steps are gentle homebodies. One reads with delight of the female Western Sandpiper that trotted over an ornithologist's arm lying extended between her and her eggs and later, when a hat had been placed experimentally over the nest, pushed herself under the brim to get to it. What it *is* about shorebirds is perhaps that they have in high degree that which gives birds their way to our hearts and imaginations. They are not, to be sure, singers like the thrushes. Yet no songbird has calls more consistently melodious than theirs. And they do sing. "Rising on quivering wings to about 30 feet from the ground," an observer—Charles Wendell Townsend—writes of the Semipalmated Sandpiper, "the bird advances with rapid wing beats, curving the pinions strongly forward, pouring forth a succession of musical notes—a continuous quivering trill—and ending with a very few sweet notes that recall those of a goldfinch." And that these slight and winsome creatures should be able to make so free of the planet and its awesome distances must strike us with wonder and amazement. Those that breed on arctic shores pass through the middle latitudes in autumn to disperse along our southern coasts, through the Caribbean and around Central and South America as far in some cases as the Strait of Magellan.

The eastern race of the Lesser Golden Plover, breeding from upper Hudson Bay westward to northern Alaska, strikes out on its autumn migration from the coast between New England and Newfoundland and probably does not stop, usually, until reaching South America—a distance of as much as 2,000 miles: hard to believe of a bird weighing no more than two or three chicken's eggs. The winter home of the migrants, in which they spend more time than on their breeding-grounds, is the pampas where, in Argentina, their close, foraging flocks made an indelible impression on the young W. H. Hudson. Birds of the western race, breeding in northwestern Alaska next door to the eastern race, winter almost a third of the globe away, in Hawaii. This takes them as far over empty ocean as the eastern birds fly, and if, as is believed, some make it to the Marquesas, the distance is twice as great, though I have not heard it suggested that they cover 4,000 miles in an unbroken flight. Other members of the race from adjacent Siberia winter in Australia and New Zealand.

Three shorebird neighbors of the Lesser Golden Plover's western race also make fantastic flights over the Pacific. The Bristle-thighed Curlew, Bar-tailed Godwit and Wandering Tattler fan out from either side of the Bering Strait to take in most of Oceania south to New Zealand. Occasional sandpipers from eastern North America show up on the other side of the Atlantic—enough so that fifteen species of them have to be illustrated in a popular British field guide. They are helped across by the strong prevailing westerlies, which blew them off course to begin with and having done so probably saved their lives—those that got there. This makes it the more remarkable that two shorebirds—the Ruff and the Curlew Sandpiper—cross the North Atlantic in the other direction often enough to require illustration in a popular American guide. Most shorebirds swim well in waters not too troubled: some are seen feeding in the rafts of seaweed in the Sargasso Sea. But theirs is not the aquatic life.

The exceptions are, of course, the phalaropes. They take to water like ducks. The two that breed around the northern rim of the world's land areas winter out at sea, in the Pacific as far south as central Chile, in the Atlantic to the Falkland Islands and the Cape of Good Hope, and down through the Indian Ocean and the South China Sea. One espies them from shipboard, smaller than Robins, riding high in the water and pirouetting in pursuit of plankton with as much insouciance as if the swells of the hoary and heartless sea, far from any shore, were hillocks of a sunny meadowland.

What are we most interested in? Ourselves, surely—surely, but not exclusively. We may find birds interesting, too; but if

we do we are likely to find them interesting not only for themselves but as symbolic extensions of our own beings, giving rein
to our aspirations and longings, as we have recalled that the
soul departing the body was by some peoples in the past given
the form of a bird. It is the restlessness of shorebirds that makes
me think of this. They belong to no place, and wherever they
are found it seems they will soon be off—for another tidal flat,
a distant beach, another continent or an archipelago half way
across the ocean's vastness. Arthur Cleveland Bent tells us of
the Semipalmated Sandpiper in his *Life Histories of North
American Shorebirds* that in Alaska the eggs laid in mid June
hatch in 17 days, that the young are fully fledged in about a
month and that a week later the birds start leaving for the
south. Several of the shorebirds on their spring migration
through New England almost meet themselves coming back
in the fall: the last of the species passing through on the way
north may be seen as late as early June and the first of those
arriving from the breeding grounds on their way south in early
July. Shorebirds from the north are occasionally seen even in
late June as far south as Florida.

Ever questing: that, if one judged by the impression given,
one would say was the essential nature of the shorebirds. And
if man, as Louis Halle has said, is as if eternally seeking a lost
and dimly remembered home, he may well see in them the
embodiments in this regard of his own spirit—a role with which
their wistful voices, as Peter Matthiesen calls them, are much
in accord.

Matthiesen, to whom contemporary writing as well as natural history is in debt, declares them to be "the most affecting
of wild creatures" in *The Shorebirds of North America*, a book
beautifully illustrated by Robert Verity Clem. Such a response
to them seems so inevitable that one can scarcely comprehend
the wantonness with which they were gunned down in the century before World War I. (Under the Federal Migratory Bird
Act of 1918, all are protected but the Common Snipe and
Woodcock.) Even our knowledge of the insensate slaughter of
the Passenger Pigeon, which once outnumbered the present

human population of the world, does not dull our sensibilities to the carnage visited upon the shorebirds. It was their misfortune to be "fat and palatable broiled or cooked." And while "to pick off a single peep, flying erratically and swiftly by, called for well seasoned judgment," according to Bent, "to bring down a score of birds from a closely packed flock required but little skill." On a March day in 1821, Audubon estimated that some 200 French musketeers at Lake St. John near New Orleans accounted for as many as 48,000 Golden Plovers. Two decades later, southward-bound Plovers were driven onto Nantucket by a storm in such a host that two gunners were able to load a "tip car" two-thirds full with those they butchered. Edward Howe Forbush, who records the event, tells also how in August 1863 Plovers and Eskimo Curlews flocked to the same refuge in numbers "almost to darken the sun" above the island, seven or eight thousand being killed on that occasion. These two species, which migrated along similar routes spring and fall, were favorite quarry because of the delicacy of their flesh, their abundance and their unsuspecting natures. Continuing, Forbush relates that "in 1890 alone two Boston firms received from the West Indies 40 barrels closely packed with curlew and plover, with 25 dozen curlew and 60 dozen plover to the barrel."

Some shorebirds have made a good comeback under protection, but the Golden Plover's has been limited and the Eskimo Curlew, once compared with the Passenger Pigeon in numbers, has all but suffered the Pigeon's fate, if, indeed, any are left alive.

One shorebird that has recovered relatively well is the chunky Dowitcher, of which Alexander Wilson early in the past century wrote of 85 being brought down by a single blast of a musket. Actually there are two Dowitchers, the western Long-billed and the eastern Short-billed—the shortness of the latter's bill being comparative: it is a quarter as long as the rest of the bird. At Little Creek National Wildlife Refuge, beside the western shore of Delaware Bay, on September 8th, one of the Long-bills, infrequent in the East, was to be made out among the numerous Short-bills and host of Peeps. I should never have dared make the discrimination on my own, but when Paul G. DuMont called attention to the buffier underparts and more clearly barred tail of one of the Dowitchers, that settled it for me.

Standing on one of the dikes separating the flooded areas of the refuge, we were still studying the bird when Paul announced a Bald Eagle. There had been instances all day long of Paul's amazing eye, for example his identification of a minute silhouette at the top of a distant bush as a Blue Grosbeak before it had impinged on my attention at all (though granted my vision is not what it once was). But his Eagle was very nearly at the limit of visibility. It was coming our way, however, and a Bald Eagle was what it was, a solid-brown immature. The ducks were in no doubt of it. Section by section as the dark, heavy-winged form grew larger they rose before it; no duck if it can help it is going to be caught on the water with an eagle for company. String after string of sturdy Black Ducks and Mallards, lighter Wigeons and small, lithe Blue-winged and Green-winged Teal took to the air and sped away. Ducks are like shorebirds in appearing to practise but one rate of flight, and that fast. On first notice, a flying flock of large shorebirds like Whimbrels may be mistaken for ducks, and on first seeing a flock of Old-squaws on the wing after a long time without, I always take them for shorebirds. But the overlapping is appropriate, for it would be difficult to say which group, scudding in on the autumn winds in wild, free flight, is the more expressive of the season.

### Autumn and the Gulls and Terns

To have a day with a top-notch field man like Paul DuMont is worth getting up for at four A.M. Son of the professional ornithologist, Philip A. DuMont and still a young man, Paul counts over 700 North American birds on his life list, his total being exceeded only by Joseph W. Taylor's 716. On September 8th, 1974, with rain threatening, there were only four of us; bird-chasers will put up with worse than inclement weather for a chance at rarities, but a few drops of water on glasses will render them useless, and without glasses there is no birding. We had gone first to Cape Henlopen, the lower lip of the mouth of Delaware Bay. Sand dunes rose steeply from the beach, with distance increasingly grown up in brush, Virginia Creeper and Loblolly Pines, many twisted, their lowest boughs on the ground. In this rather sterile habitat were several Baltimore Orioles, a Red-eyed Vireo, and a variety of warblers—a Magnolia, a Redstart, two Tennessees and several Pines. The first Pine gave Paul a bit of trouble, to my satisfaction. But he was adept at "whooshing" birds up and, when that failed, calling them out of cover with imitations of a Screech Owl's quaver. (Any bird with reason to fear an owl by night will drop whatever it is doing to harass one by day with cries of outrage or, if a predator itself, to attack it.) Those we were seeing had doubtless just come in over the bay from Cape May. Forming the upper lip of Delaware Bay across from Cape Henlopen, Cape May is a famous concentration area for autumn migrants; on the same week-end in 1935, 113 species were recorded there. The scattered bands coming in from the north are funneled down the peninsula of southern New Jersey, formed by the bay on one side and the ocean on the other, and tarry at the Cape before putting out for the opposite shore, here 25 miles away. Farther to the south, Cape Charles bears the same relationship to Chesapeake Bay as Cape May to Delaware and, thanks to the work of the bird-banding station at Kiptopeke, is now known to equal the latter as a funnel of migrants.

It was a day for terns. Rangy of build, they fly smartly with a tireless ease and grace, and, quick in maneuver, they seem at one with the air as do few other birds. Their buoyancy and zip of wing have cheered me as I crossed one or the other of Washington's two rivers on my way to work. From the stern of a riverboat I have watched them, bearers of life imperishable, as they followed above the wake through the blaze of successive middays on the great Amazon. Emitting Morse-code cries in pursuit of one another above a wild river of central India, they have been a link to me with home, and with the shores of my childhood, the abode of their cousins the Leasts, whose steelly cries of "peet peetit" to this day bring back the primal scent of the salt marshes |and the clop-clop of tidal wavelets under a rowboat. Even more than their relatives the shorebirds are they spendthrift of flight and heedless of space. Of young Arctic Terns he banded in Labrador, Oliver L. Austin, Jr., writes in *Birds of the World,* one "was picked up on the coast of France scarcely 6 weeks after it had left its Labrador birthplace. Another was reported from the coast of Natal in southeast Africa, 90 days and 9,000 miles away."

The Arctic Tern, as everyone knows, is the champion of all distance-runners. From its breeding grounds around the northlands of both hemispheres it migrates south to the antarctic pack-ice, its routes lying along the world's great west coasts—those of the Americas and those of Europe and Africa. (Some birds, however, cross the equatorial Atlantic from the bulge of Africa to the bulge of South America, then to pass southward off the coasts of Brazil and Argentina.) Even those that nest in our Northeast—a few as far south as Cape Cod—cross the north Atlantic to the coast of Europe before turning southward. An Arctic Tern sees more of the sun in the course of a year than any other object on earth.

Fragile creatures making such demands on themselves, enduring gales that can rip the stoutest canvas to ribbons, would quickly wear themselves out, you would think. Yet, as we read in John Hay's poetic study of terns, *Spirit of Survival,* a Common Tern banded as a chick was recovered a quarter-century later and an Arctic 34 years later, in Maine in 1970. Such a bird as the latter would have traveled perhaps 600,000 miles on its migrations, measured in direct flight, or, altogether in its lifetime, at least several million miles. The Common, the other Tern that breeds abundantly in both North America and Eurasia but farther south than the Arctic, which it closely resembles, seldom departs far from coasts in its migration. Still it travels as far as the Falkland Islands and Tierra del Fuego, the Cape of Good Hope, Madagascar and India. One banded in Sweden in July 1955 was recovered in Freemantle, Australia, six months later.

"Notice how the black areas through the eyes meet behind the head," Paul DuMont said of the immature Common Terns. In the autumn, for the terns as for the warblers, sparrows and shorebirds, it is good to have an expert along. "Also the dark leading edge of the wing, which shows as a dark patch near the bend of the wing when the bird's at rest." We were at the pier belonging to the University of Delaware, inside the bay from Cape Henlopen. Very dark in contrast with the gulls, Double-crested Cormorants stood erect on pilings like finials carved of the creosoted wood. Among the Commons, terns of the smallest and of one of the largest species perched here and there or scissored the air in their animated flight. "Observe the extreme wing-motion of the Leasts," Paul continued. It was true, though I had never remarked it to myself: the swiftly-beating wings almost met overhead before sweeping down in a deep arc. "The Royals are more tern-like in flight than Caspians and have a slimmer, rangier build."

Along the beach on the seaward side of the cape were both those species—big, pale-grey and white birds alike in their blood-red dagger bills and semi-crested heads with black caps pulled down, as it were, over the eyes, like masks. The few Caspians, with wider wings, were more gull-like in flight. The high-pitched, grating "kree kree" of the Royals was very different from the harsh "kree-uk" of the larger Caspians—an almost stifled, guttural scream—I had heard on the Potomac a week before, a cry of ancient seas, surely, where the bear-like ancestors of whales heaved about in the shallows. A flock of Common Terns at rest on the sand behind the first row of dunes faced all the same way, as birds will in a breeze. So many crescent moons but for their black caps, they were each a perfect replica of the others, making one think how wildly diversified a human crowd is. Paul estimated the number at 130, then counted 164. With birds in the hundreds, he said, you are likely to underestimate their number as you are to overestimate when hundreds of thousands are present.

On the beach and the water were crowds of Herring, Ring-billed and Laughing Gulls and on a bar a few Black-backed, beside which the Laughings looked like toys. We were survey-ing them when one of the number, much darker than any other, rose and took off after a Royal Tern. A jaeger! Closing in, it might have been tied to the tail of the fleeing, dodging quarry, whose swiftest maneuvers it followed like a shadow, almost within striking distance. Then, apparently satisfied that the tern had no recent catch to disgorge, it broke off. Its pointed rather than blunt, elongated central tail feathers, which Paul managed to make out through his spotting scope, identified it as a Parasitic Jaeger, which directs its piracy mostly against terns, rather than as a larger Pomarine, which is more likely to pick on gulls. The light patch at the base of the primaries could be seen, and it was noticeably stockier than the other members of the family Laridae, the gulls and terns. "I wish it were twice the size and chunkier," said Paul, meaning a Skua. I was more than content with it as it was. To see a jaeger from the shore so far from its arctic breeding grounds is an event. Sometimes the bird would settle on the water, sometimes fly off by itself on characteristically crooked wings. Then suddenly it would wheel and pursue a tern, dogging it in its twists and turns like a Satanic spirit striving to snag a virginal soul for the underworld—purely a visual image, I hasten to add.

But the best, or at least the rarest, was yet to come. It did so not as a bolt from the blue, however. All summer two White-winged Black Terns had been at Little Creek. These are birds of southeastern Europe, at home around the Black and Caspian Seas and nowhere nearer us than the lower Danube. Given their presence at the Delaware refuge, what was surprising was the rapidity with which one of them showed up for us. Com-mon Terns and Forster's were hunting over the diked waters— the latter, like the former, of the conventional tern colors of ice and snow but even whiter in effect. Five terns of an odder sort, long-winged Black Skimmers strikingly jet, white and red (of bill), were quartering the waters, graceful in speed and verve, dipping to the surface to slice it for several hundred feet at a stretch with their protracted lower mandibles. The White-winged Black Tern was spotted by Paul. Pacing swiftly and rhythmically back and forth, it was out of its summer plumage and nearly white but retained greyish markings on its neck and greyish scaly-looking areas, as Paul put it, under the wings. What on earth had brought it here, across at least 4,600 miles of alien lands and ocean? Others of its species had spent several of the warm months in the area in recent years and turned up elsewhere in the eastern United States. (Ordinary Black Terns are common breeders on lakes and sloughs from our Great Lakes westward and from France eastward.) European gulls have been increasingly reported on our side of the Atlantic—the Lesser Black-backed, Black-headed and, more frequently, the Little, which has even been breeding occasionally on the eastern Great Lakes. What can the reason be?

In the case of the terns, it may be merely a matter of more and better-equipped observers. Considering how easily a bird may be overlooked, there are probably more going astray than was ever realized in the past, or than may be today. With the gulls, it would seem that there are actually more making the trans-Atlantic crossing, perhaps simply because there are many more gulls.

During the latter decades of the nineteenth century, the demand for their plumage for millinery and their eggs for eating almost brought about the gulls' extirpation. Having upset the balance of nature one way, we then upset it the other. In the nick of time we gave protection to the larines—for terns, too, had been objects of the slaughter—and, having already drastically thinned the ranks of their natural enemies, we put the familiar gulls, of the genus *Larus,* on welfare. Our largesse—if the use of the term in this connection may be forgiven—took the form of garbage dumped in harbors, off shore from scows and inland in "sanitary landfills" and of the discharges of fish-processing plants. In the past fifty years a virtual population explosion among the gulls has taken place. A census by William H. Drury of the Massachusetts Audubon Society showed 700,000 Herring Gulls wintering along the Atlantic and Gulf coasts of the United States, mostly around metropolitan areas—and that was after 900,000 gull eggs on the coast of Maine had been sterilized in a twelve-year program of population control. For while on the whole the great increase in gulls has been welcome, it has not been so on reservoirs and airport runways—or in terneries. Gulls are merciless pillagers of the eggs and young of terns. In a study assisted and reported by Frank Graham, Jr., Jeremy Hatch, a British ornithologist, found that gulls on the 330-yard-long Petit Manan Island devoured between 700 and 1,500 chicks of Arctic, Common and Roseate Terns in a season. As Graham declares in *Audubon Magazine,* "Tern colonies are known to be shrinking and vanishing all along the New England coast." The solution in the long run is for us to learn to treat our wastes as resources. Salvaged, they would not provide the food to sustain unnaturally large populations of gulls through the winter, when scarcity normally holds their numbers down to the level at which terns can cope with them.

### The Southward Tide of the Smaller Migrants

September 21st:

Remarkable descent of warblers upon concrete birdbath in early afternoon of mild temperatures and brisk, southerly breeze. Two brightly-colored Parulas bathing at same time. Followed by a Redstart in dark female plumage, then another. Also an immature Blackpoll and a Red-eyed Vireo. Then three Tennessee Warblers in fall plumage, quite greenish yellow. Two shortly afterward in earthenware bath on other side of house. Bathed vigorously, up to their mid parts in water, for a good five minutes—quite extraordinary. One alone would surely never have remained so long. Charming to think of this little companionship, conceivably continuing through migration.

Most sumac now shining scarlet and some dogwood foliage suffused with red. But woods generally as green as ever, though much of foliage worn and chewed. Asters in bloom for some time, including the beautiful Golden Asters.

The next morning I stood in the driveway finding it hard to go indoors. Blue Jays were deep in vocal exchanges in the trees. Like Crows, Jays become very garrulous on resuming their social life in the autumn after the constraints of the breeding season. These were carrying on in a conversational undertone of quacking or queeking with now and again voices raised in a harsher, louder discourse. Surely this was true talk! "Purty, purty, purty," one would say. What could it mean? Suddenly an outcry from them heralded trouble; Jays are great ones for rousing the woods to danger, not, presumably, because they are sharper-eyed than other birds but because where others will freeze in silence they will yell to high heaven. Trouble fluttered in fast through the trees in the form of a Sharp-shinned Hawk, which put down on a branch above the driveway. Patterned in brown and larger than the Jays, it was a young female. But the hunting had been spoiled and without wasting time she crouched, was off and had sped away. A Bay-breasted Warbler I had been watching, with some of the bay remaining on its flanks, had simply evaporated, not to be seen again.

A Catbird came in at tree-top height and rested for a bit, quietly. Then, while I was looking at a vireo, my eye was caught by a Brown Thrasher high in the crown of an oak, doing a bit of preening but otherwise also quiet. This is evidently the migratory behavior of birds ordinarily denizens of the lower growth, and busy ones. Even the night-migrants among birds —as these two were—move along during the day from tree to tree, feeding as they go. Most small birds do their main migrating at night. From radar observation, it would appear that they fly usually at between 1,500 and 3,000 feet, though migrants traced by an aircraft carrier crossing the Mediterranean sent

back echoes from between 4,000 and 6,000 feet. In darkness the migrants are safe from hawks, at whose mercy they would be by day. (In Europe, Eleonora's Falcon, a smaller Peregrine proportionately longer of wing and tail, which makes a specialty of hunting insects and small birds at dusk, nests semi-colonially on rocky Mediterranean isles, beginning in August to insure its young a supply of autumn migrants attempting to cross the sea and having no means of escape.) But what is probably of equal importance to safety is that by migrating at night normally diurnal birds leave the day free for feeding, which darkness would preclude. Swallows, swifts and Nighthawks, which capture their fare on the wing and can feed as they go, and are strong flyers besides, migrate by day. So, too, does the Kingbird, "always active and exuberant," as Jean Dorst, of the National Museum of Natural History in Paris, says; its migrating flocks of up to several hundred are notably conspicuous in Central America. Bands of Blue Jays winging by at a hundred or two hundred feet in businesslike silence against a sky matching their azure are as much a part of autumn's rites in the East as the incarnadining of the multitudinous woods beneath them. But of all migrants the most difficult to overlook are the Grackles. Beginning as a rule in late afternoon, they come by in rivers overhead, also usually at between one and two hundred feet, from horizon to horizon. For several weeks in September and October we seldom drive into or out from Washington at the end of the day without passing beneath an endless streamer of Grackles just south of McLean. I say they are difficult to overlook, but the motorists in an equally endless stream seem not to see them; you wonder if they would notice pterodactyls. Last year there was one of these processions as early as July 19th. "Grackles have been everywhere in the past four or five days," I wrote on September 22nd, "pouring over the fields and through the trees to settle briefly on the branches, adding black foliage to green, or to forage over the ground, filling the woods with soft cluckings, gratings and shrillings."

To spend the whole day lying on one's back on the grass, I thought, would be the thing. There would be the luminous blue of the sky to watch for Nighthawks that come by on wings that seem to work on springs; swallows of our six species; hawks passing swiftly in power-flight at tree-top level or, with sails set, circling serenely in a buoyant, southward-drifting cushion of rising warm air; perhaps a Loon streaking by like a flying bow and arrow. Oh, to a watcher of the sky anything is possible: a White Ibis, a Raven like a black cross; an eagle in lordly disdain of the earth. And looking up into the trees at the woods' edge for warblers to materialize, three or four together, may be as good a way to catch them as to go seeking them out. One who knows how difficult it can be to spot a butterfly-colored male in spring, singing its head off in the crown of a tree only half leafed out, can appreciate what the odds are against noticing one of the little sprites as it moves in silence, rummaging restlessly, through the heavy foliage of September. When you do detect one, you still have to pray that it will hold still in the open for the two seconds you need to get your glasses on it and its image on your retina and that it will not prove to be one of those greenish or tannish indeterminates that do not quite correspond to any picture in the field guide.

All these uncertainties are comprised, for the birder, in the term "fall warblers." And when we speak of going out for the migration, it is above all, among the small land-birds, the warblers we have in mind. In their number of species as of individuals, in the floral variety and brightness of their colors as in their delicacy and animation, they are a birder's delight; in the mid-Atlantic states there are some 35 species he has a good chance of seeing in May or September. They have his gratitude, too, in that their songs give him the means of identifying them even when they cannot be seen. (Said an uncle of mine to stimulate my interest in Wagner when I was fourteen, "Think of the motifs as warbler songs.") But after the breeding season most male warblers lose their brilliance of color, which the juveniles, who outnumber them, have yet to acquire. On the southward trek, moreover, instead of coming through hard upon one another's heels in about a month, often in a wave when favored localities will be alive with them, the warblers drift through undramatically and nearly voiceless during a period almost twice as long. So when you say "fall warblers" you explain why for every five or ten birders in the Arnold Arboretum, in Central Park, on the Chesapeake and Ohio Canal on a May morning there is only one on a morning in September.

Yet many birders, if they had to settle for one or the other, might well choose autumn. There are more birds then, and the erratics are likeliest. Some displacement of migrants to east or west is apt to occur both spring and fall, but the post-breeding season is, above any, a time of wandering. Now, too, for those of us in the East, is the best time for strays from the West—though the excitement of recording one must be offset by knowledge of the fate that probably awaits it. Recalling how, one August, he had seen three Western Kingbirds perched on electric wires along a road on Monhegan Island, some sixteen miles off the coast of Maine, while friends of his had seen two others elsewhere on the island, the able nature-columnist Irston Barnes comments that "instead of flying south, these birds had flown northeast," and judges that "for all practical purposes such birds are permanently lost. They probably do not have any means to correct and set a new course." What is most extraordinary about his report is that there were five of the aberrants. Since it is hardly conceivable that the internal compasses of all five would have been off just so much as to bring them to the same place a thousand miles away, it must have been that four of them followed a misguided fifth. Strays, at least among land-birds, are usually lone individuals, like the Black-headed Grosbeak, LeConte's, Harris's, Lark and Clay-colored Sparrows and Black-throated Gray Warbler, from the West, and Gray Kingbirds, from the South, seen between Cape May and Cape Hatteras in the fall of 1973. And they are most likely to be found on the coast, for that is the *ne plus ultra* against which they fetch up.

The East Coast may for another reason be favored in late summer and early autumn by visitors many hundreds of miles out of orbit. That is the season of hurricanes. Caribbean seabirds caught in the eye of one of these circular storms will, rather than fight the 75-plus-miles-per-hour winds raging around it, accompany the relative calm of the eye as the storm pursues its course until its winds diminish or it moves inland.

The West Coast, it should be said, is by no means without its erratics from the East. Many of these have even been carried beyond the coast. The rocky, barren Farallon Islands 27 miles west of San Francisco are known for the number that end up there, recent additions having been a Veery, Chestnut-sided and a Connecticut Warbler, an Ovenbird and a Red-eyed Vireo. A Bay-breasted Warbler has been found on an island 300 miles from the Mexican mainland, according to Robert T. Orr, and a Bay-breasted and a Tennessee Warbler and a Summer Tanager in October on Clipperton Island, south of the central Mexican coast and 600 miles from the nearest other land.

But autumn has more with which to move us than the spectaculars it may bring. Stand out of doors at night in September and hear the call notes faintly raining down from the dark sky, some recognizable, like those of thrushes and the "peents" of Bobolinks. Let yourself visualize the little forms peppering the obscurity, winging all in one direction, high above black forests and fiery-glowing towns, above rivers, bays and seas shimmering like dragon skin in the moonlight. There is poignancy in the matching of insignificance against overpowering distances, of as much as thousands of miles for some of the migrants; and this is especially so in autumn when as many as half or more of the hastening motes, cheeping in exchange of assurances, are only weeks old and on their way, as Barnes puts it, "to an unknown destination by an unknown route . . . impelled by forces which they do not understand." Then if you back away far enough to see in the mind's eye all North America and the vast breadth of Eurasia, there is as much drama as you can encompass in the draining southward of dustings of birds rising from, passing over, settling upon every shore, waterway, fen, marsh, spinney, meadow, heath and acre of forest the hemisphere around, clamorous or silent, by ones and twos and by thousands, hummingbirds, larks, cranes, waterfowl, in a living tide not otherwise exampled even in the hidden realms of the deep. The southern hemisphere, we may note, witnesses no such phenomena—though that domain of the oceans has its own version in the seasonal movements of its myriad myriads of sea-birds. Below the Equator, few considerable land-masses obtrude into the middle latitudes, and of those that do, only the narrowing peninsula of South America has winters comparable to those that assail the immense territories of the upper northern latitudes. Some species desert Tasmania and southern Australia, a few reaching Indonesia. Many South African birds migrate the relatively short distance to the Congo and Tanzania and many from lower South America to the broad beam of the continent; two Patagonian swallows make it to Central America and even Mexico. But not a single land-bird of the southern hemisphere—or any other but a few procellarines—has the migratory impetus to carry it through the tropics to the summer temperate zone, as so many birds of the northern have.

### The Distributaries

In his classic *The Migration of American Birds,* published in 1939, Frederick C. Lincoln of the U.S. Fish and Wildlife Service wrote:

> Were it possible for us to see bird flights, in general, over the North American continent at the height of migration, they would appear to be in great confusion. The flight lines would seem to be intricately interlaced, some even for the same species crossing at right angles. We would witness the anomaly of birds starting their migration by traveling in a direction nearly opposite to that of their destination. Nevertheless order prevails, each species or group adhering to a line of flight that has been developed by trial and error through long periods of time.

As Lincoln points out, some of the anomalies are the result of birds having extended their breeding territories in recent times. From the newly acquired provinces, instead of taking a direct route south, the settlers return to the ancestral homeland, then follow the traditional paths. The Bobolink is a notable example. A grasslands species, it accompanied our westward expansion, taking advantage of the irrigation of the plains and the supplanting of forest with pasture and hayfields, and today in autumn returns whence it had come, flying east from as far as the Pacific northwest to the Mississippi valley before turning south.

Forty years ago Lincoln observed that the individual threads of migration routes taken by North American birds tended to coalesce into certain broad skeins. To these he gave the name "flyways." It was not the happiest choice of term. Not only does "flyway" grate on the ear, but it implies less than Lincoln intended it to when he defined it as "a vast geographic region with extensive breeding grounds and wintering grounds connected with each other by a more or less complicated system of migration routes."

In developing his conception of the flyways—as I suppose

we are stuck with calling them—Lincoln had the benefit of bird-banding records and reports of migration from ornithologists throughout the United States and Canada filed with the Fish and Wildlife Service. By 1950, when he wrote his *Migration of Birds*, a revision and condensation of the earlier work, published by his agency, such data amounted to three million items. Bird-banding has made all the difference in our understanding of migration. Since 1908, 33 million birds have been banded in North America. Today there are 2,250 licensed banders in the United States and Canada attaching a million bands a year supplied by the Fish and Wildlife Service. In the world as a whole, the extent of bird-banding, or ringing, as the British say, is at least double that. Returns run at between four and five per cent, the majority being among game birds; among warblers and similar birds, they come to no more than one in 500 attachments.

The flyways as established by Lincoln comprise four continental systems, overlapping, especially in Canada, and joining in Central and northern South America.

The *Atlantic Flyway*, with its upper corners in Greenland and northeastern Alaska, funnels birds from the northeastern two-thirds or three-quarters of Canada and the northeastern states into a corridor—the spout of the funnel—leading down between the southern Appalachians and the ocean to Florida, whence it opens out to embrace the Caribbean and eastern Gulf of Mexico. A dramatic feature of the flyway is the multitudes of anserines it pours into winter quarters in Chesapeake Bay and the North Carolina sounds—Brant, Snow Geese and Whistling Swans from the northernmost of lands; Canada Geese and Black Ducks from the area of Hudson Bay down to the upper Middle West; White-winged Scoters, Canvasbacks, Redheads and Lesser Scaups from the northern plains of Canada. Land birds of just about all the species in eastern North America converge into the flyway, the great majority reaching Florida. Here several choices offer. A great many remain in Florida. Large numbers, drawn from some 60 species, cross the 150 miles to Cuba, and here, as Lincoln states, about half in their turn remain for the winter. For the rest there are two routes southward. From Cuba they can go east through Hispaniola and Puerto Rico, then south along the Lesser Antilles to South America and never be out of sight of land. Only six species use the route, however, because as Lincoln conjectures, the total land area of the Lesser Antilles is too small to provide the food large numbers of birds would need. Alternatively, the migrants may fly the 90 miles from Cuba to Jamaica, and many do. Here lands still farther south may beckon, "but," as Lincoln writes, "from that point to the South American coast there is a stretch of islandless ocean fully 500 miles across. Scarcely a third of the North American migrants leave the forested mountains of Jamaica to risk the perils of this ocean trip. Chief among these is the bobolink, which so far outnumbers all other birds using this route that it may be well called the 'bobolink route.' As traveling companions along this route, the bobolink may meet a vireo, a kingbird, and a nighthawk from Florida; the chuck-wills-widow of the Southeastern States; the black-billed and yellow-billed cuckoos from New England; the grey-cheeked thrush from Quebec; bank swallows from Labrador; and the blackpolled warbler from Alaska."

While the "Bobolink route" is not a popular one, the highway most widely used by birds departing our shores for the tropics requires an even longer water-crossing. A "boulevard as wide as the coast between the Florida peninsula and eastern Texas," it takes the migrants across the Gulf to the coast of Mexico, to which, even if they make the nearest landfall—the northward-jutting promontory of Yucatan—is a good 600 miles. That is as far as from Philadelphia to Georgia, and for the hosts of feathered fingerlings that twice a year strike out from one shore for the other, the alternatives are to fly the whole distance without rest or pause, or drown. Some travelers of the Atlantic Flyway make the crossing of the Gulf, but the majority by far of those doing so—to which we now come—are from farther west.

The great *Mississippi Flyway* is also a vast funnel. I picture it as more of a tree, however—a pear tree, which has ascending limbs. The trunk of the flyway incorporates the Mississippi River from the delta into Missouri, whence branches reach up through the Middle West and the central half of Canada to the shores of the continent beyond the Arctic Circle. Its roots spread out along the Gulf coast of the United States and plunge southward across the water to the opposite shores. Writing of this flyway, Lincoln says that easily the longest route of any in the Western Hemisphere is that extending from the Arctic coast in the region of Kotzebue Sound, Alaska, and the mouth of the Mackenzie River to a southern terminus in Patagonia. Even by the great-circle route, this would come to 8,300 miles, as I reckon it, while a route through Central America would bring it to 9,200. Lincoln continues: "During the spring migration some of the shorebirds traverse the full extent of this great path, and it seems likely that the nighthawk, the barn swallow, the blackpolled warbler, and individuals of several other species that breed north to the Yukon and Alaska must twice each year cover the larger part of it." From the Yukon Flats of Alaska, the delta of the Mackenzie and the Arctic sounds southward through the glacial lakes of the Canadian northwest and tundra-bordered Hudson and James Bays to the ponds and sloughs of the northern plains and prairies, the Mississippi Flyway encompasses breeding grounds of waterfowl—not to mention shorebirds—probably unmatched in the world, and probably equally unmatched are the congregations that converge down it in the autumn: Canada Geese, Blue Geese, Mallards, Pintails, Ring-necked Ducks, Lesser Scaups and, as Lincoln says, "lesser numbers of other shoal-water species, as Gadwalls, Baldpates [Wigeons], and Blue-winged and Green-winged Teals." In huge concentrations, these winter over in the alluvial wetlands and marshes of the lower Mississippi and along the Gulf coast. Christmas censuses analyzed by Carl E. Bock and Larry W. Lepthien in *American Birds* show the region comprising the lower two-thirds of Arkansas, the upper two-thirds of Louisiana and western Mississippi far ahead of any other in the nation in avian abundance at the end of the fall migration. The land-birds that pour down the flyway in the tens of millions are those we have seen setting forth from the last barrier islands along a 700-mile front to hazard their lives on a flight across a desert of restless waves to the tropical shores on the other side, which the weaker fliers may not see till a full twenty-four hours on the wing. (Keep that little bird in your thoughts, flying, flying, flying, till this time tomorrow.)

The *Central Flyway* is a long corridor (rather than a funnel) leading down through the Great Plains and eastern Rockies, "a great western highway [that] also has its origin in the Mackenzie River delta and in Alaska." From those breeding-grounds, Pintails and Wigeons in especially great numbers wing southward to be joined along the flyway by more thousands of other species, particularly Canvasbacks. Among the way-stations of the flocks is the delta of the Bear River and its marshlands at the northern end of Great Salt Lake in Utah. The hundred-square-mile National Wildlife Refuge here harbors sometimes a million migrating waterfowl and many breeding species—Canada Geese, Pintails, Redheads, Cinnamon Teals and other ducks together with Avocets, Black-necked Stilts and more marsh-dwellers besides. From this important staging-area, feeder-routes send ducks westward to the Pacific and eastward even into the Atlantic Flyway. For the rest, as Lincoln says, "the Central Flyway is relatively simple, as the majority of birds that use it make direct north and south journeys." Its waterfowl passengers debouch mostly along the coast of Texas. Land-birds, of which great numbers are drained from the Rocky Mountains, are likely to go on, though not many beyond central Mexico.

The *Pacific Flyway*, which waterfowl descend from western Alaska and from more easterly breeding-grounds served by other flyways, does not carry the traffic borne by those others. The bluff Pacific coast is less attractive to waterfowl than the gentler Atlantic with its immense estuaries, and the intermontane lowlands of the Pacific states are somewhat constricted. Moreover, the coastal currents of the Pacific littoral produce more equable temperatures, if greater extremes of precipitation, than the continent as a whole must suffer, and its avifauna in general need not look far for suitable winter quarters. Two interesting travelers of the Pacific Flyway are the Cackling Goose, a dwarf Canada Goose, which breeds on the Yukon delta and winters chiefly on Tule Lake (on the Oregon-California border) and in the Sacramento Valley, and the scanty Ross's Goose, or Lesser Snow Goose, which, from its small breeding-area on the central Arctic coast of continental Canada, migrates southwestward rather than southeastward like its neighbors and ends up with the Cackling Goose in the Central Valley of California. The land-birds of the Pacific coast that leave the United States in autumn migrate through the central California lowlands and across the lower valley of the Colorado into Mexico.

A great water-crossing presents problems for birds. Some that impress us with their mastery of the air will not attempt one. Such is the Broad-winged Hawk, champion migrant of our raptorial birds after the Osprey and the Tundra Peregrine. Its style of travel is almost effortless. It soars high on a thermal updraft, then levels off in a gentle glide which from an initial climb of half a mile will take it about six. Yet, on the way to its winter home in South America it takes the circuitous route around the Gulf, avoiding any water-crossing of more than a few miles. The reason is precisely that it is adapted to effortless travel—and great thermal updrafts are wanting over the sea. In Europe, the familiar Stork is similarly a broad-winged soaring-and-sailing traveler. Breeding in the Iberian peninsula and from the Netherlands across Germany into Russia—or doing so until recent years—it migrates to Africa via the Strait of Gibraltar and the Dardanelles to avoid the expanse of the Mediterranean—though once on the other side it is capable of flying all the way to the Cape of Good Hope. (This channelization of Storks produces some large concentrations. A flock seen crossing the Gulf of Suez was 25 miles long and estimated to contain upwards of 40,000 birds.) Yet Cranes, a longer-winged practitioner of direct power-flight, cross the Mediterranean at its widest part, in the east, as does the long-winged Osprey, too, for that matter.

If water is totally inhospitable to non-swimming birds, land routes can be treacherous, too. Were they much less so than marine we should see many more birds following shores even at the cost of much extra mileage. And some terrains are very nearly as comfortless for most birds as the ocean. One of the most barren confronts Eurasian migrants when they have put the Mediterranean behind them. Between them and the mecca of the verdant tropics lies a desert a thousand miles wide stretching from the Atlantic to the Euphrates and Persia—and prolonged as an equally wide belt too arid to sustain forest across Asia to within a few hundred miles of the Pacific. Traversing the drought-stricken lands below the inland sea is one green conduit, the narrow ribbon of the Nile. Many migrants follow it. But of these, some quit it before the end to strike out across the desert. And most of the tropics-bound Europeans, crossing the Mediterranean on a front as wide as it is, continue indiscriminately on across the Sahara. During the springs of 1969 and 1970 and the following autumn, a British ornithologist, Peter Hogg, reports birds of 127 species observed migrating through an oil company's camp in the eastern part of the great desert.

The Mediterranean is island-studded and may readily be rounded on either end. Not so the Gulf and Caribbean, which also are wider. But above those formidable bodies of water North America exhibits for migrants its model character as a continent. That is attested by the orderly and well-oriented design of the flyways. They have such a pattern because the continent's longest coasts and its major mountain ranges with their bordering lowlands, watered by their run-off, are all longitudinal. Our avifauna thus has available a series of corridors beautifully adapted to north-south migration.

In Eurasia, the grain of the land is contrary. The major coasts, except on the Pacific end, and the major mountain ranges, run more east and west than north and south. The continent does not divide geographically into great flyways. "Migration routes," says Jean Dorst in his comprehensive study, *The Migration of Birds,* "are diverse, and they cover Europe with a dense network which varies according to conditions such as the weather and the species involved. It is possible, nevertheless, to distinguish several main axes around which routes are grouped." Those used by most species, he goes on to observe, lead to the west and southwest. The routes originate in "the great plains of northern Europe and the littoral of the Baltic Sea and the North Sea [and] witness the passage of countless migrants from Scandinavia, Poland and Russia." Of the 150 or so species that take this direction, some cross to England to winter in its more equable marine climate while more go on to France and the Mediterranean region. At least 35 fly the additional 2,000 miles, more or less, to tropical Africa. The other routes out of northern Europe—and I am still following Dorst—pass the Alps on the east; "these lanes are used by at least twenty-five species, of which fourteen have their winter quarters in East and South Africa. Three of them winter in India."

To an American who thinks of Europe chiefly as an arena of human history and of national states, it is a little odd to read of it in terms of the movements of birds: Rooks, for example. Rooks have their own nationalities, it appears. Four, in fact. One occupies England, Belgium and France and is resident the year around. The other three move with the seasons. There are Russian Rooks that "from the northern part of the Russian plain migrate across the large flat expanses of northern Europe into northern France." There are Baltic Rooks that "cross northern France but winter mostly in Belgium and England." The fourth Rook nation has a Polish-Ukrainian-Silesian-Austrian homeland. It takes a westerly migration route, too, but one farther to the south, leading to Switzerland, France and northern Italy. One reads of these mass border-crossings with a vague disquiet. Are the West European Rooks alarmed and aroused by the invading legions speaking in the accents of Slavic Rookdom?

What also bemuses an American reading of Eurasian bird migration is finding old familiars spread over so vast and exotic a stage. Consider the Green-winged Teal, which breeds around the northern hemisphere. The European population, after concentrating in late summer in a rich feeding-area between Holland and Denmark, scatters for the winter to the British Isles—some individuals even to North America—France, the Iberian peninsula, northern Italy and Africa, where its representatives have been found in Somaliland, the formerly Anglo-Egyptian Sudan, Kenya and Nigeria; the Siberian population, the while, is proceeding to its winter quarters in Iraq, Pakistan, India, Ceylon, Burma and even the Philippines. All that on the part of a little duck I see on the Potomac from my bicycle! There are other ducks, too, that one must regard with different eyes. Pintails, Gadwalls and Shovelers, identical to our own, breed in Central Asia and winter in India.

They are among the many ducks, shorebirds and lesser travelers that surmount the world's highest mountain range to reach the sub-continent. While the Caspian Sea attracts hosts of waterfowl and shorebirds from the north, India, with its milder temperatures, is a favorite winter haven for birds of western Siberia and Soviet Central Asia. Perhaps in order to avoid the Himalayan crossing, however, as many species as winter in India fly the much longer route to tropical east Africa. Extraordinarily, a few species migrate to Africa from extreme eastern Siberia, the Amur Falcon as far as to the Cape of Good Hope. Among a few passerines that do so is the Wheatear, that grey, black and white, buff-breasted thrush of open country which nests throughout Europe and all but southern Asia. From the remotest reaches of this enormous realm, from the Bering Strait and even Alaska, which the species has colonized, the Wheatear travels in autumn to sub-Saharan Africa. For those from farthest away it is a trip of over 8,000 miles. (Curiously, Wheatears crossing the Bering Strait pass a related species crossing in the other direction. Olive-backed Thrushes migrate from eastern Siberia, which *they* have colonized from Alaska, on a 7,000-mile flight down through Canada and the eastern United States to South America.) Most migrants from northeast Asia retreat more directly southward before the bitter continental winter, heading for southern China, the Indochina peninsula and Malaysia. For these birds the mountain barriers to the fertile tropics are the least troublesome of all those that impede escape southward from the terrible Asian cold. There is even a sea-level route along the coast and many species take it, many also coming down through the Japanese archipelago and some even reaching western Oceania.

### The Procession of Hawks

In North America, the generally north-and-south-running mountain ranges not only present no serious barriers to migration; in the east, at least, they actually further it. The Appalachians, being of a favorable bearing and on the right path and, one would judge, of suitable elevation, form migration avenues of themselves. They do so most conspicuously in the case of south-bound hawks. And, because the parade of these highly visible flyers has increasingly drawn birders to the most favored ridges in the past forty years, it has been discovered how many other birds travel them, too.

The autumn migration: for some it is the warblers, for some the shorebirds, for some the waterfowl; but of the ways in which it may be said to excel the spring, it is the processions of hawks it brings that are foremost; in spring these are dispersed. In no other group of birds is the difference between the two migrations greater; and the participants in this particular autumnal drama are to me—along with their counterparts among the sea-birds—the most imposing members of the Class Aves. It may be regrettable that the figure of the warrior has a peculiar power for us, even for those who deplore his calling, but so it is. I picture the armed knight regarding the world from beneath the vizor of his helmet with impersonal and uncompromising keenness; he makes me think of a hawk as a hawk does of him. Before the un-self-questioning intentness of such eyes intellect itself may falter.

The mountains collect hawks by attraction, but it is a barrier that produces the first concentrations. Of all terrain features that tend to channelize bird migration, the chain of the Great Lakes is the only one of significance on our continent that lies athwart the natural directions of that migration. Coming to one of these cool bodies of water, over which the air is more likely to be sinking than rising, hawks that progress by sailing have reason to turn aside and circumnavigate it. Probably Broad-winged Hawks almost always do so. Our only bird of prey that travels in flocks, the Broad-wing is also the traveler that makes most use of thermal updrafts. These are columns or bubbles of air that rise from "hot spots"—surfaces that reflect rather than absorb the sun's rays and thus heat the air over them. Milling about, sometimes in the hundreds, as they circle in one of these aerial elevators, the hawks are carried routinely to 3,000 or 4,000 feet, according to Donald S. Heintzelman, a specialist in the birds of prey, who cites a report by a Canadian Wildlife Service official, said to be corroborated by others, that they ride the thermals up to at least 10,000 feet in rounding the western end of Lake Ontario. As the mass of rising air cools and blends with the surrounding atmosphere or, if a large one, forms a cumulus cloud by condensation of the water vapor it contains, its passengers successively level off. Drawing in their outer wings and closing their tails to reduce the drag of the air, they trail across the sky, tobogganing to the next thermal on their route.

One reads of Black Kites in Europe filling the sky, but I doubt if anywhere else on earth such numbers of birds of prey pass a given point in a day as of Broad-wings some points on the northern shores of the Great Lakes. The figure reached an incredible 70,889 on September 16, 1961, at Hawk Cliff, above Lake Erie, I learn from Clive E. Goodwin of Weston, Ontario, reporter for one of the twenty-one regions individually covered in *American Birds*. "We had 49,863 along Lake Ontario that day. However," he adds, "it's been ten years since we've had those kinds of numbers, although the Hawk Cliff season totals have been running 20-30,000." Among other

noted hawk-watching stations on the Great Lakes are Point Pelee National Park near the western end of Lake Erie and Hawk Ridge on the 600- to 800-foot bluffs rising from the western end of Lake Superior at Duluth.

Above the Far South, seventeen species of the Order Falconiformes inhabit eastern North America, and the best opportunities for the best views of the entire number, all but one (the Gyrfalcon rarely comes much south of Canada), are on the Appalachian ridges, particularly the long, parallel ridges of sedimentary rock that are a feature of the central third of the range, from middle and eastern Pennsylvania through the Virginias. They are drawn to the ridges for the most part by the rising currents of air along them created by the upward deflection of the wind striking them. These are most advantageous when the wind is from the northwest, and this is also the wind that tends to carry hawks toward the Appalachians from the whole northern reach of the continent's great central lowlands. Sailing along the ridges to windward on the supportive bolster of moving air means to the migrants, whatever style of flight they practise, a saving of energy.

No one can say for sure which ridges are the most widely used. All that is known for certain is which lookouts birders have found the most rewarding. To satisfy the requirements a ridge must not only be well traveled but have an open crest commanding a wide view, so that the hawks can be seen. There are noted hawk-observation posts in the northern Appalachians. They include Little Round Top near Bristol, New Hampshire; Goat Peak in Mount Tom State Park, in Massachusetts, overlooking the Connecticut River between Northampton and Mount Holyoke; Bald Peak in Riga Forest near the northwest corner of Connecticut; and, in New York, Hook Mountain on the Hudson a few miles above Nyack, and Mount Peter, just above the town of Greenwood Lake 22 miles northwest of Tarrytown. No mountain stations yet discovered, however, are the equal of those along Kittatinny Ridge, said to take its name from the Indian for "endless mountain." Forming, in effect, the seaward front of the Appalachians for its whole course, this escarpment rises from the east bank of the Susquehanna River just above Harrisburg and, while cut by various rivers, including the Schuylkill and Delaware (at the famous Delaware Water Gap), runs for 170 miles across eastern Pennsylvania and extreme northwestern New Jersey. Its capping of hard sandstone resistant to erosion, the formation gives that state its highest elevation, of 2,034 feet, then rises to 2,278 in New York before terminating as it nears the Hudson River at Kingston. (The Appalachian Trail follows it for all but the first 25 miles.) Evidently any elevation on the ridge with a view is likely to prove uncommonly fruitful. The best known of any and the most famous post in North America for observing raptorial migrants is of course Hawk Mountain.

Probably more birders from more states of the union and countries of the world have assembled on the rocky prow here dominating a break in the ridge than in any other spot on the continent. Why this should be so comes out in Maurice Broun's *Hawks Aloft: The Story of Hawk Mountain.* This admirable account of the sanctuary, published in 1949, has been brought up to date by subsequent articles and Michael Harwood's engaging *The View from Hawk Mountain,* published in 1972, which is full of the lore of the locale and insight into its famous transients.

The celebrated eminence is located just about north of Reading and west of Allentown. Visitors from the east turn west off State Highway 143 at Albany on the road to Drehersville, which goes over the ridge through the sanctuary. Those from the west turn north off U.S. 122 at Molino onto State Highway 895 to Drehersville, where they turn east for the climb to the sanctuary. Kittatinny Ridge here makes an S-curve, Hawk Mountain rising just south of a break in the ridge in the left-hand bulge of the S. North Lookout, the principal vantage-point, is an outcropping of boulders of 1,540-foot elevation above the gap commanding the heights of the ridge on the other side of it, to the north, and those on the right, to the east, which form the middle part of the S. Other escarpments fade away far to the left. There is thus a splendid panorama of summits and lowlands from the west around to the southeast, with the hawks appearing dead ahead in the north.

Hawk Mountain came to the attention of the birding community in 1931 with reports of large-scale shooting of migrant raptors from its heights. On a big Sunday as many as 300 or 400 gunners might be blazing away at the living targets. The object was simply to bring the birds down as attestations of marksmanship and for the satisfaction of seeing them plummet to earth. Bodies were not retrieved and the high proportion of wounded were left to perish slowly in the woods beneath the shooting stands. Richard H. Pough, later to write the Audubon Bird Guides and become a leading conservationist, visited Hawk Mountain in 1932. Having seen 60 birds shot, and with two friends, picked up 230 corpses in a small area, he came back and wrote of the slaughter. With the moral support of outraged birders, Pough next year got in touch with the owners of the mountain, and in August 1934 Rosalie Barrow Edge, a fiery conservationist (whose son, Peter, now secretary of the sanctuary, I well remember from high school), obtained a lease on the mountain with an option to buy. In the following month an energetic and dedicated young ornithologist and botanist, Maurice Broun, took up residence on it as warden with his wife Irma as a full partner. Four money-raising years later, title was acquired to 2,000 acres of the mountain and the first sanctuary in the world for birds of prey came into being. Hosannas were in order and were rendered; a long step toward a decent respect for life had been taken. At the same time, however, the carnage simply moved sixteen miles farther up the ridge to Bake Oven Knob, a 1,560-foot elevation 15 miles northwest of Allentown. Broun, who was fighting tirelessly for legislation to protect hawks, wrote that he got no pleasure from the big days at Hawk Mountain "because I knew what was happening up the ridge. It just *killed* me. . . . You could go up to Bake

Oven Knob and stand by the side of the road, facing the east, in the direction of the oncoming hawks, and there'd be half a dozen guys up next to you with guns, shooting these birds as fast as they came." By that time, hawks other than Accipiters had been given legal protection in Pennsylvania, but it made little difference; gunners, unless under direct surveillance, usually did not discriminate. In 1957, however, protection in September and October was grudgingly extended to all hawks in the portion of the state containing Kittatinny Ridge. Bake Oven Knob, which is owned by the Pennsylvania Game Commission, became a prime observation post for hawkwatchers. Then in 1969 Pennsylvania adopted the "model hawk law," under which all birds of prey are protected except those caught actually attacking domestic stock. In 1972 the Migratory Bird Treaty between the United States and Mexico (concluded originally in 1936) was expanded to include the hawks, without exception. Though still widely gunned down, their killing is now a federal offense. There *is* such a thing as progress.

Today eleven or twelve thousand birders visit Hawk Mountain every autumn—about one for every two and a half hawks that pass, on which a continuous watch is maintained. Quite apart from the view of the hawk migration the lookout affords, there is no place like it for watching bird-watchers watching birds. And you cannot spend much time at it without acquiring respect for the enthusiasm that brings so many from so far and keeps them exposed by the hour to the chill and penetrating winds, as well as for their keenness of perception. When the turn-out is good it is an exceptional hawk that even gets within naked-eye-sight before being spotted. "Hawk over five!" The dominating summits are numbered on a panoramic painting on a small signboard. "Something between two and three, half a glass high." The "glass" is the field of the observer's binocular. "If you call it, you've got to identify it"; that is a witticism.

Good hawking does not stop with Hawk Mountain. In southern Pennsylvania, southwest of Kittatinny Ridge, two other noteworthy stations are located on ridges which are in fact successive prolongations of Kittatinny. One is Waggoner's Gap, on Blue Mountain, twelve miles northwest of Carlisle. The other is the Pulpit, the 2,175-foot summit of Tuscarora Mountain 20 miles west of Chambersburg.

Below Pennsylvania the migrants seem to be less concentrated. Strong northwest winds, as Chandler Robbins of the U.S. Fish and Wildlife Service observes, may cause them to drift away from the mountains. At the same time, new recruits coming in on northwesterlies from the Middle West would have a much greater multiplicity of mountains, and much higher mountains, in eastern West Virginia and western Virginia to disperse among. What is known about hawk lookouts in the southern Appalachians and elsewhere in eastern North America, and much other information on the subject, is to be found in Donald S. Heintzelman's valuable *Autumn Hawk Flights*, published in 1975. But my impression is that until more is learned, hawk-hunters will be having to take pot-luck among the crests of the Southern mountains.

But making your own discoveries is a satisfaction, as is adding to the common fund of knowledge in doing so. The main thing is not to let your birding want for the experience a hawk look-out affords. Nothing, I think, gives more a sense of the momentousness of the pull to the south than the sight of these sizable birds of fierce and independent spirit in their autumn procession. And this is the way to see them, as they pass, as it were, in review, and from an elevation that puts you up among them, often on a level with them and sometimes above. They materialize as specks in the distance on the invisible tide of air or surprise you by suddenly being on you: massive Buteos, broad wings spread as if in ritual, tails fanned out, as they soar, stately birds but not fast enough for flying prey; waspish Accipiters that can soar, too, on their rounded wings but not without frequent flapping and that take off after smaller birds like lightning bolts in a whirlwind of wings; long-winged harriers light in the air as gulls, which the adult males resemble in color; falcons rakish of build, round heads set close to shoulders, alternately gliding and snappily beating their knife-blade wings; perhaps an eagle, supreme in presence, looking as if it might mount to the sun on its immense pinions, seven feet in spread; and, a little like smaller, more lissome eagles, handsome Ospreys dark brown above and ivory below with black swatch the length of their faces, so well adapted to the fishing life that they have made themselves at home on the open waters, coastal and inland, of every land-mass of the globe but New Zealand and Antarctica.

Buteos—buzzards, as the English call them, from the Latin *buteorem*—are the constant of the migration. They make up two-thirds of the birds of prey passing Hawk Mountain, Broad-winged Hawks alone, of which as many as 17,000 may come by in a season, outnumbering all other hawks combined. (While as many as that may pass a Great Lakes look-out in a day, to see them close up, as Goodwin writes, "you would need a high-flying 'plane!") Most compact of the Buteos, the Broad-wings launch the annual pageant in September. They sail on the mountain updrafts like their fellows, adjusting wings to every vagary of air current as sensitively as a bare-footed person picking his way over stones. But the mountains provide thermals, too. The thinly vegetated ridge tops catch the early sun and begin the upwelling of warm air while the valleys still lie under the cool air of the night. Later, I suspect, as the sun floods the tilled and bare expanses of the valleys, cool downdrafts from the wooded slopes spur the rise of warm air from below.

By October the mass of Broad-wings has cleared through the central states. (It is now passing through Central America, in flocks of up to thousands.) The time of the Sharp-shinned Hawks has arrived. They begin coming through in September and for the first week or two of October they greatly predominate over other hawks in the migration lanes, coastal and montane. More than 8,000 have been counted in a season at Hawk Mountain. A fortieth as many would make it a good year for their larger replica, the Cooper's Hawk, which for uncertain reasons has been on a decline for the past two decades. The migration of Accipiters is synchronized with that of the small birds they prey on.

I am not sure to what degree the passerine migrants seek out the mountains and to what degree their flight is intercepted by the dark heights blotting out the lower stars before them or revealed in the dawn pallor on the horizon ahead and offering logical stopping places. Having put down where the earth has come up to meet them, the migrants drift along the ridges by day as they feed. From an elevation, looking down on the sea of foliage, you may see scattered individuals appear above it for a short flight before dropping back into cover. On the wooded ridges you never know when you may run into one of the straggling bands and have your hands full with fall warblers, supplemented by vireos, tanagers, grosbeaks or others. If a Solitary Vireo is among them you may be treated to its sweet, beguiling periods, poignant in the singer's seeming innocent unawareness of the valedictory mood that imbues all; it is the only bird I know that sings regularly on fall migration. . . . Whatever else may keep the travelers together, no doubt the increased security lent by added eyes tends to do so. The Accipiters are notoriously swift and agile, but their best chance of a capture comes with surprise. Forewarned, a small bird can make itself invisible.

October is the month of the greatest number of species flying the hawkways. The most numerous of them by far after the Sharp-shins have tapered off are the Red-tailed Hawks, of which the first come soon after the last Broad-wings. By the time they trail off in late November or early December, more than 4,000 may have passed Hawk Mountain.

On the 17th of the month I am in the Virginia Blue Ridge:

> At eight in the morning the west wind is pouring up the mountain in great gusts with the roar of storm waves surging in. The leaves are straining at their holds, a few racing up the mountainside with the wind and over the crest. . . . The Redtails come over individually, buoyed

aloft on the wind, tacking and mounting. One makes a playful pass at another. They hang in the wind. Facing the torrent that pours up the gap, they can hold steady as a kite on a taut string. . . . The nearer mountains in the west are still in the shadow of the one behind me, over which the sun casts level beams. The farther mountains are in sunlight, in a dreamy haze, yellow and rust with green patches. . . . A Raven over the crest puts on a marvellous display of aeronautics, tipping, swerving, wings now spread, now nearly closed as it presents an arrowhead into the wind, diving at the same speed as the wind lifts it. Apparently the whole performance is for the fun of it.

That is how hawks—surfboarders on their own wings—move along the mountain updrafts, coasting down at the same rate as the wind lifts them.

If you have only one day to give to the hawk migration, perhaps it had best be reserved for that time when the life of the plant kingdom, as it descends like Persephone into the darkness of the underground, lights up the world in one great, departing conflagration of color. Go at the height of that, when the mountains are turned into a burning Valhalla. But as a guide the weather map should take precedence over the calendar. When a low-pressure area moves across lower New England and upper New York State and is followed by a cold front, good hawk flights may be expected at Hawk Mountain two or three days later, according to Broun. The passage of a cold front is, indeed, a stimulus to migration in general. But with distance from the source of weather the correlation between weather and the movement of hawks lessens, Chandler Robbins, author of the popular field guide, *Birds of North America,* points out. Once the southward trek has begun, "the hawks will continue to fly no matter what quarter the wind is from, and they will fly even around scattered showers." But "light or moderate northwesterly winds on a cool day make favorable observation conditions on most of the Appalachian ridges."

As trees approach winter leaflessness the flights of Red-tails reach their maximum. Red-shouldered Hawks may be among them, but in a proportion of only one to ten at Hawk Mountain; this most beautiful of the Buteos has declined in numbers in recent years. Broun recounts a remarkable incident provoked by one of these, which undertook to harass an eagle passing high over the ridge. Evidently it was unacquainted with the difference in eagles. And this was a Golden, killer of wolves from the fists of Mongol horsemen, the only bird, I have heard, that does not bother to look up at intervals while feeding. Rolling over on its back, it reached up as the Red-shoulder struck, plucked it out of the air, and plunged earthward to consume it.

Red-shoulders have a trifle lankier wings than the more moth-like Broad-wings and Red-tails. The big, somewhat aquiline Rough-legged Hawks, fourth of the Eastern Buteos, are conspicuously long of wing. They come southward from their home in the Hudsonian and Arctic Zones when the rodent population declines, as Goshawks do at the bottom of the Ruffed Grouse cycle. For Rough-legs and the two eagles, all of which are most likely at the times of the big Red-tail flights of November, a count in the 20's or 30's makes it a good year at Hawk Mountain. Goshawks, largest of the Accipiters, impetuous killers of the "mad marigold eye," in Thomas H. White's phrase, are to be looked for at the same time; they have numbered almost 300. A few pairs of Golden Eagles are said still to breed in the Adirondacks and northern New England, but most of those coursing the Appalachian ridges probably come from northeastern Canada. Immature Bald Eagles are likely to have been bred in Florida earlier in the year and, strangely impelled, to have flown northward. Unfledged eagles banded in Florida by Charles L. Broley have been recovered in Nova Scotia and New Brunswick within a few months of leaving the nest, one having covered 1,500 miles in less than six weeks, Another even made it to Lake Winnipeg, in Manitoba. (A Canadian banker, Broley banded over 1,200 Bald Eagles after his retirement, beginning in 1939.) Bald Eagles have declined frighteningly in numbers since 55 were seen from Hawk Mountain in 1968 and probably from the same cause as the disaster that has overtaken the Peregrines, every breeding pair of which in the eastern United States has disappeared: the concentration of DDT in the food-chain, leading to the production of soft-shelled eggs.

The two falcons we share with the Old World have never been numerous along the Appalachians, preferring the coastal route. Both have been renowned for a thousand years among devotees of the sport of kings. The Peregrine, a great traveler, as its name implies—one bearing the insignia of King Henry IV of France that escaped from the mews at Fontainebleau was recovered twenty-four hours later in Malta, over 1,000 miles away—is probably of all living creatures, under their own power, the fastest-moving. Or, if it is not, then probably one of its off-shoot species is, the great Gyrfalcon of the Arctic (of which several have been seen at Hawk Mountain), the Prairie Falcon of our West, or the Lanner or Saker Falcons of the southern Mediterranean and southern Soviet Union respectively. Its large, deep brown eyes set in a dark, bluish-slate Hoplite's helmet (the kind with cheek-guards), it is noble in mien as in carriage, while its tractability combined with spirit and dash have always given it a stellar role in falconry. In action, flailing the air with those prodigiously-muscled wings, it is less like a flying bird than a missile hurled from a catapult. Many ornithologists would consider it the ultimate in birds, as the great bird-portraitist Louis Agassiz Fuertes did. The necessity of its inclusion on the endangered-species list, with its prospects doubtful, has for anguished birders and other conservationists epitomized all that is wrong in man's reckless and insensitive dominion. Accordingly the successful propagation of Peregrines at Cornell University has been a source of untold if provisional rejoicing. With captive birds from the reduced but surviving populations of the arctic and the West as breeding-stock, 43 young falcons were reared in the years 1973-74 and 30 in 1975. It has been a spectacular achievement. Even when falconry was a preoccupation of the privileged classes the birds were either taken from the nest (eyasses) or captured as adults (haggards); they were not bred. The question is whether those reared in captivity can be transferred to the wild and, if so, will multiply, even with DDT having been banned since 1972. Thomas J. Cade, director of the Cornell program, in an interview in *The New Yorker* says, "Falconry has provided essentially a technology for handling and keeping birds in captivity that can be taken over intact and applied to the problems of propagation and—even more significantly, I think, to the problems of re-establishing these birds in the field. By reversing the practices of falconry, I think, you can teach a domestic falcon to become a wild falcon, just as you can teach a wild one to become a domestic one." He thinks that "we should see Peregrines nesting again in the eastern United States. We hope by the end of this decade." It is extremely encouraging, though the ultimate issue must remain in doubt, that of sixteen hand-reared young Peregrines released in the summer of 1975, twelve survived to learn to hunt and kill for themselves.

In times past no one below the rank of earl was held worthy of flying the Peregrine. For ladies, upon whose delicate fists— queen's or countess's—a two-pound Peregrine would have borne cruelly, there was the Peregrine's smaller cousin, the Merlin. Where the larger bird could be flown against herons, rooks and grouse, and can strike down the swiftest ducks, the Merlin must practise upon smaller game. Still, it pursues and overtakes shorebirds as well as passerines and has been seen to dive through a flock of blackbirds and emerge with one in each fist. Its verve as I have witnessed it is the equal of any bird's. I am thinking especially of a time at Chincoteague when I watched one give chase to a Kestrel, apparently in one of the fits of temperament that come upon these high-strung paladins. The birds streaked across the marshes, the Merlin flying hell for leather directly on the Kestrel's tail the whole way, as if it were shoving the slower bird.

The bare sands and low vegetation where land meets sea make inviting hunting-grounds for falcons, and the Peregrine and Merlin migrate primarily down the coast, accompanying the southward flow of smaller birds, as do Accipiters. Jones Beach, Long Island, seems to be outstanding for falcons, and Assateague Island, straddling the Maryland-Virginia border, was formerly a favorite site among falconers for baiting and trapping Peregrines; in 1973, during a four-week period at the height of their fall migration, 136 Peregrines were counted there, all of the arctic sub-species, of course, called Tundra Peregrines. However, as a passage point of migrating hawks, Cape May, New Jersey, is second in fame only to Hawk Mountain and has been famous longer. In the days of indiscriminate hawk slaughter the bags at Cape May were unequalled. Witmer Stone wrote in 1937 in his classic *Bird Studies at Old Cape May* of a day in September 1920 when 1,400 hawks were killed and of a man who alone shot 140 in one day a year later. Most, surprising as it sounds, were killed to eat, being broiled and served like poultry. Until New Jersey adopted the "model hawk law" there was open season on Accipiters. And of hawks passing the Cape, Sharp-shins vastly outnumber all others combined, over 8,000 having been counted in one year, the overwhelming majority being immature.

Stone believed that "the normal southward flight is at a great height." He wrote that "I have often seen, with the aid of binocular glasses, large numbers of hawks circling high overhead, so high, indeed, that they appeared like small swallows or even insects, and gradually drifting off to the south." Great numbers of hawks, he thought, passed beyond the limit of vision. Like the Appalachian ridges, the Cape puts on its best shows on northwest winds, but in its case not because the migrants are aided by such winds. On the contrary. "It is only when the northwest gales threaten to drive the birds out to sea that they descend and head into the wind to save themselves and, incidentally, cause the well known visible flights." Stone was speaking not of hawks alone. "The wind will suddenly shift to the northwest, during the night, with a sharp fall in temperature, and on such occasions the whole Cape May Point area will be deluged with birds; it may be with great flights of Kingbirds or with thousands of warblers and other small passerine birds, and later in the season Flickers will arrive in enormous numbers and Woodcock will throng the countryside." He reasoned that when a north wind arises, such birds, whether migrating down the coast or farther inland "are blown off course in a southeasterly direction and more or less of them are carried out to sea, while the others, battling against the gale, bank down at the Point."

### The Perils of the Way

The thought of all the small birds carried out to sea on migration to perish in the waves weighs on the heart. That this is the fate of many cannot be doubted in view of the numbers, blown off course, that will put down on boats well out of sight of land, sometimes covering the rigging. Anthony Mercieca in a letter quoted by Robert T. Orr in his *Animals in Migration* tells how migrating warblers took refuge on a small boat in which he was sailing off the Pacific coast ten miles southwest of the Mexican border on a foggy day in May 1967:

> Most of the birds that alighted on the boat went to sleep right away, others ran around the boat trying to get something to eat. Some, after resting awhile, tried to fly away, but most returned to the boat while still others fell into the water. . . . Some of the birds stayed on the boat until it was a short distance from land and then took off for the Island.

Of those that fell asleep, the writer added, many died without awakening. Following "violent weather over the northwestern Gulf of Mexico," *American Birds* reported that "on May 7 and 8 [1974] some 5000 bird carcasses washed up on Galveston Island beaches. More than 32 species were identified; 62% were passerines, 23% were shorebirds, and the remainder were Blue-winged Teal, rails, gallinules, gulls, terns, skimmers, cuckoos and nighthawks."

Storm winds not only threaten land-birds with death at sea

but sea-birds with death on land. In February 1957, gales in the eastern Atlantic were too much for a multitude of Kittiwakes which, unable to feed in the boiling seas and weakened by contest with the winds, were driven inland in western Europe and picked up in pitiable condition, weighing from 30 to 40 per cent below normal, according to Jean Dorst. A similar fate overtook Leach's Storm-petrels in October 1952. In addition to those driven deep into Europe, at least 6,700 were found in the British Isles, injured, exhausted and suffering weight loss comparable to that of the Kittiwakes. Dovekies, smallest of the alcids, which winter off our northeast coast, are from time to time victims of onshore gales and are picked up dead or dying in city streets.

A cold wave may be no less devastating to migrants than storm winds. During the autumn of 1906 a great migration of small birds over Lake Huron was overtaken by plummeting temperatures and a heavy snowfall, with the result, Frederick C. Lincoln says, that feathered bodies were cast up on the beaches 1,000 to the mile in one section, five times as many in another. Unseasonable cold may also meet the returning migrants, as it did in the northern Great Plains in 1974. Reporting on the disaster in its August issue, *American Birds* said that "from May 15 to 24 in Manitoba, cold weather and lack of insects caused a die-off of thousands of warblers at scattered localities. On May 22, D. R. M. Hatch found on the average a dead warbler every eight inches along the shore of Lake Manitoba near St. Ambroise."

Such mortality is sad enough, though we may reflect that Nature, which takes little heed of the fall of a sparrow, has prepared the species to sustain the losses it suffers in the natural course of events. What is most painful to contemplate is the toll we take with the traps we set for the migrants. The glaring, far-reaching beams of lighthouses, particularly the fixed, white lights, confuse birds flying low in bad weather. Dashing against the source of the illumination or flying about it, they are killed, injured or exhausted. While lighthouses are being gradually replaced by electronic navigational aids, the country has been springing up in other death-dealing structures. Tall buildings can be lethal. The Washington Monument has been a notorious hazard since it was completed in 1884. The worst night at the monument was that of September 12, 1937, when 576 birds, mostly warblers and vireos, were picked up in the morning at its foot. The flood-lighting of the shaft in recent years has enabled birds to avoid it and reduced the toll. Paradoxically, however, they are also attracted to the luminous apparition. While on still nights, according to Chandler Robbins, they skirt it safely, the eddies set up around it by winds may dash them to their deaths. The Empire State Building also became less destructive with the extinguishing of the beacon light at its top during fall migration. Before then, on September 1, 1948, 212 birds of 30 species, including 78 Ovenbirds, were picked up at the base of the building, after many had been swept away, and on September 23, 1953, 63 Bay-breasted Warblers, 42 Tennessees and 32 Magnolias, among others, following a rainy night. But even without the beacon, 30 dead birds, representing probably only a small fraction of the fatalities, were found below the building on a late September morning in 1970. Even so, the total was probably much lower than the 2,000 killed by an unlighted, 1,103-foot smokestack in Ohio on the foggy night of September 30, 1973.

Of all structures, the deadliest are television towers. They are so tall—up to more than 2,000 feet in height, or more than a third again as tall as the Empire State Building. They extend over such a great area, their guy wires up to half a mile in length. There are so many of them—over 500 in the United States. Below one of them, the 1,500-footer rising from Lake Pickett near Orlando, Florida, Walter Kingsley Taylor and Bruce H. Anderson collected dead birds during the autumn months of 1969, '70 and '71. These came to 7,782, of 82 species, including Pied-billed Grebe, Green Heron, Virginia Rail, Sora and the two Gallinules among hosts of small birds. Warblers, the chief sufferers, were of 31 species. Of the worst night, that of September 28, 1970, Taylor and Anderson recall in the *Wilson Bulletin* that "birds began hitting the tower at 23:00

and continued to fall until dawn. It rained hard from 23:40 to 01:50, but most individuals started falling at 02:15. A continuous chorus of chips and calls was heard from the birds flying overhead. Individuals flew in rapid, erratic flight; many hit the two buildings, parked cars, the ground and the lower parts of the tower. Throughout the disaster birds flew erratically around the upper sections of the tower. At daybreak, living birds were crouched in exposed areas; many had damaged body parts and others were exhausted." Almost 1,600 of 37 species were killed that night. Dreadful as it was, however, that toll had been dwarfed by the 15,000 that Charles R. Kemper estimated were killed at the Eau Claire, Wisconsin, television tower on the night of September 19, 1963, and the 20,000 he estimated were killed there on that of September 20, 1957.

Such catastrophes appear apt to befall migrants that are taking advantage of a southward-moving, cool air-mass which is wedging under a stationary mass of warm air and creating a cloud layer by condensation of the water vapor in the latter. In keeping beneath the gradually lowering overcast, the flocks are brought in time down to the level of the man-made obstructions. There is no configuration of air-masses to affect northbound migrants similarly, and avian casualties in spring are comparatively light.

A low cloud cover is hazardous to aircraft as well as to birds, and to measure the altitude of an overcast, airports employ a ceilometer, which directs an intense beam of light up into it. And this, exerting a positive attraction, is even more lethal to migrants than a television tower. Drawn into the beam and milling about in it, blinded and bewildered, they crash into one another—and when two objects collide head-on at 20 miles an hour each suffers a 40-mile-an-hour impact; there is a hail of dead birds. David W. Johnston and T. J. Haines, biologists at Mercer University, writing in *The Auk*, estimated the toll of the ceilometer at an Air Force base near Macon, Georgia, on the night of October 7, 1954, at the appalling, almost incredible figure of 50,000.

By filtering ceilometer beams and operating them only intermittently it has been found possible to reduce drastically the damage they do. Darkening the beacon lights on television towers would help if it were feasible. So, probably, would illuminating the structures with low-intensity beams so that the migrants could see and avoid them, but the problems in the way of casting such illumination, especially on the super-dangerous guy-cables, are very great. Then there is the menace of the extra-sized windows liberally installed in houses built since World War II. Seeing in the panes the reflection of sky and vegetation, birds crash into them at full tilt. And how many home-owners are going to hang netting or strips of cloth in front of them or spray them lightly with a white window-cleaner before migrations? I suspect that windows in the aggregate kill far more birds than all the television towers. Add to them the birds (not to mention other animals) killed on high-speed roads, those killed by pesticides, those killed by oil dumped in the ocean by accident or design, those killed by the ever-proliferating armies of domestic cats (which every effort to have licensed is defeated by their selfish constituency), those shot illegally, and those denied a chance to reproduce by the progressive destruction of their habitats, and you wonder what prospects our avifauna has.

At least in our principles and in much of our legislation we have come a long way in the few generations since our market stalls were loaded with wild birds, including Robins, Bobolinks and Meadowlarks, killed by commercial gunners. We are immeasurably far ahead of that people which has had as long as almost any other in Europe to civilize itself, the Italians. In Lombardy alone, 100,000 songbirds are trapped, netted, or caught by lime-sticks (outlawed in every other European nation) every year to supply with decoys "the country's 400,000 licensed capannisti [who] are free to lie in wait for their skylarks and thrushes, orioles, buntings, blackcap warblers and robin redbreasts on anybody's property," as Claire Sterling reports in *The Washington Post*. (*Capannisti* is from *capanna*, the branch-covered bunker in which the gunner lurks.) "Nobody knows precisely how many migrating songbirds are . . . mowed down by Italian capannisti," Ms. Sterling continues. "The Italian League Against the Destruction of Birds thinks the national annual toll is a hundred and fifty million." (No wonder a West German observatory in 1973 found that European birds had been sharply declining in numbers. "The tomb," the report concludes, "is Italy.") In any event, the battle to preserve wildlife must go on, from the irreducible core of hope that the extermination of its varieties may be stayed until contemporary civilization suffers the drastic reverses it so richly invites.

### Pathfinding in the Skies

How do migrating birds know where they are going?

Nothing has centered so much scientific curiosity on birds as the puzzles presented by the twice-yearly journeys made by most of those of the higher latitudes, some only up and down a mountain, others as much as half way around the globe. Only a minority of birds migrate, it is true. The more equable the clime, the greater the proportion of the avifauna that is stationary, though even in the tropics some species shift quarters with alternating wet and dry seasons. There may be both migratory and stationary races of the same species, as in the Fox Sparrow and Junco of the West coast, even migratory and stationary siblings—for among some species the females go south while many males remain on the breeding territory. Moreover, birds are of course not alone in migrating. There are insects, fish, reptiles (marine turtles) and mammals that in a regular cycle travel a thousand miles or more back and forth— though in the case of insects faring so far (notably the Monarch Butterfly) it is a different generation that makes the return trip. But in no other class of animals is migration so spectacular as among birds or are the questions it gives rise to so tantalizingly, so arrestingly posed. In his foreword to the 1963 American edition of Jean Dorst's widely acclaimed *The Migration of Birds*, Roger Tory Peterson says, "I wonder whether we shall ever arrive at the ultimate answers to the riddle of migration." Though science must of course do its best to, I for one should not be greatly disturbed if the puzzle in the end proved too much for us. The world will be poorer without romance, and at the heart of romance is mystery. "Probably the knottiest problem in all ornithology," says Joel Carl Welty, "is how a bird finds its way home."

To one who has not given much thought to birds, it is not knotty at all. All the young have to do is follow their elders, and these, for their part, have only to retrace the routes they learned similarly in their own youth. In fact, however, the young in many cases migrate independently, without mentors to guide them. Much migration takes place during moonless nights when landmarks would be of doubtful visibility and over seas devoid of landmarks to begin with. Some birds when transported to places beyond any terrain they have ever seen will yet manage to return. Man has turned this faculty to his account. From the time of the Pharaohs and of ancient Greece and Rome until the invention of wireless telegraphy, pigeons trained for the purpose provided the fastest means of communication between an expedition and its base over distances too great for mechanical signaling. Frigatebirds have been similarly employed by some Pacific islanders.

That birds in orienting themselves make very general use of visible terrain features such as we depend on when out for a walk or ride is without question. In doing so they have several advantages over us. They have a visual resolution as much as two or three times sharper than ours. They are assisted, too, by an extraordinary power of visual association. B. F. Skinner, using food as a reward, trained pigeons to peck at a certain spot on an aerial photograph presenting the kind of view a bird would have on flying overland and found that even after a lapse of four years his birds knew where to peck.

The face of the earth offers many "lead-lines"—rivers, mountain ranges, coasts, borders between grasslands and forest, rock-outcroppings. It could be argued that birds of migrating species are born with the relevant maps imprinted in their nervous systems, as many are with templates of song and nest-building. As for nocturnal flight, the view is heard that even on moonless nights there is sufficient starlight to illumine essential terrain features, though if the migrants were in fact guiding on these they might be expected to prefer a night of full or gibbous moon, whereas no such preference has been detected; birds will migrate even under an overcast that must blot out all light. An alternative explanation could be that nocturnal migrants get themselves launched on the right course in the evening by still visible landmarks and then hold it by maintaining the same angle to the wind. Much evidence, moreover, seems to indicate that the wind plays an important part in avian orientation when other clues to direction are lacking. It is argued, however, that a bird flying blind in a moving air-mass will always have the sense of the wind blowing directly in its face, just as a blindfolded swimmer in an ocean current will meet the resistance of the water head-on regardless of his or the current's direction; neither would have any knowledge of the course he was steering with respect either to the movement of the medium or to the land. A gusty wind would presumably reveal its direction to a bird by its buffets and thus tell the bird at what angle to the wind it is flying. However, it is hard to imagine how an even shift of the wind to a different quarter could be detected by a bird unless it had reference points on the earth or in the heavens.

If we were dependent exclusively on field observation of wild birds for our knowledge of avian capacities, it might be possible to maintain that the migrants simply took their direction from the lay of the land with the wind to keep them on course as necessary. Or it almost might. There would still remain some refractory cases. It would still be hard to account for the ability of Golden Plovers, Bristle-thighed Curlews and Wandering Tattlers to make their landfalls on Pacific Islands thousands of miles from their points of departure and of Greater Shearwaters, after ranging the Atlantic from its southernmost to its northernmost reaches to return to the little islands of Tristan da Cunha, a cluster a mere 30 miles wide, 1,500 miles west of the Cape of Good Hope and 2,250 east of Buenos Aires. There are the Shining and Long-tailed Cuckoos of New Zealand. The former winter in the Solomon Islands and Bismarck Archipelago, over 3,000 miles away and farther via Australia, while some of the latter reach the Tuamotos, 2,600 miles away with an absolute minimum of 1,500 over empty ocean and probably much more, unless a much longer, indirect route is taken with empty ocean reduced to a minimum of 1,000 miles.

Where field observation, assisted by banding and radar surveillance, tells us what birds do, experimentation can teach us what birds are able to do and, up to a point, at least, how they do it. Much has been undertaken.

Initial experiments were in transporting birds from their familiar surroundings and seeing what they would do when released. Sending birds out in the expectation of their return has, of course, as we recalled, been man's practice for two thousand years and more with domestic Pigeons, descendants of the cliff-dwelling Rock Dove of the Mediterranean-Caspian region. For all this time, Pigeons bred for the purpose have been able to "home" with sufficient consistency to make them valuable as messengers, even though, practically speaking, a Pigeon will return only to the loft in which it has been reared and mated—which does not preclude moving the loft, however. Innumerable Homing Pigeons have reappeared at the loft after having been released in territory quite strange to them, from distances of up to a thousand miles or even more.

Some students have held that no extraordinary powers are involved in these feats. The successful performers, they have observed, are the beneficiaries of many generations of selective breeding for reconnaissance ability and speed on the wing and have furthermore been trained in many practice flights, usually over increasing distances. What a Homing Pigeon does, in their view, is to fly around the release point in expanding circles until picking up a familiar configuration of the landscape, which tells it where the loft is. They cite the practice of Pigeons of visibly circling about after their release, the greater speed and consistency of returns among Pigeons flown always in one direction from the loft, and the high proportion of Pigeons that fail to return from long-distance flights from unfamiliar territory. In the case of wild birds that, when transported away from their nests and released in strange surroundings, manage to find their way back, their view is the same: the percentage of those returning is low enough to warrant ascribing their success to luck in a hit-or-miss quest for clues to location.

There has been some justification for skepticism about birds' super-capabilities. Working with certain figures on percentages of wild-bird returns from increasing distances, a mathematician has showed that random search would have accounted for them. Experimental releases of Homing Pigeons at great distances have resulted in a wide scattering of the birds. Then there is the frequently cited experiment conducted by Donald R. Griffin of Harvard with Gannets. Capturing a number of these long-winged sea-birds at their nesting colony on Bonaventure Island, off the Gaspé peninsula, he took them to release points as far as 213 miles distant and observed developments. First, he found that those released along the coast returned sooner than another group released at Caribou, Maine, 100 miles from the St. Lawrence and 140 from the sea. Secondly, by following the second group in an airplane and plotting their peregrinations on a map, he showed that, rather than setting off toward Bonaventure as a "homing sense" would have led them to, they went off in various directions, through twisting and curling paths that were clearly exploratory in nature. Of the 16 in this group, ten were found back at their nests within a little more than four days, the fastest having covered the 213 miles in twenty-four hours.

Many birds, we have learned—those of stationary species unacquainted with migration—are quite at a loss when removed from immediate home surroundings. Trials of four non-migratory species of European birds showed that six miles was the farthest distance either of two titmice could be taken from the nest and return, nine the farthest for House and Tree Sparrows.

At the same time, experimentation has taught us that birds have powers of orientation unsuspected in the past.

We have learned to begin with that even in species in which young and old habitually migrate together, the former are able to take the right course on their own. This was shown by William Rowan, in Alberta, who held back a number of trapped young Crows until others of the species had departed for the south, then released them. Of the "some 60 per cent" recovered, he was able to report that "not a single bird had deviated significantly from the standard fall direction." Similar results were obtained by Frank C. Bellrose, a wildlife-management specialist, who trapped and confined over 1,000 young Blue-winged Teal in Illinois, then, weeks after the last wild Teal had departed, released them in batches over a period of several months. Those subsequently recovered in the south—54—had, again, migrated in the direction taken by the adults.

We have also learned that young birds moved from their birthplace to an area distant from it will migrate along the same compass-bearing that their forebears have taken to winter quarters and will follow it for about the same distance, even if they end up in unfavorable habitats. This was first established by Ernst Schüz, who removed infant Storks from their nests in the Baltic region and reared them in western Germany. In this case, however, not all migrated in the ancestral direction, to the south-southeast; there was a tendency among them to follow the lead of the local Storks and fly southwest. A more consistent pattern emerged among young Storks and young Herring Gulls transplanted to areas where their species do not breed—some of the Storks to England. Recoveries left no doubt of the dominance of the inherited directional proclivity or of the youngsters' ability to follow it. Even more arresting was the behavior of young Starlings trapped in the Netherlands by a Dutch ornithologist, A. C. Perdeck, and released in Barcelona. Ignoring the attractions that have made Catalonia a popular winter haven of Starlings, the transportees flew on westward, just as they would have if quitting the Netherlands, to the full width of the country.

Such experiments were to test the actions of displaced young on autumn migration. Werner Rüppell experimented with spring migrants. He trapped some hundreds of Hooded Crows on their way northeast at Rossitten (now Rybatschi), a famous station in a migration corridor on a neck of land in the Baltic, and released them at distances up to 640 miles to the west and southwest. The majority of the 176 young crows recovered had, like the fall migrants, carried out their migration by pursuing a course parallel to that to which they were bred and in doing so established a new breeding colony well to the west of that in which they were hatched, one they also maintained in subsequent years. Most interestingly, they migrated to winter quarters also west of that of their fellows.

So—as Geoffrey T. V. Matthews sums up in his *Bird Navigation:* "The young bird is thus innately equipped at least for the simple procedure of a bearing-and-distance flight to a hitherto unknown area." I do not myself see what is so simple about it; but in truth much more demanding performances have been recorded in further experiments. "The displacement of older birds . . . produced very different results from that of the young birds," Matthews continues. "There was a strong tendency for the recoveries of these older birds to lie in the direction of, or actually within, the normal winter and summer areas. They ignored the 'standard direction' and the example of local passage migrants at the release point. The difference . . . is best shown in Perdeck's work with Starlings."

What Perdeck did was to trap in The Hague 11,000 Starlings on their way from countries bordering the Baltic Sea to winter refuges farther to the southwest, in Belgium, northwest France and the southern British Isles. He then took his captives south*east* to Switzerland for release. Later, recoveries showed that the young had resumed the ingrained southwest direction, which took them to southern France and the Iberian peninsula, while the adults flew from Switzerland *north*west to their habitual winter quarters on the two sides of the English Channel. If the ability of the latter to reach a known objective via a course quite outside their experience and that of their ancestors was surprising, the subsequent behavior of the young was no less so. The resurgence in the spring of the inherent directional impulse would have sent them northeast to the environs of Budapest. Instead they took a more northerly course that brought them back to their native lands in the Baltic countries. Then in the autumn, with equal unexpectedness, they turned up in the winter home they had acquired by displacement the year before, in southern France and the Iberian peninsula. Perdeck's experiment was repeated with Chaffinches, and with the same remarkable results, "the young birds orienting according to direction," as Dorst puts it, "the adults to a true goal"; furthermore, the young, again, adopted the winter home they acquired by displacement and returned to it the next autumn "by true-goal orientation."

What these performances certainly appear to tell us is that migrant birds have not only an innate directional sense but an ability to steer for a particular area without need of clues provided by known landscape features. To determine whether this is so, wild birds of many species have in the past half century and more been trapped at their nests, transported to greater or lesser distances, released and their returns recorded. Of 26 House Martins transported between 316 and 450 miles, seven returned; of 143 Cliff Swallows between 40 and 115 miles, 63; of 21 European Common Swifts 150 miles, 10; of 38 Alpine Swifts 1,020 miles, 12; of 80 Common Terns between 94 and 456 miles, 36; of 61 Leach's Storm-petrels between 163 and 2,980 miles, 48. Of five Wrynecks (a relative of the woodpeckers) transported from Berlin to London, two made the 560-mile return trip within 12 days while another returned from Salonika—a distance of 930 miles—in the same length of time. A Red-backed Shrike, also from Berlin, made the 760-mile trip from Marseilles in 13 days. Sooty and Noddy Terns have homed from 850 miles away, Barn Swallows and Starlings from 1,150 miles, White Storks from over 1,400.

Slow times made by many homing birds—much slower than they could have made in sustained, straight-line flight—have raised the question of whether they were confused or allowing themselves generous rests. To reduce the likelihood of the latter a marine species was forced to fly overland. Geoffrey V. T. Matthews took 152 little Manx Shearwaters from their nesting colony on the Welsh coast and released them deep in Europe, between 125 and 265 miles away, under clear, sunny skies. Of 131 known to have returned, over half did so during the first two nights. Those released in the afternoon made speeds of between 16 and 35 miles an hour for the course, averaging about 24—a very respectable showing. Those released earlier in the day did less well, but probably only because they had to await darkness before making for their nesting burrows to avoid capture at the entrances by the much larger, marauding gulls.

While the nest has been assumed, no doubt rightly, to exert a particularly strong pull upon a displaced bird, one ornithologist has tested the homing of passerines removed from a winter haven. L. Richard Mewaldt trapped 411 Golden-crowned and White-throated Sparrows down from the north at San Jose, California, and flew them for release to Baton Rouge, Louisiana, over 1,800 miles away. The next winter, 26 were recaptured at San Jose—a higher proportion than it sounds inasmuch as the mortality of sparrows during a year of such trial should probably be reckoned at more than 50 per cent. That same winter Mewaldt flew 660 birds of the same two species, including 22 that had returned from Baton Rouge, to Laurel, Maryland, a distance this time over 2,400 miles. Of these, 15 were recaptured at San Jose the following winter, among them six of the Baton Rouge veterans. To those six small birds, frail and of indifferent powers of flight, that triumphed over such vast stretches of alien lands on the strength of an attachment, one's heart goes out.

If there is something touching about the little sparrows, there is something scarcely less so—as there is equally a demonstration of birds' drive and ability to find their way home—in the Canada Geese that were captured in Missouri, pinioned, and, having been released or escaped from confinement in several wildlife refuges in the northern plains, were discovered resolutely plodding northward, one having traveled 25 miles.

The longest homing flights so far recorded are those of Leach's Storm-petrels and a Manx Shearwater, each of which covered over 3,000 miles from one side of the Atlantic to. the other, and those of three Laysan Albatrosses from Midway Island. Of these, two flew home from the state of Washington—a minimal distance of 3,200 miles—and the third an astonishing 4,000 miles, at least, from the Philippines, though requiring 32 days for the trip.

To the layman struggling to get a grip on Geoffrey V. T. Matthews's *Bird Navigation,* a Cambridge University monograph, it is immensely refreshing to have the author cast aside detachment and out of the jungle of technical language speak as follows:

> Delving into the problems of bird navigation has its intellectual rewards, but there is an excitement in dealing with the navigators themselves that has little to do with scientific discipline. It was certainly not unremarkable to open a burrow on a Welsh island and find therein a Manx Shearwater ringed AX 6587, when that bird had been sent over 3,000 miles to Boston, Mass. Added piquancy was given when the letter announcing its release 12½ days before, came 10 hours later. Reversing the process, one could not be indifferent to the fate of seven tiny Leach's Petrels when releasing them on the Sussex coast; nor fail to be relieved when a cable arrived reporting the return of the first two, in under a fortnight, to their nests on an island off Maine, again over 3,000 miles away.

Matthews goes on to render the all-important judgment that "the sheer distance involved in some of these successful flights renders explanations of homing in terms of chance quite unrealistic. In addition, evidence has accumulated . . . that Pigeons, of good stock and in good weather conditions, will home from unknown points at straight-line speeds close to those of normal flight. This is especially so when the birds are in small groups. There may then be an element of competition, or, perhaps, less tendency to be diverted." Conceivably the consensus of a group proves more reliable than individual judgments of direction. The Shining Cuckoo, though belonging to a family of individualists, collects in flocks for its long overseas flights.

What the skeptics of Pigeon-homing had not allowed for was

the great unevenness of the distribution of the homing ability not only among species of birds but among genetic strains within a species. If, on long test flights, only ten out of 100 Pigeons returned to their own loft, the rest being picked up elsewhere, and the ten were more or less different each time, then the successes could be attributed to lucky chance. If, on the other hand, it was more or less the same ten each time, then it was a case of a small minority of talented individuals in a mass of mediocrities. And, as with human beings, that seems to be the way it is.

The true homing of Pigeons was demonstrated in 1967 in Massachusetts by M. C. Michener and Charles Wolcott. Their technique was to attach a tiny radio transmitter to the Pigeon's tail and keep tuned to its signal with a direction-finder. So equipped, ten birds were flown individually and repeatedly from a point 35 miles west of the loft and their courses traced. Inasmuch as no two courses out of 36 flown were the same, it was evident that the birds were not flying from landmark to landmark. Indeed, when they came within sight of familiar buildings identifying their home base they then *shifted* course to one directly to the loft. What they were doing was flying a learned directional course. That came out when the releases were shifted to points 20 miles south of the loft and 30 miles north of it. Without exception, the Pigeons took off on the inappropriate west-to-east bearing to which they had become accustomed. However, after five miles or more, even up to 50, the growing discrepancy between the course it was flying and the direction of home evidently got through to the bird—whereupon it would turn and head for the loft on an extraordinarily accurate bearing, in some cases no more than two degrees off. *There* was true-goal orientation.

That brings us back to the question of how birds are capable of it. That there is any one sovereign technique at their command we may well doubt. If they are possessed of "most miraculous organ," in Shakespeare's phrase, it is one available to them in very varying degrees and probably only uncertainly at best. The number of birds that go astray on migration and in homing experiments is evidence of that. The truth probably is that in meeting the exigencies of direction-finding, birds muster a patchwork of inner resources which may or may not see them through, as we do in meeting the exigencies of our lives, with comparable results.

A discovery that put the scientists far ahead in the process of answering the big questions was announced in 1949 by a German ornithologist. Gustav Kramer, who kept passerine birds in outdoor cages, found that his subjects became restless during the periods of their normal migration and, furthermore, tended to face or flutter in the direction in which they would normally migrate, spring or fall. To test their proclivities fairly, Kramer designed a circular cage with a circular perch running around it. This became variously modified by others to provide automatic recording of the occupant's movements and obviate the necessity of hours of observation. The most ingenious system in point of simplicity was devised by the Americans Stephen T. and John T. Emlen of Cornell and the University of Wisconsin respectively. Their cage has a sloping lower wall of blotting paper and an inking pad at the bottom so that with every movement up the incline the captive leaves tracks, the density of which indicates the strength of its directional tendencies.

Meanwhile, Kramer had made a second discovery, and an electrifying one. He found that Starlings in cages under sunny skies displayed consistent directional headings, while under an overcast their movements were random. He also recorded similar behavior on the part of Red-backed Shrikes and Blackcaps, and to these species other experimenters soon added others performing like them. Those who tested free-flying birds, including Pigeons, said that they, too, lost orientation under cloud-covered skies. The case for the sun as a reference point in navigation was virtually clinched by experiments of Kramer's in which, first, mirrors were used to shift the sun's apparent position and, secondly, an artificial sun was used in a dark room. In both cases the Starlings oriented on the ostensible sun.

But what is far more remarkable than that birds should guide on the source of light is that in doing so they can maintain a straight course while the reference point itself moves from one side of the sky around to the other. The sun's azimuth for the bird—the angle between the direction in which it is heading and the direction in which the sun is to be seen—must be constantly if slowly changing if the migrant is to stay on course. What this means is that the migrant must contain a mechanism that tells it what time of day it is so that it will know what the azimuth is supposed to be. To a bird seeking to steer a course northeastward, the internal timer must say: "It is dawn and the rising sun should be on the starboard quarter, on an azimuth of 45 degrees. . . . It is mid morning and the sun should be on the starboard beam, on an azimuth of 90 degrees. . . . It is noon and the sun should be on a starboard azimuth of 135 degrees. . . . It is 4:00 P.M. and the sun should be on a port azimuth of 160 degrees." These are fairly fine correlations, but we have no alternative to believing that they are those on which migrants operate, if only approximately. "There is general agreement on the existence of intrinsic rhythmic processes, whether these be neural or hormonal in nature, which serve as the 'clocks,'" Matthews declares. "In natural conditions, the rhythms are kept in step with external rhythmic events. . . . Of these, the light/dark succession of day and night is one of the most important."

If it were to be shown that a bird's internal clock could be artificially advanced or retarded and have the bird out of phase with sun-time by the same degree, then the existence of the clock would surely be demonstrated. And precisely this was done by Klaus Schmidt-Koenig working with Homing Pigeons. Dividing his subjects into three groups and a group of control birds that were left in natural conditions, he installed each of the former in a windowless room in which an artificial cycle of day and night was maintained. In one room the cycle was six hours ahead of sun-time, in another six hours behind, while in the third the difference was twelve hours, so that natural day and night were reversed. When the subjects were judged to have accommodated to the imposed regime they were released individually and alternately with control birds. It was expected that birds in the first group would head in a direction 90 degrees to the left and those in the second 90 degrees to the right of that taken by the controls and those in the third in a direction opposite to that taken by the controls. The deviations were not so exact but were close enough to prove the point. As striking as these results was the demonstration by some of the Pigeons that despite their timers' having been thrown off, they could beat a prompt and direct return to the loft.

Schmidt-Koenig's experiment with Pigeons has been duplicated with wild birds, with similar effects. It may be added that an ability to orient on the sun has also been found among bees, fishes and reptiles.

With diurnal migrants shown to navigate astronomically, the possibility of their nocturnal fellows' doing likewise naturally suggested itself. The night, however, affords no such dominant and regular beacon as the sun; the moon, in addition to contracting and expanding through its phases, rises and sets an hour later every day and is absent from the night sky half the time. Was it conceivable that the stars, mere points of light, yet sprinkled the length and breadth of the heavens in overpowering numbers, could provide the markers the migrants would require?

So it has appeared. A shock wave of excitement again ran through the ornithological community in 1955 with the announcement by Franz and Eleonore Sauer—Germans like Kramer—that hand-reared Blackcaps and Garden Warblers in a Kramer-cage under open, starry skies had oriented in the direction in which they would normally migrate. Again in the spring the warblers demonstrated the appropriate directional urge and so, subsequently, did others, and also a Lesser Grey Shrike, trapped by the Sauers in Africa. The following years brought corroborative results with a variety of other birds tested by different investigators—always with the proviso that orientation was dependent on clear nights; cloud cover produced haphazard movement. In one of the experiments

Frank Bellrose released captured Mallards at night at points between 11 and 33 miles from their homes, each with a tiny flashlight attached to its foot. Under clear skies all took off in the direction of home without hesitation, while fog apparently confused them and caused them to fly at random. The Emlens reported that most of the Indigo Buntings in their blotting-paper cages oriented correctly spring and fall even with the lower 38 degrees of the sky blocked out, and that some did so even when nine-tenths of the sky was covered by cloud and only a few stars were visible. The moon, far from assisting in orientation, has been found to impede it, presumably by reducing the visibility of the stars.

Meanwhile, the Sauers had tested some of their warblers in a Kramer-cage installed in a planetarium. What they found was that the responses of their subjects were comparable to those under the natural sky. While not all investigators have had such clear results from the use of a planetarium, the Emlens' Indigo Buntings not only oriented appropriately under the artificial heavens, but, when the projector was reversed to place Polaris, the North Star, in the south, they reversed their orientation with it. Other experiments of the Emlens' suggest that it is the stars within a radius of 35 degrees of Polaris that provide migrants with the essential navigational clues. Inasmuch as half these stars become invisible at any given time, along with Polaris itself, within five degrees of the Equator, however, birds migrating very far into the southern hemisphere would find them unavailing.

Presumably birds could orient on constellations of the southern as well as of the northern hemisphere—though the necessity of having to do both would seem to be asking a great deal of them—but if constellations are the markers, how do birds adjust to their rising four minutes earlier every evening, until a year takes them full circle, back to the starting line-up? Not only are the constellations in a progressively different position every night, but, as Matthews points out, because the earth reaches a given inclination to the sun slightly earlier every year, the spring sky gradually becomes the autumn sky in the course of 13,000 years, which is perhaps not a very long time in terms of the genetic imprinting of a species.

Nevertheless, it seems indisputable that birds do navigate by the stars as well as by the sun. Whether they can do so by the earth's magnetic field has been a matter of speculation and dissension for over a century. During World War II, one observer—O. A. Knoor—reported that flocks of Scoters and Scaups became bewildered and fell out of ranks when struck by a radar beam, then, upon its being deflected, regrouped and resumed their course. The same phenomenon has been observed by others, while equally birds have been seen to be unaffected by such beams. In any case, it is far from clear that susceptibility to radio waves would mean sensitivity to the earth's magnetic field.

Dorst declares that "not a single experiment in eighty years has disclosed any such sensitivity." (Among such experiments, birds have been flown with magnets attached to wings or tail to see if they would be thrown off course.) However, he is candid enough to add in a footnote that common mud-snails have been found able to orient themselves by magnetic fields and that "new experiments will be necessary."

One such was recently carried out by Charles Wolcott, who had demonstrated the true homing of Pigeons with radio direction-finding. It was part of an effort to ascertain what birds "are using to find their way in the middle of the night, inside a cloud." Wolcott equipped a group of Pigeons each with a coil of wire on the top of the head, another coil around the neck and a minute back-pack containing an electric cell to create a magnetic field and one of Wolcott's transmitters, for tracking the bearer. The birds were released 30 miles west of their loft at Stony Brook, New York, half with the north pole of the magnetic field at the top of the head, half with the polarity reversed. Most of the latter, with the south pole above, flew straight home while the former took the opposite direction. "This suggests," Wolcott writes in *Harvard Magazine*, "that the birds really are sensing the magnetic field in some way." Meanwhile, William T. Keeton at Cornell had taken two sets of Pigeons, one with internal clocks shifted by six hours, one unaltered, released them under a total overcast and at a site neither had seen before and found that both headed for home. "Therefore it is concluded," he wrote in *Science,* "that the sun is used as a compass when it is available, but that . . . orientation [is] possible in the absence of both the sun and familiar landmarks."

If we find that birds are indeed sensitive to the earth's magnetism, it *might* help solve the *real* riddle of avian navigation. That birds are able by guiding on the sun or stars to fly in a desired direction is surely marvellous, as it would be if they are able to guide also on the magnetic poles. But when a bird is shut up in a box and taken hundreds of miles to the southwest, how does it know that flying northeast will take it back home again? How does it know where its home is? Unless it has a way of "seeing" the site around the curvature of the earth, the site must have characteristics that relate it positionally to other places in which the bird may find itself.

For human beings every spot on earth is located in terms of its latitude and longitude—how far north or south of the Equator it is and how far east or west of a line drawn through Greenwich connecting the Poles. These are its co-ordinates. A navigator who does not know his position on the planet's surface—its co-ordinates—may obtain the information by "shooting the sun" at noon with a sextant. The orb's angular height above the horizon, given the day of the year, will, by reference to a table, tell what the latitude is while the time difference between noon at the navigator's position and noon at Greenwich (noon being the moment when the sun is at its zenith) will tell the longitude, depending on the accuracy of the chronometer. At night, position is determined similarly by the elevation and bearing of two principal stars at a given moment, again with reference to tables. All this, even for human intellects supplied with fine instruments and the computations of astronomers, is tricky business and impossible under cloud cover. (Hence the popularity of radio beacons by which a ship or aircraft, determining the direction from which it receives each of two of them, can locate itself on a chart on which the beacons' positions are shown.) How on earth can the unaided nervous systems of birds ascertain co-ordinates, and what co-ordinates?

One proposition has been that birds are receptive to both the earth's magnetic field and the Coriolis force and to gradations in them, and that intersections of lines of equal magnetic force and equal Coriolis force supply the equivalents of latitude and longitude. (The Coriolis force is that which is generated by the earth's rotation and imparts a rotational tendency to moving bodies, including winds, the direction of rotation opposite in the northern hemisphere from that in the southern.) However, the proposition is unsupported empirically. Ornithology, moreover, appears to be convinced that birds are without any mechanism that could conceivably detect the minute fluctuations involved if, indeed, they can detect either force at all.

That birds may be able to derive latitude and longitude from the sun, somewhat as man does, has been suggested by Matthews. If the sun's path as we see it be visualized as an arc drawn on the interior of the inverted blue bowl of the sky from rim to rim—that is, from its rising upon the horizon to its setting—then the closer to the Equator you are, the more nearly perpendicular to the rim the arc will stand and the higher its zenith will be, while the closer to either Pole the more parallel to the rim and the lower its zenith. Accordingly, the degree of steepness of the arc indicates how far north or south you are—your latitude. Now if you move around the earth from east to west carrying a watch and not changing its setting, you will find that the farther you go the less far along on its arc the sun will be at any given time of day. (In Madrid the sun stands at its zenith when in Washington it will not reach the zenith for about four hours.) Traveling in the opposite direction, the opposite is true. Thus from the sun's position on the arc it is possible to determine longitude—how far around the earth you are from a base point if you know what time it is at that point.

For a bird to apprehend its location by this means it would have not merely to take in the sun's position in the sky but to know how far along on the invisible arc it was. That means it would have to be able to see the movement of the sun (which, like the minute-hand of a watch, is too slow for us to be able to do so) and from the tiny segment the sun would describe while under its observation extrapolate the remainder of the arc, or most of it. A bird would also have to possess a stubborn internal clock which would resist resetting by the changing times of dawn and dusk as it was borne through changing lines of longitude—as if a human voyager kept his watch on the time at home while he crossed different time-zones. Matthews shows how a bird might be equal to all these demands. Unlikely as it may seem to us that it could meet them, and unconsciously, too, any other method by which it could derive co-ordinates will probably seem no less unlikely. Possibly, too, a bird can locate itself in relationship to a goal by the stars through means analagous to sun-reading and to our own technique for doing so, but this would be even more amazing.

And as if the difficulties for birds of navigating by astronomical phenomena, as we perceive them, were not enough, there are Keeton's Pigeons, which headed for home from unfamiliar surroundings and under an overcast. There is the case of the female Purple Martin in Michigan that was removed from her nest and young, released at 10:40 P.M. 235 miles to the south under a sky blanketed by a double layer of clouds and was back at her nest by 7:15 the next morning.

Perhaps, as Peterson suggests, we shall never fully solve the mystery.

By the last week of October autumn's final chapter is under way. On the 19th, at the epitome of its glory, the first White-throated Sparrows appear (I note) while the two Kinglets are still much in evidence—tiny creatures so compact as to be neckless—and the last Olive-backed Thrush is at the bird-bath. From the bank of the stream a Winter Wren skedaddles—a dark little peg-tailed gimmick; you would think it would be lonely. The next morning the fields are rimed in four degrees of frost. A heavy fall of leaves follows. Hard freezes on the 21st and 22nd bring the first Juncos and a brief stopover by two Hermit Thrushes in the Dogwood near my window. Silent in movement as two small brown shadows, motionless in repose after the characteristic lifting and subsidence of the tail on alighting, the thrushes seem mere thoughts of birds, as yet uncorporealized. The hardy Myrtle Warblers have acquired the appearance of winter birds in drab brown, furry-looking plumage.

There are reprieves. On October 28th a Horned Grebe, bird of the rough winter seas, is to be seen on the river and near by the first group of the raft of Ruddy Ducks that winters here—so many floating teapots with tails for spouts. But the day is mild and sunny. A Song Sparrow, a Tufted Titmouse and a Mockingbird are singing. It is an extension of spring's lease, more even than the persisting small sprays of goldenrod and aster, and a comfort to the wayfarer of advancing years. (Never say die to youth!) It is a comfort, too, in its indication that the song of birds is not gonadal merely but is an emotional expression to be called forth, as today, by pleasant associations.

But for all its color and excitement and regretful looks backward to times of song and flowering, autumn is a losing season. All wanes. Every gust leaves the woods barer than before. By the end of the first week of November they are virtually denuded.

Yet all is not over. It is for this stage that nature reserves a crowning demonstration, heralded by one of its great voices. The sound is one you are seldom immediately sure of, when the first audible presentiment comes down wind of a clamor in the northern sky. The Geese! It is out of doors then in a rush. What a summons it is, that high, broken, incessant baying out of the wild and solitary spaces of the North, like the sounds of an army returning with battle honors from a frontier beyond the imagination of stay-at-homes. And there they come, the dark, strongly beating forms, forward-striving in the outstretched necks, all in one rank, wing-tip to wing-tip in that extraordinary, broad V-formation—an incredible sight in the humdrum sky above the suburbs. Cry havoc! No, it is not havoc they cry but the untamed and untamable, the un-quenchable springs of our common vitality, clarioned in the heavens by the passing phalanx that all may hear.

Only the setting in of the hard freeze in the north could send those stalwarts southward down the sky roads When the Canada Geese come through, winter cannot be far off.

# ___6
# WINTER

### The Scourge and Its Compensations

All seasons are good. Even if the proposition gives you trouble, it is something to tell yourself in November. No part of the year is as hard to see pass as those last mild days of autumn, when the sunlight is intensified and enriched by the remaining red and yellow foliage. They come as a recrudescence of summer after the first cold spell, and because, I am told, the redmen considered them the most propitious time for attacks upon the encroaching settlers, whose harvests were then in, they came to be called Indian summer. There are those who like winter: sports addicts and many urbanites. But the former, by and large, are interested only in the near-frictionless surfaces that snow and ice, quite incidentally, put under their runners and the latter mostly in the resurgent cultural and social seasons and bright lights. Apart from them, few would call winter their favorite time of year. On the other hand, even fewer have never exclaimed over the newly fallen snow, the clean, sparkling, virginal mantle spread over all in purification made visible. Winter is cold and winter is dark, but the cold brings invigorating air and the dark its justly celebrated antidote, the open fire on the hearth.

There is, however, a virtue in winter I cannot remember ever having heard acclaimed, though to me it may be supreme. We do not have to enjoy it. In a benign season, when all nature beckons, as it is said, we are expected to rise to the occasion and not miss out on what offers. When the world is in flower it is easy to feel that not a moment is to be lost. We must gather rosebuds while we may. We tend to mirror nature's moods. In the glory of high spring, when the earth seems romantic and singing at heart, in love with life, we receive a powerful impulse to be no less so, and if we are equal to it, ours is the glory too. Only we may not be, or for very long at a time. We are not sufficiently youthful and carefree. And then our hearts are heavier for the ways in which we are wanting. With every year, spring reminds us more of our diminishing capacity to be what it would have us be.

Not so, rough and cheerless winter. It comes bearing malice and makes no secret of it: the devil take you if you cannot bear its brunt. We seldom feel we are missing out on anything in winter, except the chance to get away from it to the country's two southern corners, or beyond. The pleasures that may come to us under winter's sway, akin to those that help redeem old age, are like extras, above and beyond our allotment—money picked up in the street. While the cold reigns, mere survival absorbs life's energies. Reflecting nature again, we feel it enough to make it through to spring. We feel it with special force when the soulless northwester strikes, roaring through the bending, wildly thrashing trees, and the house, which nothing can warm, creaks and cracks in its joints and seems ready to depart its moorings. We suffer then for the small minority of living creatures that face out the season rather than going south or underground. So we do, too, on those very different winter days that exhibit nature at very nearly its most beautiful. That is after a freezing rain when the sun comes out in a blue sky to glitter and glisten on a landscape sheathed to the least twig and pine needle in crystal, here and there flashing with diamond sparks of red and blue and green. The world of glass is an enchanted one. But for birds, their sources of food encased in ice, it is a deadly enchantment. If the freezing rain comes on top of an accumulation of snow, grouse that have taken refuge for the night in a drift can find themselves prisoners in the morning and, in default of a thaw, starve to death.

It is scarcity of food, of course, that makes winter a threat to birds rather than cold *per se*. The annual movement southward is the alternative to mass starvation. Given nourishment and shelter from the wind, birds in general can endure very low temperatures. A neighbor of ours who raises Peacocks brings them through the winter without heat, though the mercury here sometimes drops below zero. Chickens, which are only domesticated Jungle-fowl, are kept in unheated houses much farther north. A dozen or more Baltimore Orioles, of a species that normally migrates in autumn to southern Mexico or beyond, regularly winter in Kinston in eastern North Carolina where William McG. Orr, Jr., keeps them supplied with grapes, grape juice and orange slices. (When I first heard of this from a relative of his, my rather grand suggestion that the boarders were perhaps Goldfinches was left to be withdrawn with as much grace as possible in the face of color photographs subsequently produced.) That birds, so seemingly fragile, stripped down as they are to slacken gravity's hold upon them, can come through the severities of winter that many endure, speaks in the highest degree for the engineering proficiency of natural processes, what we should call genius if we displayed it.

The most deadly manifestation of winter on our continent, at least south of the Arctic, is probably the fierce and icy wind, armed with lacerating snow, that races across northern prairies and plains of the heartland with nothing to stay its onslaught but scattered thickets and belts of cottonwoods and willows along the major streams. "Blizzard" was the term coined for it by the settlers, whose previous experience had provided not even a word for it to prepare them for the combination of furies. "A hard, granular snow was driven horizontally, cutting and blinding any face that was turned into it for long. Not even our hunting fever could temper that terrible wind," John Madson recalls of the blizzard of November 11, 1940, in *Audubon Magazine*. "The world about us was closed out by an encircling wall of wind and snow. . . . The storm had caught a vast waterfowl migration over the Midwest and had bludgeoned countless ducks down onto the sloughs, ponds and rivers. We saw mallards beyond number that day. Each sheltering riverbank had its huddled flock, and some numbered into the hundreds. We would blunder up on them and they would try to fly up into that roaring whiteness, only to be battered back down onto the river." But on balance the day was a good one for the ducks. "Hunters were dying by dozens on the Upper Mississippi and northern lakes and marshes, where waves were breaking over their blinds and freezing or drowning them."

Ducks and geese can ordinarily count on being south of the blizzards' reach but are equipped to come through when caught. They are well insulated and have reserves of fat to live on until the weather moderates and they can escape. At normal migrating speeds, ten hours of flight would put them four or five hundred miles to the south. The Grouse—Sage, Sharp-tailed and Pinnated—have no such option, but they can do as their eastern cousin does and hole up very comfortably in a snow-drift. The introduced Ring-necked Pheasant seems not to be on to this. It adapts much better to agriculture than its native relatives; travelers in South Dakota will see billboards making such claims as "Pheasant Capital of the World" to lure gunners. But it depends for cover on dense brush-growth and the like, and when snow buries this, especially when it also covers the grain-fields, the species can suffer catastrophically. The winters of 1947 to 1950, according to Madson, took the life of "virtually every South Dakota pheasant west of the Missouri River." A dead female Pheasant is among the birds shown in *Audubon Magazine* as they were photographed by Ed Bry following an unseasonable blizzard with 50-mile-an-hour winds and blinding snow that blasted North Dakota for thirty hours ending in mid afternoon of May 1, 1967. A Mourning Dove is also shown frozen to death in the snow. Coots, pictured marching across a frozen slough, were hard hit, suffering the highest casualties among marsh birds. But the Redpoll in some stalks of weeds and Horned Larks feeding close to the ground on cropland blown clear of snow are facing adversities they were bred to, and a flock of Robins has found a haven in one of the thickets that sheltered other songbirds. Probably the worst meteorological disaster known to have befallen birds on our continent was the mid-March storm of 1907, which pelted 1,500 square miles of southern Minnesota, overwhelming a vast movement of Lapland Longspurs, which were borne earthward under the weight of the clinging flakes to perish in such terrible numbers that those littering the frozen surface of two small lakes alone were estimated to total three-quarters of a million.

While we in the East are spared such extreme manifestations of continental climate as desolate the northern plains, we have blizzards, too. In the Northeast, snow may drift to the second floor in the lee of a house; those enclosed passageways between houses and barn in Maine were not installed whimsically. But our countryside does not lie naked to the scourge; refuges are nowhere far. It is possible nonetheless that we lose more than a few wintering birds in conditions of unusual stress. I have never seen a winter-killed bird and I suppose the majority of birders in the East have not, but of course the odds against coming upon the corpses would be high. Disasters do occur. Bluebirds and Phoebes have suffered drastic setbacks taking years to repair by arriving in the north too early in spring and being caught in a late snowstorm. Frederick C. Lincoln tells of a blizzard that struck South Carolina in 1899 with the worst cold known there in two centuries, leaving thousands of Fox Sparrows, Juncos and Woodcocks to starve to death and wiping out probably nine-tenths of the Bluebirds and Pine Warblers wintering in the area.

Our worst winter winds, by a proportion of ten or twenty to one, come from the direction of the Great Lakes. They may reach gale force, these northwesters, but they are seldom snow-bearers. They are too sterile for that: emptiness on the rampage, they seem to me. They put me nervously on edge. To be reconciled to them, as far as possible, I have long tried to find something to be said for them, some constructive purpose they serve. Well, they do break dead branches from trees so that new wood may heal over the juncture and close it to fungal attack, and the really savage ones blow any mounds in the woods bare of leaves, permitting mosses and

Partridgeberry to grow on them. But I still resent them, and so do birds. Their feathers are blown about and the smaller ones, certainly, have difficulty navigating in gusts that threaten to snatch them away. They are also depressed, like me. You can tell that from their silence. A northwester in March, when half a dozen species have begun to sing, will shut them all up, as cold in itself will not. Blowy days, when the objects of the pursuit stay under cover as much as possible, and mute, are the poorest of all days for birding.

They are days for the zoo, for those with access to one. The bird-house, abode of Touracos and Troupials, Sun-bitterns and Golden Conures, auditorium of whistles and cries that, in the warm, rich air, require you only to close your eyes to transport you to the rain-forest, provides the poor man's tropical holiday. Zoos grow ever more enjoyable as the bare, crowded cages of yesterday give place to larger in which an approximation of the captives' natural habitat is striven for. How much more congenial it is, how much more like transubstantiation to their native country, to watch a pair of Roadrunners in a roomy desert setting or Penguins swimming beneath or climbing upon a rocky coign of Antarctica than to see ten times as many birds in a concrete cell! In a modern zoo birds may in general, I believe, be appreciated without misgivings on the score of their suffering greatly from captivity. I should not care to answer for the birds of prey or other powerful or active flyers, but the majority of captives are probably compensated for the loss of freedom by security against predator and hunger which inhibit freedom in the wild. William B. Conway, Curator of Birds at the New York Zoological Park, relates several occurrences tending to substantiate this view. In 1950, when a storm broke the window of their large cage, some Red-billed Blue Magpies of the Himalayas, evidently frightened, flew off and might well never have been seen again. The next day, however, they were back and waiting to be fed. And a wing-clipped African Crowned Crane, having regrown its pinions undetected, made repeated flights over the zoo but each time returned to the "African plains." Similarly, at the St. Louis zoo, three Horned Screamers got loose, soared high overhead and then returned to their enclosure.

The acceptance of birds of their captivity in a modern zoo says nothing, however, of the fearful sufferings and mortality of wild creatures at the hands of trappers and local dealers—the suppliers of the importers. Before I read of these horrors I thought appreciatively of the unique chance zoos afforded to see at close hand the living embodiments of exotic avifaunas, recalling some in the aviaries in Rock Creek Park: the pink-throated Princess Parrot of Australia tirelessly calling "ko leesh, ko leesh"; the Blue-breasted Quail of Indo-Malaysia, no larger than a woman's fist; the Bornean Great Argus Pheasant, with a bare, blue head and neck emerging from a smooth, brown greatcoat of feathers polka-dotted on the over-sized wing quills; the Rothschild's Starling, white with a narrow black mask and black tips to wings and tail; Grey Frog-mouths, large of head and eye, perched motionless upright, like gargoyles. I recalled watching a dusky Inca Tern cheeeeping for food from an indulgent visitor and thinking how zoos, by bringing you close to birds in an absence of fear on their part, reveal that which you might never observe in the wild, in this case the Tern's speculative, seemingly self-aware expression that was almost human compared with the rather blank look of the narrow-faced Scarlet Ibises in an adjoining enclosure. Zoos fill an important place, but the importation of wild animals should be prohibited except from countries in which an international agency can ensure the humane treatment of captives from the time of trapping. And animals of rare species should not be eligible for importation at all except by responsible breeders.

### On Intimate Terms

It is not only at the zoo that winter can bring us into proximity with birds. A feeding-station puts us into partnership with them against the weather's hostility. In exchange for seed, suet and water they lend a redeeming animation and warmth to the generally bleak scene. How the Chickadees and Titmice come trooping in when you resume the setting out of sunflower seed in the fall! Their joy and excitement are unmistakable. In they come bouncing three or four at a time, and hours later it is still going on. If birds are ever disheartened, they do not show it. And if the truth be that a bird on the way to disheartenment is a bird that will probably not live to get there, the knowledge is ours and not the bird's. Birds know no lasting burden of regret for what is past or anxious premeditation of the future. They are contained in a present that is usually sufficient to their needs, and being so, and vivacious withal, they help us to be so, too. In the defensiveness toward life that grows upon us after childhood—and is so terribly sad in a child who has had reason to acquire it—we are partially disarmed by birds. There is perhaps under their influence a reversion to feelings we had about the world as children. While I think this is equally true at all seasons, we enjoy a closer community with birds when other life is withdrawn. Whether there's a special providence in the fall of a sparrow, as Hamlet asserts, I do not know. But one can believe such a providence sees to the little rounded shapes to be made out at the feeding-tray in the grudging light of a winter's dawn and at the close of day, in the quarter-hour between dog and wolf. Those at dusk are, with us, always Cardinals. Except for them, I might add, birds will be found at the tray in dimmer morning than evening light, perhaps because they are hungrier after the long night or reckon the owls are less so. Cardinals are quite crepuscular. All through summer, well into August, the male's measured notes in the grey lightening of dawn, pure as if struck from a crystal goblet, are the first sounds of day.

It is generally agreed that winter is the best time for taking up an interest in birds. This gives you a chance to learn the common species when there are only a score or so in the familiar countryside. Then, as early spring brings others, you can keep up with them as they arrive one by one. In this way you have a good grounding before the full array moves in. A feeding-station, moreover, whether your own or a friend's, brings birds admirably close. It gives you a chance to see them not merely as elusive, doubtful objects in the field of a binocu-

lar but in as clear detail as they are depicted in the guide books—or are seen in the zoo. We have had 27 species come within five feet of our windows, either to suet and sunflower seed on a balcony railing or to the terrace below, where we scatter baby-chick scratch-feed. (Of finely cracked corn, this seems to be acceptable to seed-eaters as a substitute for the much more expensive millets in specially prepared mixtures.) Three additional species have visited the large suet-holder ten feet up the trunk of an oak thirty-five feet from the house: Crows (constantly), Pileated Woodpeckers and twice, incredibly, a Red-shouldered Hawk, which the last time displaced a Crow and, grasping the wire mesh with its talon and half hanging from it, tore with its beak at an extruded strip of tissue. Of those coming to the bird-bath, I have counted forty-five and have doubtless missed some.

In making your environs hospitable to birds the most important element is cover. Dense shrubbery, preferably some at least evergreen, supplemented by conifers with thick growth from the ground up, offers refuge from enemies and shelter from the weather together with nesting-sites. (For cavity-nesting species, bird-houses are of course called for, built to specifications set forth in numerous publications.) If food and water rank below cover it is simply because they are more likely to be obtainable through the birds' own efforts. In the warm months, when food is least difficult for birds to come by, a landlord can be most of service by making sure of the unfailing availability of clean water. All birds drink and most of them bathe. Some are skittish at the bath, satisfying only the letter of the requirement but making a great virtue of it. The Carolina Wren is one. It buzzes at the surface of the water and instantly buzzes off, to flutter violently, as if drenched. I find this behavior unaccountable. If the bath is to be perfunctory only, why bother with it? Surely birds are not capable of hypocrisy! Robins more than any seem to enjoy a good dousing. They duck and flail the water up around them in a deluge, three or four at the bath at once. Even in the middle of a day of uninterrupted rain one of our Robins, already wet, went in for a dip—perhaps absent-mindedly. Birds frequently bathe in winter. I have seen even a tiny Carolina Chickadee have a quick flutter in the water after a wet day with the temperature barely above freezing.

Wintering songbirds fare best by bogs and swamps and where weeds bear plentiful seeds, where old trees with shaggy bark and dead wood harbor insects' eggs and larvae and a good crop of berries clings to branches. (What shrubs to plant for birds, if you have a place for them, is also the subject of ample printed advice.) Even here, however, their lot will be eased by food supplied them. And birds still have to drink. When natural sources are ice-bound, providing water can be even more important than in summer. To keep it from freezing, electric immersion heaters for bird-baths are for sale. I achieve the same results by keeping the water in a seven-inch flower-pot saucer which sits in the open top of a five-quart oil-can (of the kind thrown away by all service stations) this in turn containing a low-wattage light bulb in a socket fixed to its bottom. (A layer of insulation around the inside of the can conserves heat and a small can turned upside down over the bulb prevents its shattering when condensed moisture falls from the saucer.) The sound of water dripping into a bird-bath increases its allure, a fine spray even more.

Writing this on a May morning, I have just cast my eyes over at the bird-bath (keeping one's attention confined while sitting within sight of a bird-bath or feeding-station is impossible) and to my excitement seen a little bird like a bit of hot Mexican noon flutter to the rim of the concrete. It is, at this moment, my favorite warbler—a Cape May. On its way north to nest in the spruce-fir forest, the Little Tiger of the Trees—*Dendroica tigrina*—showers itself and becomes number forty-six for the bath.

Sometimes even on a warm day the bath will be ignored for an hour or more; but then one bird at its ablutions will bring a succession of others, all seized by the idea. Birds are notoriously suggestible. It would seem that they are so even to some extent in their diet. The charge is made in disparagement of their mental powers that birds are in this regard inflexible. Brant, it is true, came near to extinction when the eel-grass on which they depended was all but wiped out by a disease—though in truth enough of them switched to sea-lettuce to keep the species going until its staple food recovered. But a feeding-station rather impresses you with birds' adaptability. Chicka-dees and titmice, though insectivorous, learn quickly to come to sunflower seed, the like of which they have never seen before—reminding one in this of their English relatives which, it will be recalled, discovered how to remove the tops of milk-bottles for the cream beneath. They and nuthatches, wood-peckers, Mockingbirds and Carolina Wrens catch on to suet with little delay, highly novel a food as it is to them. Wherever such foods are provided, those birds, if in the neighborhood, seem to resort to them. It is rather a mystery to me how they know what they are doing, and that the new feeding habit should now be conventional for their species. At my own station I see examples of a departure in diet that only two or three individuals, within my observation, have ventured upon. Though all are clearly cases of birds of one species emulating those of another, they are startling to me. The visit of the Red-shouldered Hawk to the suet-holder was one; it was obviously doing what it saw Crows doing, as the Crows had doubtless taken their lead from the smaller birds. Twelve or thirteen years after we started putting out sunflower seed, two at least of our Downy Woodpeckers started eating them, wedg-ing them in a crevice and "hatching" them open with their bills, as nuthatches do. Our Red-bellied Woodpeckers now regularly join the seed-eaters on the terrace for cracked corn, though only by laying their heads on the side and grasping the grains between the lateral edges of their bills can they pick them up from the asphalt. "Successful species accept generalized diet and display considerable enterprise in finding it," Robert O. Paxton observes, in *American Birds* adding that "Robins at Moose Jaw, Saskatchewan, obtained minnows at an open spring hole in the river ice and swallowed them whole, head first." That rather surprises me about Robins, which I have never known to come to suet, in even the win-triest weather, but the Red-bellied Woodpecker's enterprise is as evident as its vitality. Given to reiterating a loud, complaining cry tirelessly, the bird might, I sometimes think, be called the Red-belly-aching Woodpecker, but it captivates me nonetheless with its oddly stilted and theatrical movements of head and torso at the feeding-tray, not to mention the burnished Chinese red of its crown and nape, and I am delighted that the species is prospering. Paxton, incidentally, contrasts the Red-bellied's spread with the Red-headed Woodpecker's poor showing in the past half-century.

When we stop providing sunflower seed in May, our resident pair of Cardinals switch immediately to suet. And the Cardinal is another successful species. From having been almost unknown in New York in my boyhood, it is now colonizing northern New England, its northern spread accompanying reports of its increase in its original homeland. If the increase has not created an excess of numbers, forcing many to venture into new territories, it has at least supplied the exodus and replenished the ranks of "the repeatedly decimated colonizers pressing against the survival frontier," as Paxton puts it, referring to Cardinals found frozen in the front lines.

In short, birds alert to their opportunities can profit from the dietary examples of others. That I was not more surprised to have a Cape May Warbler at the bath was because for three days it has been coming to the two suet-holders. I have been astonished by that, even though early last spring each of a pair of Pine Warblers nibbled suet from the balcony holder several times a day for a week. To have such dainty little flower-birds at one's board puts one on the right side of the universe.

But I feel the same of less exotic visitors, especially of our Carolina Wrens, when, accustomed to having chopped cheese provided for them just outside the glass door to the kitchen, one of them on finding the larder bare will hop up and cling to the door-frame, looking in to see if we are there to get the message. (Although he remarks on the heavy toll of Carolina Wrens taken by the winters of the early sixties where they had spread northward, Paxton speaks of the species as another that has expanded, while the Bewick's Wren has fared poorly.) Vera says the male sings from close to the door to apprise us of his wants, and it must be so. He is a great singer, hardly, I think, missing more than two or three days running, if that, the winter long. With Oliver Herford

I heard a bird sing in the dark of December;
A magical thing and sweet to remember.
"We are nearer to Spring than we were in September."
I heard a bird sing in the dark of December.

Sometimes there will be alternating singing between him and a male at a neighbor's house, and one winter day a third male from down at the stream joined in. Ethological theory would doubtless tell us that territorial claims were being refurbished. But one knows better: in a drear and inimical world, sentinels on the ramparts of wrenhood were affirming to each other the importance of their kind in the scheme of things. Sometimes, as I remarked, our male sets out to provoke the neighbor's, or so we are persuaded if only because his insistent and emphatic singing will shortly elicit a response. (We have, too, since I first wrote that, the example of the Yellow-throated Vireos previously recounted.) The two will each sing a phrase in turn. Sometimes the phrases are different, then again the replying male will adopt the initiator's song.

Winter is the time to get on intimate terms with birds. It requires no great patience then to bring some of the smallest to take food from the hand (especially if you have a shop-window mannequin to stand in for you). And one never forgets one's first experience of the sharp little claws' clutch and the quick scrutiny of the tiny, shining black eyes less than two feet from one's own. Mine came when I was eleven, in a nook of Central Park where an elderly woman had accustomed some Chickadees and a Red-breasted Nuthatch to come to the hand for peanuts. In general, the smaller the bird the tamer. For one thing, the larger the bird, the more likely it is to be one that is shot at. It should be possible to derive a loosely applicable size/tameness formula, viz.: eight times a bird's weight in grams is the distance in yards to which the bird will ordinarily let you approach before fleeing (unless it is hiding and believes successfully). Thus the 8W=D for a half-ounce Chickadee would be four yards, for a two-ounce Robin sixteen, for an eight-ounce Crow fifty. That is the idea, anyhow. But some birds can be won over much more readily than many smaller than they. The Catbird is one, even though not around when scarcity of food helps overcome a wild creature's caution. We had a Catbird that took cheese from our hands with little doing on our part, and friends of ours in Washington, D.C., had another with a special fondness for raisins. This bird, which could be recognized by one of its tarsi that went off to the side, was an habitué of the rear deck of their house for eight consecutive summers, until killed by a neighbor's cat. One wonders if it did not enjoy similar arrangements with a family in a winter home on the Gulf coast. It is known that some birds migrate in autumn as faithfully to a particular spot as they do in spring to their nesting-site.

I am inclined to attribute the Catbird's tractability to its gentle-seeming nature. Yet its cousin the Mockingbird responds with almost as ready a trust to appeals to its appetite. And the Mockingbird is a very different creature otherwise—a bold, dashing troubadour. A resident Mocker can become an intolerable bully at the feeding-station. As the days lengthen after the turn of the year he begins to act up, taking over proprietorship of the suet-holders and sailing in to drive off any patrons smaller than himself. The theory is that birds giving a grey-and-white effect like his own chiefly exercise him. Anyway, the human resident, unless he is prepared to supply only the larger woodpeckers and jays, or shut down altogether, usually has no choice but to trap the Mocker and relocate him, as we have had to do several times, however regretfully.

By bringing birds closer, as winter provides a natural opportunity to do, we learn more about them as personalities. How much can be discovered has been shown by Len Howard, the English woman who, moving into a Sussex farm cottage, set about to make friends with her bird neighbors. Her continually astonishing account of her experiences in *Birds as Individuals*, appearing with a foreword by Julian Huxley commending her observations, attracted great attention when it came out in 1952, for it revealed heretofore unsuspected—or merely suspected—depths and complexities in avian psychology and differences in attitude and behavior that could set individuals of a species apart from one another. The secret of her success comes out in her remark about the sensible response of a pair of Blue Titmice and one of Robins to her succor of their nests, threatened respectively by a cat and by insecurity of position. She said she had no doubt that the two couples "would not have behaved intelligently if they had feared my presence. Often bird behavior is judged when the bird is panicked with fear of the watcher."

Roger Tory Peterson, in an introduction to the American edition of the book recounting his and James Fisher's visit to Miss Howard's bird haven, tells how the living-room was "for birds to live in. Cereal boxes, shoe boxes, and mailing tubes were tied beneath the ceiling for her Titmice. . . . There were times, Miss Howard informed us, when as many as seventeen of the boxes were occupied." Continuing, Peterson recalls how

> a Great Titmouse flew in the open door and instinctively I ducked. One does not expect birds to fly *toward* one. Another Great Titmouse came in through the window, and then a Blue Titmouse. The birds were a little cautious at first, because of the two strangers, but they soon seemed to accept us. Soon there was a constant stream of birds entering and leaving.

The price of living "in continual company of numbers of birds," as Miss Howard acknowledges, is considerable. There are such matters

> as cleaning up, having things spoilt, the rooms always looking as if prepared for the sweep, with newspapers spread over furniture and books covered with cloths; then the disturbance of sleep, for they hammer furiously on the panes if I shut the windows at dawn to keep them outside when nights are short, and they do all they can to prevent

my concentrating upon anything except themselves. But there are even worse problems. Living with birds, it is impossible not to get fond of each individual. But their lives are short and there are many tragedies.

She speaks of the "havoc wrought by cats unless I am continually on the watch," the Jackdaws and Magpies that take nestlings, the "injured ones among my many birds, dependent upon me for their recovery."

> In one way or another my birds demand attention from dawn until dusk. . . . While I am trying to write this page some are perching on the typewriter, some pulling at my hair, others flying to my hands and falling off as I start to tap the keys.

The avowal helps lighten the burden of shame one feels over living at less close quarters with one's avian neighbors. But what Miss Howard has learned of birds must reshape our conceptions of them. From having lived with chickens I knew that individual differences among birds can be appreciable, but I should never have thought that they would enable even the keenest observer to give names to scores of tenants, let alone to distinguish the broods of sixty young Great Titmice "by their voices and details of utterance in their fledgling calls." Miss Howard brings out astonishing capacities on the part of birds: their quick perception of human intentions (". . . so sensitive that they learn at once what is forbidden and what is allowed, although they have no conscience over disobeying when one's back is turned!"); the mutual devotion of which a pair of small birds are capable; how a bird may visibly die of grief over her desertion by a mate; the fascination a young bird may find in a later brood of siblings; the cleverness of birds at discovering hidden food and the quickness of an uncommonly smart Titmouse at learning to open small boxes; a territorial male's tolerance of an injured rival and the willingness of another to let neighboring males trespass to obtain water during a drought. That is only part of what one would scarcely have believed.

The feeling above all that Miss Howard imparts was expressed by a local electrician who was brought up short, amazed, by the birds alighting on her and, his eyes shining, kept murmuring, "How wonderful!" Then he said: "But why shouldn't it be like that? It ought to be like that."

In an article in *Natural History*, citing figures indicating that 43 per cent of the households in Amherst, Massachusetts, and almost 28 per cent of those in Boston feed birds in winter, at an average cost of about $8.20 each in the latter, Richard M. DeGraaf and Jack Ward Thomas observe that extrapolating from the Boston figure would show almost $3.5 million spent on feeding birds in Massachusetts in a year. For the nation as a whole, they quote an estimate of $50 million. That, as they suggest, gives an idea of the potential ecological consequences of this popular practice. Scarcities of food in winter normally act to limit or reduce the numbers of a species exposed to them, and probably our provender enables many more to survive farther north than otherwise could, just as the refuse we provide has nurtured a proliferation of gulls. Feeding-stations may well have contributed to the dramatic northward push of the Cardinal and Mockingbird, the more northerly wintering of birds like the White-throated Sparrow and Rufous-sided Towhee and the extraordinary spread of the red-fronted, red-rumped House Finch where introduced from the West into New York City in 1940. Undoubtedly they help explain the sensational eastern spread and more southerly winter travels of the Evening Grosbeak, formerly a bird of the Northwest.

What could never have been foreseen is that feeding-stations would foster an Argentine parrot's invasion. Fortified by sunflower seed and millet, pairs of the grey-headed, green Monk Parakeet, escaped from captivity, have been able to winter in the United States and build their huge, communal nests as far north as New York State. Flocks of Black-hooded and of Canary-winged Parakeets that have turned up in the northern states probably owe their survival, at least in part, to the same commissariats, and the Rose-winged Parakeets of the Indo-Malaysian tropics, which have wintered and bred in the northern environs of New York City, certainly do. Parenthetically, it might be added that while the accretion to our avifauna of such colorful and interesting exotics would be easy to welcome, introduced species that establish themselves, as few manage to do, generally succeed at the expense of the natives. The extinction of the Carolina Parakeet, which formerly ranged into the northern states, presumably left an unoccupied ecological niche, which an alien relative might fill without disrupting the *oikos*. However, a true replacement could be expected to attack fruit crops, as the original did—and the Monk Parakeet is notorious in its homeland for its depredations upon both fruit and grain.

### Invaders from the North

Feeding-stations may attract some of the birds known as irregular winter visitors. Typically these are inhabitants of the circumpolar boreal forest and forest frontier beyond it whose southward movements are occasioned by a failure of their usual food-supply—conifer seeds in many cases. There are good years and bad for Evening Grosbeaks, Pine Grosbeaks, Pine Siskins, Hoary and Common Redpolls, Red and White-winged Crossbills and Bohemian Waxwings, but what a birder calls good is bad from the birds' point of view and vice versa. Raptorial birds that prey chiefly on animals subject to fluctuations in numbers, as Goshawks on Ruffed Grouse, Rough-legged Hawks and Snowy Owls on lemmings and hares, are also forced south in years of lean pickings. The presence of the two hawks is noted only by specialists, but the appearance of a Snowy Owl, ghostly and conspicuous, usually makes a stir locally and is only too likely to bring out the gunners. Twice in recent years one has commanded attention for a day or two at a time on the roof of a public building between the White House and the Department of State.

Known simply as the Waxwing in the Old World, the Bohemian Waxwing, as it is called over here with reference not to Czechoslovakia but to its vagrant movements, feeds largely on berries. A short yield brings about the mass irrup-

tions familiar in Europe and the American West, as many as ten thousand having once descended on the parks in Denver. Few of the wanderers ever reach the East, but the gap in our avifauna, which otherwise would be grievous, is nicely filled by the Cedar Waxwing, which we may have the year around, so long as fruits persist on the branches to attract the tight, swift, freebooting flocks. Waxwings create a sensational first impression. With their sharp, black faces beneath pointed crests—a black mask pointed both front and rear and divided by a white line running back from the bill—their body color an indescribably soft, textureless brown, tails tipped in yellow and secondary wing quills as if in beads of red sealing-wax, they strike everyone as seeming the products of oriental art, and the more so for their unbirdlike way of perching for a time motionless, a flock of a dozen or two nervelessly still.

The Crossbills are queer creatures, of which I should give much to see more. They are quite tame, as some of the other northern visitors are; a Pine Grosbeak feeding on small crab-apples by the door of Louis Halle's home in Westchester

County would take food from our hands. They are like diminutive parrots both in appearance and in climbing about on all threes—hand-like feet and beak—and sometimes even hanging by one foot; little reddish (or green and yellow) parrots oddly to be found knocking the snow off the spruce twigs as they forage for the cones. Spruce forests are their home, but they foray to the Pitch Pine barrens of Cape Cod and have even bred there. Both in the Old World and the New they are known for their erratic wanderings. Flocks may reach any part of Europe and in our country even end up on the Gulf coast. In the north, chancing on a likely area, they may settle down to nest, then after a season or two disappear again. They may nest as early as January or after mid summer —have, indeed, been found nesting in every month of the year.

Pine Siskins—dusky, streaked versions of the Goldfinch, lowlighted, as it were, with yellow—are nearly as aberrant as the Crossbills, whose habitat they share and, sometimes, traveling companionship, too. They desert one breeding area for another, forego a breeding season to remain in the south, may be plentiful for one winter and absent for two or three. Siskins often consort in old fields with Goldfinches and Redpolls, the little rosy-tinged finches with red forehead and black chin of the extreme north. If there is a feeding station in the vicinity these free-rangers may be counted on to find it, as may Evening Grosbeaks, whose speeding, high-flying flocks, announcing themselves with calls unexpectedly like bold House Sparrows', shower down on a nearby tree, so incongruous with winter in their dashing patterns of yellow, black, white and grey that seeing is almost disbelieving. Siskins, Goldfinches, Grosbeaks, they settle on the sunflower seed and munch and munch and munch. And when they leave are soon back for more.

### Winter and the Ponds and Marshes

The continent's northern reaches—that is to say its shores down through Canada and its interior down through the northern plains states—have a meagre winter avifauna, it is true. But even a little below, species begin to be numerous, and they increase markedly the farther you go toward the coast as well as toward the south. The Christmas censuses have brought that out. (The fewest species recorded in a recent year were five at Bancroft, Ontario, and seven at White-horse, Yukon Territory, as compared with 201 each at San Diego and Freeport, Texas, the most.) While the intense rivalry among participants in these steeplechases seems to me at odds with the needs of the spirit that send us to birds to begin with, I must say it lends itself to making sure an area will be assiduously combed. And we may learn from the census-takers that for profitable birding in winter, the place to go is where the ice-free waters are, in bogs and marshes, seashores and open ocean and, if in ponds and lakes as well, so much the better. As far north as fresh waters and coastal marshes remain unfrozen you may find waterfowl from the icebound sloughs and lakes of the north and some summer birds risking the winter instead of accompanying their fellows southward. Broadly speaking, the line below which open fresh water is generally plentiful the year around passes through the area where we live, bending southward inland, northward toward the coast. East of us is Chesapeake Bay, into which the Atlantic Flyway funnels, and beyond it the coast of Maryland. Here in the vicinity of that line, outward of the shore, is another, more or less the farthest south reached by sea-birds of the frigid ocean off Canada and New England: Eiders, Glaucous and Iceland Gulls, Razor-billed Auks and Dovekies.

And now I must ask myself if winter may not be after all the most exciting season for birding, at least for us here in the overlap of two winter worlds. It seems so when you come to the coastal waters. As you approach the Chesapeake Bay you will know it by the flocks of Canada Geese wheeling rest-lessly about against the sky. Their powerful flight is that of a driving impetus within the flock or—it seems more to me today —of a supreme earthly will behind them. And what a clangor! It makes you think of an indiscriminate alarm of church bells. It lacks the clarity of bells, and yet it rings and in variety of pitch could be a wild, random pealing from a belfry. It is odd that the geese should be so vociferous, the swans so silent.

These—Whistling Swans—come next as you travel toward the Bay, at first sight always rather rocking you back because of their size, which the deliberateness of their wing-beats emphasizes, and that unearthly whiteness. You think of them as argosies of swans in their whiteness, somehow sailboat-like as they fly with flat strokes before the breeze.

In the environs of Blackwater National Wildlife Refuge, stripped cornfields are suddenly seen to harbor herds of geese; it is the white wedges on their chins that give them away. They could well be llamas or guanacos. Grazing animals, they have their legs set well forward to balance a horizontal body and well apart for lateral stability, and perhaps this gives them their sedateness, too. Swans standing beside them are much the taller. The spectacle of the two together in generous numbers conveys a feeling of the largeness there is about our continent, not of physical dimensions alone but in the sense in which we speak of a largeness of nature in some great and magnanimous human beings. And correspondingly one thinks of the meanness and niggardliness to which it could be reduced by the theft of its riches, which we have so long been thieving—to the end, one supposes, that it will be a fit abode of spiritual paupers. . . . Where you have crowds of geese and swans and not a sound, the quiet is almost eerie. But you are as apt to have scattered individual geese exchanging exclamations. The honk of a Canada Goose breaks sharply upward between halves. "Co-hick," it sounds, or "co-leek."

Inside the Refuge, a Great Blue Heron is hunting in the open water of a marsh, an adult. At only a hundred feet distant, the white on the head and the black slash mark over the eye, like a brush-stroke carried well past the head, are conspicuous, as are the plumes on the back and breast. It stands erect and, though its neck seems fully extended, raises it a little more. It puts its head off to the side. It is perfectly motionless. Then—bang! Down the head goes, hitting the water with a splash, and up it comes, wagging. Evidently the strike miscarried. The hunter moves forward, step by stealthy step, with each stretching out its neck a little more. You would swear it could go no farther, but another step sends it up another notch. Totally intent, it moves its head again for a different view. The lunge is too fast for the eye. This time the quarry, whatever it is, is seized, tossed back in the throat and swallowed.

From a gravel road crossing the Refuge on the dikes a flock of white Snow Geese may be seen on the other side of the water at the edge of a field. Though they are at rest, one or two are continually stretching up to beat their wings, showing their black primaries. These, with the beating of the wings as the birds presently take off, a dozen or two at a time, cause the lines to twinkle. The Loblolly Pine woods in the background are dark but the outer foliage is yellow-green in the sunlight, and against this the geese pass twinkling, rising to twinkle against the blue. One flight is entirely of adults, glistening white, white as a snowfield in the sun. The young are dingy above. A few of the birds are quite dark with white heads: Blue Geese, which are not common here. They are birds of the Mississippi Flyway, breeding at its head in the lands bordering the Arctic Ocean, where the Snow Geese breed, too, but on a wider arc, from northern Alaska to northern Greenland. (Because the two sometimes hybridize, science has decided to write off the Blue Goose as merely a variant plumage of the Snow. Yet, breeding in proximity to the latter, the Blue has retained its identity from time immemorial, while the Mallard, taking advantage of our leveling the forest and flooding valleys to advance from the west to the Atlantic, has been hybridizing so generally with the Black Duck as probably to doom the latter through absorption with no suggestion from science that they are one species.) There is another concentration of Snow Geese at the northern end of Assateague Island, in the marshes on the inland side, and when a disturbance puts up two hundred or so in the distance they wheel about like sea-birds over a tropic isle in a great and continuing clamor of shocked and indignant honking—the rightful heirs dispossessed of their land.

Blackwater is on the way to Assateague, a National Seashore cut by the Maryland-Virginia line. The portion of Assateague below the line is another National Wildlife Refuge and one to which birders are drawn as bees to clover.

Here something might be said about the Wildlife Refuges, which, to the number of 356, have contributed invaluably to the preservation and improvement of wildlife habitats. That we owe the purchase of land for the refuges to receipts from federal duck stamps bought by gunners as shooting licenses is unfortunately true—and a disgrace to a rich nation that could find no other means of financing it. That gunners are in a small minority of those taking advantage of the Refuges— only one in fifteen—does not put the traditional dependence on duck stamps in a better light. On the strength of the fees they pay for the privilege of shooting, gunners are vocal about the debt owed them by conservationists. This debt birders would be readier to acknowledge had gunners not for decades resisted a switch to steel shot, claiming that their gun barrels would be damaged, though tests have showed that the average gunner would have to use such shot for ten years or more before damage became even perceptible. Meanwhile, ingested with their food, lead shot is estimated to poison hundreds of thousands of waterfowl fatally every year.

What should also be known about the Refuges is that, while in Fiscal Year 1973, duck stamps paid $7.1 million for land-acquisition, $2.7 million in general appropriations were allocated to the same purpose and over $25 million to the system's operating costs. In other words, the public is footing 75 per cent of the bill. Against the revenues from the duck stamps, moreover, must be set the value of the wildlife that falls to the gunners, who have no more title to it than anyone else. In the National Wildlife Refuges alone in Fiscal '73 they killed nearly 200,000 gamebirds, nearly 9,000 deer and nearly 175,000 fur-bearers. (The figures are from *The Washington Post*.) "Refuges" is increasingly a misnomer, for, under the enthusiastic leadership of the Department of the Interior, inveterately two-faced, almost half of them have in recent years come to be opened to gunning.

The Chincoteague Wildlife Refuge on Assateague is one that is open, but only for shooting deer. Mercifully, birds on the island are protected. Outside the summer months, it is one of my favorite places. In winter, when its popularity with the public is at a nadir, you may well meet no one at all at dawn on a week-day.

At six-thirty A.M. on February 18th it is still almost black dark on the road across the Refuge. In the east, however, a faint, dull red glow on the horizon seems to emanate from embers just below. A crescent moon and the Morning Star shine above it with an occult brilliance. Every five or six seconds a light flashes twice in quick succession on the pine-trees; topping the Loblolly woods behind me, Assateague lighthouse is sweeping the hidden Atlantic with its beam. It is too dark for me to see anything as I walk, including any signs of life, but twice I hear a splashing and a whir of wings accompanied by irate nasal quacking as a flock of Black Ducks takes off. There is no warier duck.

Around the ruddy glow in the east, the sky is turning a luminous deep blue and is reflected in the wide lagoon the road skirts. Between sky and water the pine forest and the isolated stands of pines might have been inked in upon back-lighted, dark blue glass. As the light gains, the coldly burning white lights bestrewing the heavens pale, the moon to thin to a mere paring, Venus to disappear. The clouds, low-lying on the far horizon, resemble a greater and more distant forest. On such a morning the windows of the soul are opened. It is not in sleep that the spirit is released from the body but at dawn, to partake of the universality of things in a cosmos starting afresh. . . . I turn off onto a lane atop a dike where the afternoon before a covey of Bob-whites had zoomed off ahead of me, little winged cannonballs emitting a chorus of peeping and twanging notes. More ducks rise with alarm cries as I walk on, and herons, too, Black-crowned Night Herons with a short "quahk!" and Great Blues with a prolonged "waaaaaaark!," as if I were throttling them.

How could one ask for more than to see the world materialize out of the receding darkness? The ducks seem to feel the charge in the ether. From the time there is light enough to read by, the air is seldom empty of them. Black Ducks streak across the sky, two or three of them together, always in close formation, wing-tip to wing-tip, but staggered, often parachuting down onto the water in a pose understandably beloved of sportsmen's painters. Wings forming an arch, heads rather up, they govern their direction by tilting this way and that to put down with hardly any other motion apparently just where they meant to all along. Canada Geese are taking to the air as well, showing their strength in their deep, heaving wing-beats when they slog into the wind, and, by contrast, their lightness as, with shallow, easy strokes, they run before it. Snow Geese are near enough the road for the light rust-colored stains on their faces to be visible, and their incongruous sneers, produced by that wedge of black where the mandibles join. They are really sturdier-looking than the Canadas but their honking is higher-pitched and more perfunctory.

The marshes are fecund. Herons are everywhere, even those I think of as semi-tropical, Great Egrets yellow of bill and Snowies whose head plumes the breeze lifts—astonishing in the freezing morning cold. Here and there is a Night Heron in a tree, svelte and beautiful, black on the crown and back with that lovely, soft pale grey on the wings and white beneath; what did Nature have in mind? It sits hunched up, lozenge-shaped, misanthropically, jewel-red eyes preoccupied with the inner heron. . . . A female Sharp-shinned Hawk with the blue-grey upper parts and rufous-barred lower of an adult comes by, taking it slowly and plainly hankering for her breakfast. She is followed by a brown Harrier, speeding down wind, twice breaking itself to turn on its wing-tip, vertically, thinking it had spotted a prey, then hurrying on to take by surprise any that might appear. A Song Sparrow or Myrtle Warbler—and the latter especially abound—would appear hardly to have a chance. Even the ducks are not taking any and rise as they see the hawk coming.

How one responds to the spare spaciousness of the barrier isle, the land's last low-spread advance between sky and ocean! The trees huddle together in their exposure, the clumps of woods set apart by golden cordgrass marshes, themselves divided by open leads of water and the great lagoons and lesser ponds fringed by thickets of Wax-myrtle like attenuated little trees and its companion, Silvertip, in the semblance of low-lying, grey cloud-banks in the early light. One is unburdened and given over to that openness, to the boundless, which the ducks set to life as they scoot by or come rocking in for a landing on those stiffly bowed wings, as if it were a stunt. Fish Crows in a flock over the woods are definitely performing. They draw the attention first by their short, skeptical *quaks,* like clipped caws emitted in a paper cup. They are cavorting around one another, very companionable, as I doubt you would find the larger Common Crows doing, but as you picture Daws around an English cathedral tower.

Woods on the frontier of the sea's realm have a special secretiveness about them. A forest of low, many-branched Loblolly Pines, some like candelabra, through which a loop walk of 1.6 miles is invited, has depths within depths, and the wind in the needles enjoins a *hush* with every small gust. On a bay in the woods the sun just reaches a flock of fifty or sixty Green-winged Teal. Cute, dressy little dumplings and very animated, they rise in the water one after another to beat their wings among much excited peeping, as of toys. Watching cautiously in deep shadow as I am, I am none the less espied by some Black Ducks at the far side of the flock, and, quacking shame! shame! they bring the whole mass into the air with a tremendous whirring and clatter of wings. . . . Two young women with binoculars whom I later encounter had seen three Woodcocks in the woods the evening before. I dare not report my major find, for it was a bird that Does Not Count and highly implausible besides. Shortly after entering the woods I had been brought up short by a sound that is to me as rousing as any to be heard, the dauntless crowing of a cock. Following it with mystification and silent applause, I soon came up with the originator, a domestic rooster, right enough, but a splendid fellow with bright red comb and golden hackles, escorting a hen. Wherever they came from, they had evidently been pecking at some grain put out on the road for the famous Chincoteague ponies.

By now other ducks have appeared, among them a dozen Gadwalls, in appearance greyish female Mallards with a pronounced black rear end in the drakes, much in evidence when they tip to feed. A score of Shovelers are tipping, or dibbling, closer by, kicking their orange legs, pitter-patter, to keep vertical. Their heads when they come up, green velvet in the drakes, are as dry as before they submerged. Like the Elephant's Child, whose snout was pulled into a trunk, the Shoveler has a face that is mostly nose. Pintails and Wigeons (note the white patch toward lower rear) are feeding on another lagoon as are Whistling Swans, looking dead while their heads and necks are under. The Swans have absurdly small voices for their size. You can approximate their calls by whistling *whoo*. The pitch varying as it does, a flock at a distance could make you think you were hearing children at play. In the marsh Red-winged Blackbirds are already singing, sounding as if musical dice were being cast.

### Winter and the Ocean

Beyond the dunes lies a harsher world. Though shunned by most birds, which it has little to offer, the winter beach is by no means birdless, and it powerfully attracts some human beings. For these, it is enough to top the last rise of the sandhills the sea winds have shaped to know the sentiment *Back again at last*. The boundless prospect of the ocean is limitless in space, the voice of its waters, crashing and seething on the shore in their solemn and steady pulse as they have without respite over eons upon eons, limitless in time. You cannot stand witness to that unfolding of the infinite and remain the same, not be paradoxically revealed in all your littleness and yet be redeemed of that littleness. Is there also a sense of return to the beginnings of life? If so, there is perhaps also a sense of the sea as the ultimate grave of all. The heavy seas of winter, which chew beaches away, as the lighter waves of summer restore them, have here at Assateague uncovered all that remains of a ship's hull, the layered timbers of the bottom held together with spikes several feet long. To gaze upon it is to hear in the muffled drum-beats of the breakers a dirge for the seamen lost with it. From this, this restless eternity of waters, we all came and to it, sooner or later, all that remains of us returns.

But the knowledge one has of one's feeling about the sea throws no light on the feelings about it of the birds that consort with it. Some that do seem quite out of place beside it. Could anything contrast more with those breakers that charge in, bellowing like bulls, to reach up the beach and slack away with the hiss of frustrated serpents than the dainty, lovable Sanderlings that hurry after the deflated monsters to probe excitedly in their trails, then scurry back at the last instant before the bared teeth of an oncomer? They fly past you over the surf, two or three or half a dozen together, to settle on down-bent wings, dropping lightly onto their reflections in the watery sand. *The* winter shorebirds of our sandy beaches, the Sanderlings are pale as the grey beach itself. With heads drawn back as they run, they are like bobbins stuck with a bill and legs. Unless they are rushed, the blur of legs is altogether in front of the place of juncture with the body, an oddity adding to the effect of mechanical propulsion. Dark-eyed and sweet of face, they seem an expression of life's innocence, altogether unlike the Herring Gulls in whose pale eyes one reads, as it were, an ancient and illusionless habituation to the remorseless sea. Yet, as Arthur Cleveland Bent says of the Sanderling, "few species, if any, equal it in world-wide wanderings. Nesting in the Arctic regions of both hemispheres, it migrates through all the continents and most of the islands, to the southernmost limits of South America and Africa, and even to Australia." Its guileless simplicity must be proof against the connotations of the covetous immensity it dares.

So must a relative's. The Purple Sandpiper winters even farther north than Sanderlings do. The rocks, shaggy with seaweed, on which it finds a living do not occur naturally on our east coast below Connecticut. However, coastal engineers with their revetments and groins have created new opportunities southward for the species. One of its favorite haunts is a seawall of boulders lining the channel that divides the lower end of Ocean City from Assateague Island and extending off shore as a breakwater. Thirty or forty, quite tame, may be found foraging for algae, pouncing upon one trove after another as if the spread might at any instant be yanked away from them. They are the darkest of our sandpipers, as befits rock-dwellers, and, of course, are more grey than purple, but their bills at the base are orange-yellow, as are their legs.

The jetty at Ocean City is a favorite haunt of birders as well. In the Christmas census of 1973, when Ocean City's 158 species was one of the highest above the nation's southern periphery, the birds at the jetty included four Common and seven King Eiders and a Lesser Black-backed and four Black-headed Gulls. This is about the last regular southernmost resort of the eiders, those ducks like short-necked geese; perhaps they find on the rocks the mussels they fancy. (The King is only a straggler south of Canada, but the Common Eider winters in great rafts off the elbow of Cape Cod.) A small flock of Old-squaws (a name abominably inappropriate) off the jetty on my last trip raised another question about birds and the ocean. A rising north wind had set the seas running, sending one hard upon another in the rush for land, and the little ducks, of devil's-food cake with sugar icing, were rising and falling as if on accelerated elevators, except when they were under water, all together. How could birds get their sleep in such a heaving bed? The thought of being swung through such circles even when awake is enough to make one giddy.

Old-squaws, which winter on deep fresh-water bodies and along and off the coast, are my favorite ducks. Little Eskimos with heads that look furry, like seal's skin, close up, they are the most active of all our anserines. When not diving—and they have been caught in a net at the incredible depth of 200 feet— they are likely to wheel away in a sportive flight, getting off fast and hurtling over the water on limber wings; it is a puzzle that a bird so chunky at rest can be so lithe in the air. It goes with their liveliness to be garrulous, and the nasal tooting of a flock is audible from afar, like the honking of diminutive geese.

I like to have lunch by the Ocean City jetty and toss bits of bread to the Herring and Ring-billed Gulls that cluster on the beach there. They are quick to spot a promising visitor and converge on him. Surrounding him, they seem to egg one another on, like small boys, to go closer, and some Ring-bills come within six feet. You may look for Bonaparte's Gulls there, too. The smaller the gull, the more tern-like (and the larger the tern the more gull-like) and the Bonnie, our smallest, little larger than a Flicker, is quick and light in the air. A flock of some thirty I saw from the jetty coming in from out at sea late in the afternoon could have been shorebirds in the tightness of their formation and abrupt shifts of course, appearing alternately as grey and as white, snowy brilliant against the darkening sea as they caught the beams of the sinking sun. To the north, as many as 200 will meet the ferry from Lewes, Delaware, as it enters the canal for the slip at Cape May. Jampacked on the water, they rise with a chorus of grating and peeping notes to hang above the water churned up by the ship's propellers, one and another diving to the surface for a spoil. A sight to hold one's gaze they make, the multitude of wings beating in exactly the same tempo, each with the white stripe down the forward edge, by which you may know the species.

The ferry is a real ship, and the fifteen-mile crossing, taking a little more than an hour, is the nearest thing to a sea voyage I know at the price. It is in winter, at least, when the raw chill keeps the un-bird-minded mostly within. I watch the gulls and try to figure out how they follow us without a perceptible beat of the wings. Those overhead could well be taking advantage of the updraft caused by the wind's striking the vessel; they are mostly to windward. Like hawks coasting along an Appalachian ridge, they could be gliding down a simultaneously rising billow of air, in equilibrium. But some, drifting forward, then aft, falling well astern, all with scarcely a visible other movement, seem too far off the vessel to benefit from the currents it sets up. Perhaps they are exploiting the columns of rising and falling air that are said to form over ocean water that is warmer than the atmosphere. One is to picture the air flowing up the inside of the column and down the outside, or vice versa, and the columns to be pressed together, so that they assume an hexagonal form in cross section. It is a queer conception, to me, but sea-birds are said to soar high on the columns or, as the wind tilts and even flattens them (queerer still!) coast upon them.

Floating astern, a gull will drop to the water, then with only a few beats of the wing—and these evidently more for balance than thrust—recover its station above the ship. A maneuver favored by gulls accompanying a ship overhead (it is the one described by Leonardo da Vinci) is suddenly to tilt and slide away down the wind nearly to the water two hundred feet away, then bank with the nearer wing-tip almost awash and, rising with easy strokes, rejoin their fellows. A Great Black-backed Gull that hung above us on one crossing, mostly to leeward, had the stature of an eagle as, like a monarch unbending to lead the cotillion at a court ball, it swept around the orbit and, white of head and tail as it presented its dark back to us in swerving around the far side of the circle, looked in particular like the Bird of Washington.

With ill luck you may see no more from the ferry than on a poor day on the outer beach, apart from funebral Cormorants: a string of Scoters and a few Loons, along with the Herring Gulls.

Birds or no birds, the beach is always, when the surf is running, a fulfillment. Let it even be raining or snowing, and the waves rearing on one another's traces to plunge and explode in thunderous vibrations instill in the human heart some of their own wild vitality. Thus it is with an on-shore wind. But comes the westerly and all changes. The waves fight it for a day, their crests swept back in white manes, but by the second they are nearing exhaustion; after their long trek against the wind they can manage to rise only a foot or so at the end and crash with a nerveless plop. (They are, however, blasting the coast of Europe, or preparing to.) It can be punishing then on the beach. The icy westerly fries the side of the face and the glare is searing as well. Usually there is a gull on the wing in sight off somewhere, its object undivinable, and, if you walk on, a Loon riding low in the water well outside the surf.

A Loon gives me a little of the feeling of a submarine. There is the same pared-down purposeful build above and below the waterline, the same suggestion of the ocean's dim and chilling underworld in which both pursue their ends, of utter loneliness as you think of darkness overtaking them at sea. Only there are many souls for company in a submarine, only one in a Loon. And what goes on in that solitary psyche, what impression reaches it of the medium of its existence?

The Common Loon winters off all the shores of North America between the arctic and Mexico, and most of this immense range it shares with the perky little Horned Grebe, in proportions a tiny goose with sharp bill. Seeing five of these together well out from the beach at Ocean City made me think that the Loon is the only bird I know that exhibits no inclination to company. (Raptorial birds, forced to disperse by the exigencies of hunting-grounds, do not count.) Yet the very next day I had to back-track on this. I was at Cape Henlopen at dawn. The wind, out of the northwest the day before, had swung around to the southeast, bringing on the softer air a sense of life's renewal, and on the seaward side of the long point constituting the Cape the surf was coming up again. Well off shore Loons were flying southward, often several together, eight in one flock—companionably enough. Nearer by, on the water, one of smaller, trimmer build was alternately kicking under and suddenly being there again—a Red-throated Loon, a somewhat more northerly species and now also, of course, in drab winter dress.

Vera and I had found a dead one of these on the beach with a fish's tail protruding from its bill. Extracted, the fish proved to be over eleven inches in body length and two and a quarter in maximum width—almost half the length of the bird that had tried to swallow it, to their joint extinction.

A little black-and-white pilotboat was making a rendezvous with a freighter, and whenever I raised my binocular to it another Loon or two would cross the field of view, perhaps also a beading of Scoters in a straightaway close to the water. Farther out, beyond sight, was the realm of another avifauna. For the pelagic species of the cold waters, as for strays from the Caribbean in summer, you ordinarily have to take to the sea yourself. And, without having to be a yachtsman, you may. Charter boats catering to deep-sea fishermen are available to bird clubs for off-shore excursions.

Picture yourself in one such. And for atmosphere, rather than for ornithological coups, I suggest *Captain Bunting*, of Ocean City, a 35-footer, on February 3, 1974.

Departure is scheduled for 6:45 A.M. Some forty members of Washington and Maryland bird clubs have assembled in the dark for breakfast at a wharfside restaurant. Along with the camaraderie there is dubiety about the weather. The dawn cannot even be described as half-hearted. With the low, grey sky is a wind out of the north. While departure is delayed, eight or nine small flocks of Old-squaws come in off the ocean for the bay, recalling Napoleon's "whiff of grapeshot." Note is taken of two Ruddy Turnstones on a piling, brown and white sandpipers marked, seemingly, with an ink-blotting on the lower face and breast.

That the ocean is rough is apparent from the start. The boat is pitching and rolling as soon as it clears the breakwater, and half a dozen passengers are immediately stricken, to spend the entire day stretched out in the cabin on benches along the bulkheads or at their foot. The motion is so violent that walking, or lurching, more than a step or two is impossible without something to hold onto. No one breaks a leg, as a fisherman did on a recent voyage, but several fall. The waters that rise abeam of us to shrug us off their shoulders are so sombre, so opaque, so marble-glossy they make one think of a dark rock, like basalt, in fluid form—liquid obsidian; and they are of a menace to match their hue. To be down among the rearing herd of waves, looking up at their peaking summits, is very different from seeing them below a great liner's promenade deck. Shark-like in rapacity, they seem, and they are nothing loath to hurl themselves on one another. On the glimpsed horizon, where two systems are in collision, the breakers gnash their teeth at the heavens.

Even more than by the scene from the beach is the imagination puzzled by the anomaly in this cold cauldron of the ocean, heaving up its brute waves as far as the eye can reach, of the myriad delicate carriers of life, warm-blooded and quick—the sea-birds—to which their implacable habitat is normal, even in essential aspects benign. They actually shun the land.

The continual casting of fish offal from the stern—"chumming," it is called—assures us a following through the morning, while the supply lasts. Herring Gulls and a Black-back or two are soon joined by Gannets, and all the way out, for forty or fifty miles, we have four or five accompanying us, though they pay no attention to the bait. After perhaps fifteen miles, when the land is quite out of sight, the Kittiwakes begin appearing. Within an hour they are all but swarming around us, thick as bats astern.

The Gannets frequently sail by close enough for their eyes to be discernible and to elicit exclamations of admiration from the birders. Seen in profile as they glide on level wings—and their wing-beat is never but shallow, as if they were merely patting the air—they seem to have but little body, despite what one knows of their size. Racy of form, with the long, tapering wings set back for perfect balance—they have a wing span of six feet, twice their length—they are flying crosses pointed at all four extremities and are of the purest, whitest imaginable alabaster unruffled by a single misplaced feather, the head tinted with buff, the outer wings black almost to the joint. They fly with the head slightly erect, giving them a commanding appearance, and the bill a little depressed. Two that alight on the water ahead of us and have to take off again regain the air quickly with powerful kicks of their big, fully-webbed feet.

The Kittiwakes fly on wings somewhat bent back and bowed and, like other small gulls, with much zip. Where the larger convey the feeling of the steady force of the sea wind as they ride it, the dextrous, nervous Kittiwakes make you think of the air as sprightly and volatile. They are like all gulls, though, and Gannets, too, in their fondness for that grand, long glide to leeward, down to the water and up again on a few buoyant wing-beats. And on that desolate herd of pitching seas that strike chill to the soul when you think of finding yourself through some mischance floundering alone among them, the Kittis settle down in a tight flock in the manner of Bonaparte's Gulls, as if they were doves from a cote on the barn roof, and all fly off again in a spirited, light-hearted throng. The wing-tip appearing to have dipped in India ink, like the Gannet's, is diagnostic. The young are more distinctive, so marked with dark on the mantle as to present the sign of a broad M in flight.

Against the weather, which the Kittis take nonchalantly, I am clad in thermal underwear, woolen shirt and trousers of Army issue over that, then sweater vest under a full knitted pullover topped by a quilted storm-coat with a rain suit over all. The other passengers are similarly attired—and we still freeze. The deck of the cabin is covered with the bodies of the seasick and others are bent over and pale on the benches outside. Probably everyone else is a borderline case at times. I have a poor couple of hours after consuming the ill-chosen sardine sandwich I had brought and visiting the noisome head.

Enough hands are on station, however, to raise a lusty shout of *Skua* five times—a remarkable gleaning of a real arctic customer like this one. Twice the cynosure is close enough for an impression to be had of it: a dark, heavy-set gull with bluntish wings and a white patch at the base of the primaries. The one cry of *Alcid* proves baseless, which is a disappointment.

That is on the return voyage—the interminable voyage back. The boat is bucking the wind, and after rising for a wave it smacks down into the next, sending up a fountain of spray which shoots clear to the stern and beyond. Those of us who have not sought refuge, and courted nausea, in the crowded infirmary of the heated cabin are huddled together in its lee, braced one way or another against the cavortings of the vessel, gloves soaked with spray, shoes with the water sloshing about on the deck. And only the day before and a few miles away, behind the beach, I had seen half a dozen Tree Swallows and two white herons—immature Little Blues!

We are still twelve or fifteen miles from an invisible shore when that cry of *Alcid* turns all heads toward a bird astern of us in the distance flying hard, with crisp wing-beats, coming our way. It turns out to be a Mourning Dove; no wonder it had been misidentified. Where in the world is it coming from? How did it get so far out before heading landward? It appears to be making a maximum effort, and, while fighting a head-wind, is keeping up with us. At times it veers off to one side of us or the other. How does it know in what direction land lies? Does it know? After perhaps five minutes that seem much more it veers entirely off to the side and is lost to sight. . . . But not to mind. The picture of the winged particle of life, perhaps frantic, even panic-stricken, pitted against the roiling universe of lowering clouds and spuming waves, calling up the vision of countless small birds in unequal contest with the sea, is not so easily expunged.

As for the birders, they will oversubscribe the next charter trip in the hope of better weather and some of those refractory alcids.

# ____7
# SPRING

### The Glorious but Uncertain Coming

Time is a wheel, one year in circumference, that brings to pass all points on its compass in regular sequence in a cycle endlessly repeated. But the wheel not only revolves on its axle, it also rolls forward. The days of the year follow one another year in, year out, as they have always done, but each dawns upon an earth that has changed since its last visitation. Time is progressive as well as cyclical. That this is so is constantly borne in upon us in the human world; modern man works conspicuous and irreversible alterations in his surroundings in a twelvemonth. The older we become the more the human world in which we grew up and feel at home is replaced by another more alien to us and more hospitable to the young, it seems, to remind us of time's forward motion and consequently of its theft of the sands of our life. On the other hand, in the world of Nature time is most conspicuously cyclical. The earth under Nature's regime changes but imperceptibly in the whole of a human lifetime, except as fires or storms or landslides may cut a swath through its vegetation soon to be healed. Though granted that we ourselves will have changed in the interval, April in our sixties is the same April we knew at sixteen.

Individual beings inescapably grow older, but for the rest Nature is continually reasserting the past, not denying it as civilized man does. The more we live in the natural world, the more attuned we are to cyclical time, time ever renewing. That is probably one reason why, as in youth we turn to Nature, all athirst to consume a world revealed to us in its enchantment and far horizons by the dawn burst of awareness, we turn to it again in age. Then we who cannot accommodate ourselves to the destruction of cherished landmarks and new departures in modes and standards, which the young take in stride, are sage in the ways of the four seasons as our juniors will be only with time.

I have become (in my own eyes) sufficiently sage in those ways to recognize that there are not four seasons at all, but only two. Our names for the two, spring and fall, are both descriptive of movement, and movement is of the essence of time; the wheel is always rolling. Summer and winter, as we use the terms, suggest periods each of like days following upon one another; and that, indeed, is how they feel for a time, as it might be they were here for good. But a graph of average daily mean temperatures, like one of day-length, will show not a level summer plateau and level winter floor but a continuing curve in the form of a wave. Summer and winter are only the roundings off at the top and bottom, the turnings of the tide. Even as far south as Virginia, only six weeks separate the full leafing-out of the Big-toothed Aspens and the first reddening of the Tupelo's foliage, while not a day passes in summer that is not spring for some flowers, autumn for others. Only a month separates the latest spring from earliest fall date on which one might expect to see a migrant shorebird. In winter the gap may be even narrower. One January 19th I saw a trio of Turkey Vultures migrating south against the blue, balancing on a cold northwesterly, like sailboats in a chop, and within an hour heard the first Cardinal singing, "Tsi-boo-i tsi-boo-i tsi-boo-i," making it the last day of autumn and the first of spring.

The first day of spring! Who that has been through a northern winter can ever forget the balm of the first signs of spring? Perhaps I am thinking of youth, when time is so much longer, a week as a month is later, and, lacking habituation to the course to steady us (not to mention the ballast of matrimony, career, etc., etc.) we are more vulnerable to externals, exhilarating or depressing. I am certainly thinking of my own youth and of winters that lowered upon New York State and New England, until it seemed that it had always been winter and always would be, grey and pinching. And how cold it could be in a drafty house with but one register through which the heat of an irregular coal fire was transmitted to a single room or hallway above it! How cold especially in an upstairs bedroom after the fire had been banked for the night. One must have been through that, or worse, and have been wearied to the soul of accumulations of sullied snow, giving the earth the air of a dirty and unhallowed old age, and a hopeless one, to know the inner resurrection that comes as, one night, one hears a dripping from the eaves and can tell from a softness on the moist air that the thaw has begun. Or the annunciation may come with a mild day and a Song Sparrow's brief, spangling upsurge of sunny notes or a Red-shouldered Hawk's prolonged wild crying, torn out of its breast, you would think. On the south side of a ledge of rock a lichen will be found to have put up its sporeheads and in the swamp the flower spathes of Skunk Cabbage to be growing up through the panes of ice.

Today, February 12th, there are these same signs of spring in northern Virginia.

Though the thermometer two mornings ago stood at twelve degrees, the Red-shouldered Hawks have begun their courtship. For ten minutes at a stretch they perform with vociferous abandon. *Kee-ah, kee-ah, kee-ah,* the male screams while winging about over the woods. The cry is rather pained, complaining and strident to human ears but not, I am sure, to the female, who is also flying about and replies in a softer and somewhat hen-like double-note. They are handsome birds, rust-colored on the shoulders, the closely barred underparts an almost orangeish light brown. "Kee-ah, kce-ah," the male protests, the usual Red-shoulder seclusiveness cast to the winds. He has been tried too far. "Kee-ah, kee-ah," he screams. He is now climbing in wide circles, beating strenuously. Satisfied of his height, he levels off, then turns earthward and goes into a steep descent. Nearly closing his wings, the tips against his tail and only the shoulders extended, he comes down in an accelerating, sloping dive—a thrilling sight. He is almost in the tree-tops before he spreads his wings and casts up. Again he swings out in a wide,

steep spiral. Up and up. Regaining his pitch, he once more
turns down and, picking up momentum, drops like a bomb.
This time at the bottom of his stoop he wings swiftly away . . .
as I hear a faint echo of his cries in the distance, which he is
doubtless gone to deal with.

Within a fortnight the beaks of Skunk Cabbage are up;
beaks or hollow bison horns, streaked with purplish red and
veined with blood vessels enclosing the flowers arranged like
sparse kernels on a tiny ear of corn. But the first flower of all,
in bloom beside the door on February 20th, is the little waxen
bell of a Snowdrop, directly beside a melting snow bank.
Chickweed is green and growing and so are the inch-wide
green doilies of an early mustard. Our Cardinal began singing
nearly a month ago, joining the Carolina Wren, which was
caroling even on the morning of twenty degrees of frost. Tufted
Titmice are singing, too; have been off and on all winter, like
the Wren. "Peeta peeta peeta peeta," they call, little lost souls
in the woods trying to find one another.

With March comes a brief, unseasonably warm spell, as one
often does early in the month. And this, you say, is what life
is meant to be. There is a feeling of luxury about it, as of an
indulgence from On High, as if Heaven itself had come to
earth. A Grackle is creaking—singing, in its view—in a tree outside the window (open for the first time) and reawakens the
twelve-year-old in me to whom, in my first spring as a birder,
even a March Grackle in Central Park was a thing of wonder.
Later, six are to be seen flying northwestward against clouds
like the thinnest sheets of combed cotton against the pale blue.
Eight Robins also pass going north, though not the first ones
of the year; a few, even a small flock, may drop by at any time
during a mild winter to pluck the fruit from the hollies. A tight
flock of Cedar Waxwings speeds by in the same direction. Forcing their way out of the dank earth, the first crocus buds have
opened into yellow-orange chalices, making me think that if
I were looking for the justification of a faith I should find one
more persuasive in the spring flowers than in any formal reli-
gious exhortation, ever. At dusk from the low boggy woods

there percolates the vocal equivalent of those flowers, the first Hyla's call, then others responding, in a variegated medley of eager peepings. How touching the sound is, and how trustful! Talk of faith: this is the very voice of faith, faith that—that what? If I knew, I should perhaps know what faith is warranted. Faith that life will prevail? Soon after the Hylas, sometimes before, comes a chorus of runs up tiny xylophones, from the equally diminutive Chorus Frogs. The two acolytes of spring can turn a swamp into bedlam, and an eerie bedlam in that, standing close by on a cloudy afternoon, hearing cries loud enough to issue from quail-sized vocalists, you see nothing to account for it. You take another step forward and the sounds peter out, and might never have existed outside your imagination. At night the tintinabulation sounds directly beneath our windows instead of two hundred feet away. A morning now, after mists have softly possessed the countryside, will discover the tops of the dead weeds occupied by silvery pockets of spider-web like gossamer parachutes, inverted.

March 3rd brings a reversion. The temperature drops. An icy rain steals in and turns to snow before tapering off. All the same, the first Phoebe materializes, right on schedule. There is as little drama in the manner of its coming as there is much in the fact of it. The next day it is inspecting the shelf under the porch eaves on which it nests every year. The Carolina Wren is carrying nesting material to the box it also regularly occupies under the carport roof. The drama of life itself is in its unflagging challenge to the brute forces, and that is how we see it in spring. The array of living things presses unremittingly against the rear-guard of winter, exploiting every opening. Frequently the pioneers get ahead of the season. Winter, like a chivvied beast retreating to its lair, will turn upon the presumptuous celebrants and, driving on into the Deep South, put the quietus on them. The frogs settle back into the mud; the early flowers fold up, may be buried by snow; the Phoebe disappears, presumably to a wet bottomland where some flying insects may still be found, or a few berries. The winter-resident birds carry on as usual, but this is a trying time for them. All the easy pickings are gone and of the new crop of foodstuffs there is only a beginning trickle. The feeding-station is never more important than now. How the Crows still find enough for birds their size is a mystery. But they are as energetic as ever. When a Red-tailed Hawk sails over our woods, local corvidom is after it in a trice with shrieks of righteous, even ecstatic, indignation.

Winter is highly temperamental. One never knows which lands in the temperate zone will be punished, which largely spared. However the season may be going, one learns to take nothing about it for granted, especially not to be deluded by an apparent early visitation of mild weather. The Washington area's worst snowstorm in the past quarter-century, catching the Forsythia coming into bloom and leaving power-lines down for as long as a week, came on March 18th. The Blizzard of Eighty-eight that brought New York to a standstill and killed 400 persons, struck between March 11th and 14th, and one year ten inches of snow fell on the city in twenty-four hours beginning on April 3rd. It is such surprise onslaughts that play havoc with vulnerable migrants like Bluebirds and Phoebes. We have had snow flurries here in Virginia on April 17th and the northern plains are not out of danger of a lashing through most of May. Winter's eccentricity makes for great irregularity in the occurrence of early vernal events. The time of the first crocus and of the first calling of the froglets varies by more than a fortnight with us. The only certainty in March is that life will make the most of the mild spells that can be counted on and let not a day pass to assert itself when winter begins to recede from one of its forays.

No victory was ever celebrated in more modest accents, in sweeter, more benignant strains and hues than spring's. The Robin's tempered singing, gentle and cheerful in its swinging cadence, could prepare you for Ceres's step among the daffodils, among the tiny white blooms of the luxuriating chickweed, the white-flowered little stalks of the mustard *Cardamine*, and the first delicately flushed stars of the Spring-beauty, soon to bestrew the woods as if poured from Ceres's own cornucopia. It is mid March. Down where the wet meadow meets the flooded woods the gurgling, liquid crowing of the Red-winged Blackbirds, beginning with the *konk* of an object dropped in water, is the voice of the spring thaw across the continent. The singers toss the cue back and forth. The first Wood Ducks leap dripping from the stream, and later a half-dozen of them alight in the high branches of an oak, like doves. (Wood Ducks seem slow to grow used to man. Even those nesting just above Washington in backwaters of the Potomac are quick to take alarm and go winging off with the squeals of a captured pig, these subsiding to an anxious *oo-ee-uk oo-ee-uk*, then to the sound of distant lamentation.) Even the unpromising habitat of the upland pine forests is not without its affirmation of the reawakening. High in the trees is to be heard a song like a brief Chipping Sparrow's, to my ears the tinkling of a silver tambourine. The Pine Warbler is back, to go to my heart again with its sunny breast, gay little musical sprinkling and lively mounting from branch to branch, all brightening the sombre, wire-needled pinery rejected by other birds.

Mid march and the Elms, with which Washington is uniquely well endowed, are as if richly fruited in raisins, such being the color of the opening flower-buds. Of all the rites of the twelve-month, of all the natural spectacles our country displays, that which for its beauty and scope is made least of is beginning: the flowering of the deciduous trees and the unsheathing of their leaf-buds. Among them, in suburb and forest, March belongs to the Red Maples above all. Coming out with the sunshine-yellow Forsythia, the Red Maple's flowers hang in clusters, long-stemmed, typically reddish little bells with long red clappers for pistils and yellow stamens, so that from a distance they look orange-red. But they vary greatly in color from tree to tree, from pale gold or pale yellow through brass to magenta, with many a rhubarb red. The flowers evolve into pendants of little winged seed without one's noticing any change, for the colors remain as bright and wide in range as before. By then—and I am looking ahead—the oaks are in bloom, too,

hung with tassels of pale, verdant gold and honey gold while other trees are breaking out their foliage in spurts of lambent green. Then the woods and countryside, wherever trees may be, are a brocade worked in soft-tinted but luminous silks. The little bouquets ornamenting every twig are of colors subtler than autumn's and glow with new beginnings, with hope and promise. Yet the tapestry seems scarcely to be remarked by those who in autumn crowd the roads of the Berkshires and the Skyline Drive along the northern Virginia Blue Ridge to see the flaming immolation of the living year. The difference would seem to be that one is an accredited spectacle, the other not.

Spring, the morning season, is of all times of year, a becoming, not, like the other seasons, a fulfillment, a running out, a sleep or death. It brings that most delicious state of mind, of happy expectancy. How can it not be one's favorite? Yet I sometimes think that March is the least likable of months. It is the bringer of setbacks. Winter's rear-actions do not so much distress me of themselves, however, as in their manner of striking. March is the month of northwesters. They come charging through from the continent's northern interior, crystal-clear, ice-edged, desiccating, the void given velocity, the negation of spring's pregnant softness. On the first day they are likely to bear navies of tumbled, white, grey-bottomed clouds evenly dispersed over the blue sky. These come about, I understand, as the cold wind sweeps in under a static mass of warmer air and raises it to temperatures low enough to condense the water vapor it contains. By the second day the characteristic intense and fleckless blue of the Polar Canadian air-mass it brings is likely to have set in, as sterile as the deep blue ocean waters. "I am reconciling myself to the northwester"; meet it is I write it down, watching some Buffle-heads on a lake, the drakes as bright as snow-white sparks. "I think it must be good to submit one's soul to its cauterization." After that reflection I must set a notation for April 5, 1975—for the treachery of March is that the month may outrun its lease by a week or more.

Most disagreeable 48 hours of the year, I believe. Blistering northwester, which began day before yesterday morning, is, this mid afternoon, continuing hardly abated. Power-lines are down all over the place, roofs have been blown off, a barn blown over a highway, blocking traffic, trees down on cars and a woman killed under a felled tree at the zoo. Below freezing past two nights and only 38 degrees by noon today.

Before subsiding on the sixth day, the northwester had reached a gust of sixty-three miles an hour, killed three more persons, and blown so much water out of the Potomac into the Chesapeake and out of the Chesapeake into the ocean that huge mudflats sloped down from where the shorelines of river and bay had been. "Owed to the West Wind," the pictures of wreckage and stranded boats could have been called.

The reason for March's brutal winds, we are told, is to be found in the warming up of the earth to the south of us, which creates a general updraft and a potential void beneath it, which air from the north rushes in to fill. Spring comes in against the current, as it were. I thought of this two weeks after that death-dealing northwester watching Swallows—Barn, Tree and Rough-winged—flying up the rock-torn Potomac, close to the water, in the teeth of another northwester, much less strong but still chilly—on April 20th!—battling for headway as spring itself has to do. It is the wind, always, that calls the tune, not the calendar. Depending on its quarter, it turns July into autumn, April into winter, at any season brings to pastoral hills and vales the atmosphere of the Grand Banks of Newfoundland, visits Greenland cold on the Southland in January or banishes with benign and blessed spring the bitterest weather of fall or winter. If the Deity is serious about having us forgive our enemies, then let him remit our transgressions by sending the south wind to wash gently and warmly over us when we are shrunk with cold.

### The Stimulus to Migration

The farther along in the calendar, the less difference there is in the time of the vernal phenomena from year to year—the more reliable the season is—and the quicker the tempo of change: the more momentum the season develops. This means that by March, whatever the weather may be doing in the temperate zone, a spirit of restlessness is astir to the south of it, in the scrub woodlands of Mexico, on the savannas of Cuba, Central America, Colombia and Venezuela, in the rain-forests of Yucatan, the Greater Antilles and South America, on the pampas of Brazil and Argentina and along shores fronting the Antarctic Ocean—wherever North American birds resort for the winter. To be on schedule at their breeding grounds, these must soon be on their way, if they are not already so.

The first waves of spring migrants to reach us in the north are birds that had retreated in fall only to our own southern states. They account for all arrivals through the Catbird, Brown Thrasher, Ruby-crowned Kinglet, Tree Swallow, Palm Warbler and Louisiana Waterthrush—though many members of most of those species winter also well to the south of the United States. How these know when to start north is a question that has always been readily answered: they do so when the increasing warmth tells them the time has come. But how about the migrants that winter in the tropics, where the seasonal change in temperature is negligible and—more awkward still—below the tropics in the southern hemisphere, where it grows cooler as it grows warmer in North America? It is not signs of spring these latter see around them when they start northward but of autumn.

The problem first presented itself to ornithologists of the northern hemisphere as the question of what set off the southward migration in the autumn. What gave birds the urge to quit their breeding-grounds and head for the lower latitudes? Here, again, the obvious answer—the onset of cooler weather—would not suffice: too many birds left while temperatures were still high and insects at their most plentiful. Black-and-white Warblers have been known to arrive in Key West, Florida, and Yellow Warblers to set out across the Gulf of Mexico in mid July, even before the maximum temperature had been reached in their breeding-territory.

What put ornithology on the right track—as it would seem to be—were indications that light was at the bottom of it. Experimental evidence to that effect was derived by William Rowan in Edmunton, Alberta, who it was that had found a directional sense in migrating young Crows. Confining Dark-eyed Juncos in outdoor cages after their fellows had migrated to the United States, Rowan gradually lengthened the day for one set of them by means of artificial illumination of increasing duration. The result was that testes of this set grew during the bitterly cold weather to a size normally attained only in May. (Further tests have seemed to show that the effect of the increased day-length is indirect and that it is the added hours of activity on the bird's part, which it promotes, that causes the physiological changes.) Upon releasing the captives, he found that birds kept under normal conditions of light—the control birds—and those with testes of maximum size remained in the area while those with testes in process of development or regression disappeared, presumably moving on in response to a migratory impulse. Such an impulse would not arise in those in a condition associated with the stationary periods of wintering and breeding. Juncos being difficult to trace, he repeated the experiment with Crows, which are easier, carrying it through October and November. Upon their release, some of the light-treated individuals went south with the control birds, which was normal, but an unknown number did go north.

It seemed that increasing hours of daylight promoted gonadal development and migratory movement. But was it gonadal development that provoked the movement? In any case, how did the process come about in the tropics, where day-length was virtually constant, and in the temperate zone on the other side, where spring migration began during diminishing day-length?

Studies by Albert Wolfson at Berkeley of Dark-eyed Juncos, in which there are both stationary and migratory subspecies, showed that by the end of March the testes of the migrants, which were then beginning to set out for the north, were only four cubic millimeters in volume while those of the stationary birds had grown to 220. Other experiments have demonstrated that castrated birds will migrate. So, as Wolfson concluded, there is no cause-and-effect relationship between gonadal development and the migratory impulse.

But if gonadal development did not regularly precede migration, the deposition of fat did. That had been known for some time. Experience with captive birds had taught that migratory restlessness in the autumn is accompanied by a marked accumulation of fat, in which energy is stored. This accumulation lasts until December, after which it is renewed on a somewhat lesser scale before the spring migration, to decline drastically in the breeding season. Wolfson's studies of the Dark-eyed Junco and Barbara D. Blanchard's of the White-crowned Sparrow brought to light that the migratory subspecies were substantial accumulators of fat, the stationary subspecies not. Subsequently, an examination by Eugene P. Odum of the University of Georgia of over 300 birds of ten species killed upon striking a television tower on the northwest coast of Florida indicated that the farther a bird is prepared to migrate the higher the proportion of fat it tends to contain. White-throated Sparrows, which had reached their winter home, contained fats averaging only 6.2 per cent of their weight while the proportion in warblers of three species, which ordinarily would have flown on across the Gulf to the tropics, averaged over 30 per cent. Odum's estimate was that a fat-content of 27 per cent would carry a small bird on a non-stop flight of at least 600 miles. A Ruby-throated Hummingbird goes from a fat-content of between 11 and 15 per cent in June to one of between 41 and 46 per cent on the eve of migration. That comes to about two grams of fat—less than one-fifteenth of an ounce—and this, we are told, is fuel enough to take the little creature 800 miles! A bird migrating three or four thousand miles cannot, of course, carry fat enough for the whole trip, but its physiology is such at this stage that it can replenish burned fat at a prodigious rate.

Evidence has accumulated that the migratory impulse is to be explained not as an isolated phenomenon but as part of an annual cycle through which birds pass, the stages of the cycle being, from the beginning of the year: (1) molt, (2) fat-accumulation, (3) spring migration, (4) breeding, (5) molt, (6) fat-accumulation and (7) autumn migration. (Not all birds have the first molt.) This in turn has suggested glandular activity as the regulator of the cycle, itself subject to regulation by day-length, or photoperiodicity, as the scientists call it. Experiments have in fact shown that the cyclical secretion of hormones by the thyroid gland and their reabsorption are related to the bird's physiological cycle. "Our information," Jean Dorst says, in *The Migration of Birds,* "is still incomplete and highly contradictory, but these glands do seem to play a part in migration, although their action is no more direct than that of the gonads." From the thyroid, researchers have looked to the pituitary, which controls the thyroid. Now, indeed, according to Dorst, "most authors believe it governs the annual sexual cycle." That the pituitary operates to some extent on its own is shown when birds from one hemisphere are taken across the Equator to the other and continue to breed when it is summer in their former homeland, which is to say when it is winter in their new. In this they are clearly obeying an "internal rhythm," as Dorst observes. It would, however, surely be only a question of time before the transplant's cycle adjusted to the local seasons. This has happened in the case of the European Storks that came to settle in their erstwhile winter haven in South Africa. They underwent a six-month shift in rhythm and now breed in the southern hemisphere summer.

Wolfson believes that the action of light sets the timing of all the processes determining the migratory cycle. The answer he and others have proposed to the question of why the pituitary is not initially stimulated into action (setting in motion the deposition of fat and the migratory impulse) by the light that migrants from the temperate zone encounter upon reaching the tropics, is that the gland is in this stage in a "refractory" phase and unresponsive to external stimuli. When it again becomes accessible to the influence of light, day-length, it is true, is not increasing. Indeed, for the migrants that have passed on through the tropics to the southern temperate zone it is actually diminishing. However, it is still a full twelve hours, or not much less and—if this explanation is correct—great enough to administer the stimulation the pituitary requires.

### The Flight Northward

Whatever the impulse that stirs birds to return to their breeding-grounds, it is irresistible. It is as if a psychic wind swept the lands below us, picking up the wintering birds in their multi-millions and bearing them off, as the autumn wind plucks leaves from the trees and takes them with it. Actual winds have little to do with the launching of birds from the tropics. In our clime, the migrants do seem to move most readily on favoring winds, spring and fall. But wind appears to be decisive only when strong; then, favorable or unfavorable, it grounds most of them. Once on their way, the travelers seem to pursue a course almost impartially over forest, llano and desert—and over sea, too, at least to a width of 500 miles, one would add but for the birds that travel the updrafts and hence avoid a water-crossing, along with some others.

In respect of birds' attitude toward a sea-crossing, the Black-poll Warbler and the Cliff Swallow offer cases in point, and opposing ones, as Frederick C. Lincoln shows. Arriving on spring migration at the northern end of South America, one strikes boldly out across the Caribbean for Cuba and Florida while the other, having set forth several weeks earlier, takes a circuitous westerly route, up through Central America and around the Mexican coast of the Gulf. One might expect the swallow, the more powerful flyer, to make the challenging, direct over-water route, the little warbler to hug the shore, but in actuality it is the other way around. The explanation is that the Blackpoll, which migrates by long overnight hops, resting and feeding by day, loses less by making its hops over water than it gains by keeping the total mileage down; whatever the hazards and hardships of a 500-mile sea-crossing, they are less on the average than those entailed in an extra 2,500 miles by land. The Cliff Swallow, on the other hand, a day migrant that in any event passes a large part of its waking hours on the wing, hunting, loses nothing by spending as many of them as necessary wending its way along a coast abounding in its prey and gains by avoiding the crossing of a rationless sea.

One pictures the throngs of small birds that have made the crossing of the Caribbean or the Gulf expending their last strength to make the far shore, dropping exhausted into the low tangle of brush growth and stunted pines behind the dunes of the barrier islands. And so they may if the crossing has been a hard one, against strong head-winds or battering storms. But the more usual event, it seems, is for the migrants not even to stop for the shore but to wing on over the coastal plain. As well as testifying to extraordinary reserves of energy available to them, it argues a consuming impatience on the part of the travelers to reach their goal. Yet the other evidence is that they obey no urgency. As a rule they travel only as far in a day as they could in an hour or two by stretching themselves. It makes sense for them to allow time enough for leisurely progress, and that is the kind they appear generally to make. If they keep pace with the spring, their advance on that account would be unhurried. As John Kieran observes, "From the Gulf of Mexico to the Canadian border a man could walk northward with the spring and not fall a day behind it." The Canada Goose makes just such a measured advance. Following the thaw northward, its leading elements depart the mid United States about the first of March and arrive in northern Canada about the end of April—a distance a goose could cover in three days. The proprietors of other feeding-stations must have had experiences like mine with birds tarrying over. The Cape May Warbler I mentioned in the preceding chapter hung about for three days at the height of the spring migration, evidently relishing the suet, and every year we have a Fox Sparrow that lingers with us for a week or ten days in March, its warm, reddish-brown and kingly size—for a sparrow—helping to make up for the month's less winning ways.

There are exceptions to the practice among birds nesting far to the north with a long way to go. These, to arrive in time to make the most of the brief high-latitude summer, would find themselves passing through still chilly weather if they started early enough on the last 1,500 miles to allow for dawdling on the way. The Blackpoll Warbler, whose passage in the spring winds up the land-bird migration in the East, is one. To reach the northernmost part of its breeding territory at the upper limits of the forest in Alaska, it accelerates from perhaps 25 to 200 miles per day. The Grey-cheeked Thrush, which breeds even beyond tree-line, traveling from its winter home in South America as far as the two sides of the Bering Strait, gets up to 300 as it nears the end. The Blue Goose is another bird that holds back to avoid outrunning the season, then sprints to its destination. It lingers in the coastal marshes of Louisiana, where it winters, until the end of March or early April, when it may fly non-stop all the way to Canada before putting down in the Hudson Bay area for a final delay, then pouring into its breeding grounds on lands bordering the Arctic Ocean during the first half of June.

There are insufficient banding records to show whether individual birds habitually follow the same route north that they take going south, but with few exceptions—and those not easy to explain—where a species occurs in fall migration it occurs also in spring. One eccentric is the Connecticut Warbler, which in fall migrates down the seaboard side of the Appalachians from its breeding territory in central Canada but in spring, on arriving in Florida from the tropics, heads northwest to pass up the Appalachians' inland side. The most striking case is that of the Lesser Golden Plover. From its breeding-grounds in arctic Canada, the eastern race migrates southeastward to the Nova Scotian and New England coasts, strikes out over the ocean to the Lesser Antilles and South America, then flies south through Brazil to the pampas. It returns via western South America, Central America and Mexico, thence winging northward through Texas and the plains. Some of the young in the fall, however, migrate down the Mississippi Flyway, making one wonder if this was the original migration route in both seasons, from which the fall route was for some reason pushed farther and farther east. The vanished Eskimo Curlew, in the days of its abundance, had about the same migration pattern as the Plover.

### The Irreversible Tide of Spring

The Canada Geese, keeping even with the isotherm of 35 degrees as it moves northward, are most likely to pass in numbers through the central Atlantic states around the middle of March. Along the coastal plain where horizons are wide, their V's may be seen so far off they could be fine darning of rents in the clouds, or even at distances at which a large flock will seem no more than a wisp of smoke subtly changing shape as the wind bears it along. The view at our house being restricted by hills and trees, they have to come fairly close for us to see them. In any case, we hear them first. . . . And, no, it is not distant dogs. Once more, *the geese are coming*—and this time northward bound! Then, there they are, the sky-borne string of dark, evenly winging, portentous forms proclaiming their advance in the cacophony of explosive honking, ringing like a liberation. The clangor drifts back to us when the celestial chargers are long out of sight.

If you are susceptible to nature and keep in touch with the natural world, you know how strong the incentive is to *make something of it*, not to let its manifestations, which touch you to the quick, fade into oblivion. Great is the impetus given to photography by this need. Another solution, however limited, is to keep a record of the train of events, of the natural occurrences you witness. If you do this, you are almost sure to find that the pages fill up fastest in spring. At no other season do the tokens of change so appeal to our notice, do we so look forward to what each new day may bring. No other do we so yearn to see realized: please, oh gods, heap my plate higher with spring!

There are three springs in our lives: the spring of the day, the spring of the year and the spring of life itself. The last, life's spring, comes when we have had no experience of its other seasons and hence we are apt to appreciate it only in retrospect, and with an incurable nostalgia. As for the first, few of us are up and abroad in the early morning except on the way to work and oppressed by its anticipation.

"The Memorial Parkway and the Beltway were roaring with traffic. You think of the commuters as a levy of *fella* being herded to toil on the Pyramids." I had been out for an early morning walk on the Canal towpath. It was mid April. The open grassy expanses were as if half snowed over with Spring-beauties. Virginia Bluebells, rather coarse of foliage, held up their clusters of down-pointing trumpets azure as the sky, opening from pink buds. White-hearts—Dutchman's Breeches—had bangles of down-pointed white arrowheads on stalks above the mounds of grey-green, palmetto-like leaves as smoothly laid on one another as feathering. In the course of a two-hour walk I saw only an elderly man in a yachting cap with his tall, attractive daughter, whose long hair swung as she strode along. Even on a Saturday or Sunday you see surprisingly few walkers out early; indoor work in office and household saps the spirit for such enterprise, I am afraid. Yet to be abroad in the spring of the day in the season of spring is to know again, as well as one can, that third spring, the spring of life.

April 15th. It is my favorite week-end of the year. In the near darkness I drive through mist lying on the air like fine-stretched silken floss, and the river, when I reach it, is largely obscured in mists, the sun showing through as an orange orb, the trees taking form, hazily, as one approaches them. Why is it so terribly moving? On a mudflat are two Greater Yellow-legs, little more than silhouettes in the mist, into which the river fades away, out of which a few Black Ducks come winging. The Yellowlegs, almost up to their bodies in the water, make occasional quick jabs at it as they walk stiffly, bobbingly. While one bathes, ducking its head repeatedly, a third comes in, flying with legs outstretched behind, then, on bowed wings, sets down, running a few steps. Their cry is a clear *kew-kew-kew-kew*, as if aggrieved and pleading in a cause of which they have become uncertain.

Farther along, where the path—a bicycle trail down the river to Mount Vernon—crosses a marshy embayment on a trestle of wooden planking, a pair of Green-winged Teal is to be seen among the new shoots of Pickerelweed. The drake is a fashion plate, his sharply patterned plumage so smooth not a feather is discernible in its surface, the silky green swatch enclosing the eye as carefully brushed back as a model's pompadour. A mood of suggestiveness holds the morning in spell. And perhaps that is what is so moving about the early hours of a spring day, their suggestion of possibilities no more to be pinned down than the mists. These are still rolling off the river, disclosing patches of quiet, dark water, when I stop on a grassy elevation. At the foot of it the piles of a ruined pier are occupied by a dozen Ring-billed and a few Herring Gulls with, surprisingly, a Bonaparte's in dark nuptial hood. While I placate the crude (but grateful) inner man with coffee from a vacuum bottle and a doughnut, the gulls cry from below, from the realm of mist and river, their wild, yearning "Klee-aaah klee-aaah" an assertion of sentience against the inanimate and heedless sea. It is a voice of a different world from that of the Mockingbird swiftly and with warm fervor capping one lyric passage with another in a Red Oak dripping tassels of golden braid. All the while, every fifteen seconds from across the water, warning ships of a shrouded headland, comes the clear peal of a bell, a sound that must reach one, reverberant with diverse and solemn associations, from a past far older than oneself. So it comes to me that there are other springs than those I had thought of. There is the dawn of our race in forests as mysterious and withheld as those that take shape out of the morning fog and, farther back, the dawn world in which all things had their beginning and their promise and life commenced its grope toward consciousness, called up in the Herring Gull's cries.

Back from the river lilacs are in bloom and the wisteria is hung with its celestial grape-clusters of silvery-lavender peablossoms. Dogwood flowers are uncurling, still small and greenish; they do not open fully formed as true flowers do, the "petals" being bracts—modified leaves. The woods are showing green nibs of foliage buds, those of the Tuliptrees in the form of tiny bananas with the skin partly peeled back, those of the Hickories of Dürer's praying hands. Seizing the chance between the last hard freeze and the closing over of the forest canopy, the little woods plants are displaying their wares in showy modesty. Patches of ground are as if sprayed with Spring-beauties, one of the first and the longest blooming of them, and the supernally white flowers of the poppy Bloodroot have been out for some days and, even longer, the pale blue cups of Hepatica (of the Buttercup family) in the heavenly shade you would think the devotees of the Virgin would choose for her blue robe. How can you not feel a comprehensive hope when you behold such loveliness emerge from the dank, sullen earth? And how, when under the soft, southwesterly zephyr, a universal love seems to suffuse all, can you not but be shaken to realize that the Nature that produces this is the Nature that terminates lives in suffering and terror, in wholesale slaughter, and evolves the labyrinthine horrors of parasitism? Best to recognize it not within your capacities or responsibilities to resolve the ultimate enigmas. Try to be reconciled to the fearful ambivalence in the reflection that in Nature's most heartless as in her most beatific there is a constant that commands our unfailing awe and wonder, and that is the intricacy and precision of natural processes, the unity in which all discords are harmonized . . . and among those processes those that bring plants of a common species into bloom at separate locations on the same morning. How is it managed? Until a certain day between March 23rd and April 9th (as usual I am speaking parochially) the Common Blue Violets have progressed only to whorls of half-dollar-sized leaves. Then on that day scattered plants open their first flowers and on the morrow, or within forty-eight hours, all around you are bouquets of them.

In this magic week of which I am speaking the early violets are at their most profuse, the blue-lavenders, the whites, the yellows. In congregations through the woods, all in the vicinity at the same stage, the May-apples' leaves are being unfurled—fairy parties setting up their beach umbrellas. Among the crowded blades of Trout Lilies like little green gonfalons marked with blood, the small, yellow lily-flowers hang downcast, hiding their beauty. Transfiguring their setting, the fruit trees are all in bloom, pears having led off and been followed by cherries, plums and crabs. Against the still largely wintry woods they stand like ballet dancers, all bouffant pastels, white and rosy. Narcissus are joining daffodils edging greensward studded with dandelions among which bees are busy. In this week, too, the mighty crowns of the oaks are fleeced with those glowing metallic fringes, the Whites, with palest gold, lagging the Reds and Blacks, and the heavy bunches of seed the Red Maples bear on slender stalks show their bright, wide-ranging colors akin to those of wines, from white wine to red through sherries and *vin rosé*. Pine twigs are tipped with candles of new growth. At dusk a bat swoops and the toad in the yard joins his fluting *vibrato* to the strenuous pipings from the bog.

The first thunderstorm is almost a month past. It came up with massive, dark grey clouds that were like the universe's internal organs, against which a Red-shouldered Hawk bearing a prey to its nest winged dramatically, as if it were the thunderbird itself—came up with the rushing sound of an express train, audible nearly a minute before it struck, the wind bending the pines like wheat, hail mixed with the rain. Rending the heavens with a splitting detonation, crashing and booming their length like a maddened bull, a thunderstorm is intimidating. It puts us on notice that man's will is not yet supreme. Thunderstorms in the East of April 4, 1974, were tornadoes in states to the south and west, cutting swaths of destruction through human works and killing 322 of the occupants by the evening's count.

In advance of the rain there is apt to be a spell, bringing, to me, the supreme tableau of spring, when tinctures of green in the budding woods, the grass now lush for the first mowing and the flower-clouds of the fruit trees catch the sunshine and stand out in almost supernatural radiance against the slaty bulk of the nimbus formations. The rumblings of thunder, growing apace, are the timpani of the overture—for overture it is, this time of spring's setting in. It is the best week of the year because better is yet to follow, so that it comes with anticipation enhancing its charms. The fullness of spring in May, when the threat of cold winds and late frosts has at last been put behind, the storm-windows are exchanged for screens and the tide of birds' northward migration reaches its crest, is tinged with regret that one cannot stay the passing days.

Until then you look forward to each new day for what it may bring. One morning an ecstatic few notes of song, all cutting edge, burst from the stream valley and instantly peter out, as if the singer were abashed by its violation of the quiet: a Louisiana Waterthrush. (A warbler with a flat-headed, narrow-looking face, it has the same coloring as a Spotted Sandpiper and the same habit of rhythmically pumping its body from the head backward, as if it were possessed by the beat of inner music. Why should life at the edge of inland waters have given two utterly unrelated birds such similarities?) Our Brown Thrasher's arrival is announced by the patches of leaves on the margin of the lawn and driveway; and soon you see the lanky, rather gawky forager, about the size and color of the leaves it is tossing over its shoulder. The Catbird you may hear first, the rambling song not as musical as you would expect from so sweet a bird but otherwise in character, an unpretentious, quiet, reminiscent-sounding soliloquy. The House Wren you always hear first, and there is no mistaking the stuttering, bubbling-over song.

Meanwhile, two that you are likely to encounter at eye level among the still-bare branches remind me of Frank M. Chapman's remark that you never forget your first warbler. Well, my first could not be found among any in Chester A. Reed's *Bird Guide*—not, as it turned out, being a warbler. It was that bird as fairy-like as any we have, the diminutive, large-eyed, unfearful, olive-colored, oval Ruby-crowned Kinglet. I have never forgotten it or my first actual warbler—which my twelve-year-old peers and I could also not find in Reed. At that age you are ready to believe in species yet unrecorded by science, but with half a dozen of the unknowns glowing yellow and wagging their tails in Central Park's famous Ramble, along with the Kinglets, that hypothesis seemed scarcely tenable. We finally got word from a more experienced bird-chaser. What we were seeing was the Palm Warbler (a native, by the way, of Canadian Zone forest bogs), but the eastern race, much yellower than that depicted in Reed. "Ay me! . . . The course of true love never did run smooth."

In spring one has the sense of birds' simply blossoming forth. All of a sudden, there they are. It is not surprising that until two centuries ago they were widely held to have been there all along, hibernating (a notion properly ridiculed by our sophisticated selves, until we found, somewhat sheepishly, that the Southwestern nightjar called the Poor-will does hibernate, on ledges in caves); come warm weather and they had only to revive, full-voiced, like frogs. The newcomers give no sign of travel weariness but reappear in the landscape at the peak of their vigor. "Hark! from the woods a loud whistle pierces far through the clearing," wrote Florence Merriam Bailey, who would "hurry out, full of eager anticipation" on spring mornings before I was born. "The Great-crest has come!" And it is warranted, both as to the loudness of the Great Crested Flycatcher's burry, ascending whistle, which is as exuberant as a boy's, and to the exclamation-point.

The Whip-poor-will has come! A metronome to a nocturne, it is a tropical voice. Now is night transformed. The frozen stillness, black or moon-shrouded, that would pierce your vitals with chill steel has become a rich expectancy, a soft, breathing darkness deep in secrets. We are safely in my time of year: "That time of year thou may'st in me behold. . . ."— not in my extern, heaven knows, but in my heart.

Warblers have come!—among the tail-bobbing Palms, burnt orange on their crowns, a Yellow-throated Warbler in formal black and white with brilliant yellow bib, agile as a monkey, two chesty Parulas, the shape of arrowheads, and that warbler

I never see without the sense of surprising a treasure out of Nature, a Prothonotary, the orange-yellow of its head and underparts, set off by the soft grey of its other plumage, that of the richest yolk. The Prothonotary is singing energetically, opening its bill like a pair of scissors and jerking the notes out: "Chee chee chee chee chu," descending on the last note with a decisive quality about it, as of "I told you so." It is a swamp bird, and at the edge of the water a number of solid black Rusty Blackbirds with pale yellow eyes are singing constantly, a thin, squeaky ghost of the Red-wing's lusty up-welling. In a weedy pool the presence of a small flock of Blue-winged Teal is betrayed by the white half moons on the faces of the drakes; and these, as they take off, objecting with small, stifled quacks, show their powder-blue wing-patches, like strips of the sky.

You see in spring small flocks of Robins and blackbirds fly-ing north, swallows zipping by, Swifts skittering across the sky, a northward-bound Osprey, long-winged and easy and buoyant in flight. But the spring migration hardly gives you the sense you have in the fall of the great movement of birds. You are more conscious in spring of the warblers as sources of song than of bands of them drifting by. The gentle rain of bird calls from the night skies of autumn is for some reason, not, I think, just because of the smaller numbers returning, less to be heard in spring. The Grackles, joined by Starlings, Red-winged Blackbirds and Cowbirds, have their spring roosts numbering millions, but the great rivers in which they pour by in autumn are lacking, as are the parades of hawks along the mountain ridges and at Cape May and the kettles of traveling Broad-wings. Witmer Stone, reporting the passage of hawks in autumn at Cape May at a height rendering thcm all but invisible, wrote: "Whether there is a northward hawk flight in spring at a great altitude I cannot say, but if not how and by what route does the great autumn host return?" It is a good question. One thing is evident. Because the East coast and paralleling Appalachians run from northeast to southwest, southbound migrants over a great sweep of the continent will tend to fetch up against them whereas those northbound would tend to depart them. It seems likely, too, that the chill earth of spring does not provide the strong, ascending currents of air that form over warm areas in autumn, helping the soaring hawks to mount high and collecting the kettles of circling Broad-wings. If such is the case, the probability is that the northbound hawks, rather than passing at great altitudes, come through at little above tree-top level, and singly. They are, however, concentrated to some extent against the barrier of the Great Lakes, this time on the southern flank. Those rounding Lake Ontario on the east have made Derby Hill, near Mexico, New York, a noted spring look-out, as they made it the first objective of the Hawk-Watchers Association upon its formation recently in Syracuse. It must, indeed, be quite a station. On October 15, 1973, on a northwest wind, more than 40 Parasitic Jaegers and two Pomarine were seen from it.

### Migration Through the City

With less to make us aware of the great tidal currents of birds in the spring, it is not surprising that we seem to receive them by spontaneous generation. And one kind of place in which the overnight avian flowering is incongruously profuse is in the large city parks, which are as oases in deserts. Of these, that which treats birders to probably the greatest display is Central Park in Manhattan. New York lies on the coastal border of the Atlantic Flyway. Below migrants passing over it at dawn it spreads the most extensive panorama of urban desolation in the western hemisphere. From the air in the early light it must appear as a Hades of buttes and canyons created by volcanic action, dimmed by the noxious vapors still hanging over it from the eruption, pierced by myriads of apertures through which the internal fires still glow fiercely. But, heavy as the pall may be, the natural contours of Central Park, the green grass, the trees and shrubs picked out by the budding foliage are discernible to the hungry transients flying up Manhattan and, veering toward it, down they come.

Central Park is of course not the only magnet among the

great metropolis's parks. John Kieran, in *A Natural History of New York City*, says, "I honestly believe that Van Cortlandt Park [at the northern end of the Bronx]—from the swamp on the west to the oak woods on high ground on the east—is as good a place to find spring warblers as any area of similar extent in any part of North America. In the eastern section alone, a half-mile strip of oak woods with wet undergrowth and a roar of traffic on both sides, I have found twenty-six species of warbler in one spring season."

The claim may be justified. But I doubt that there is such a compression of species so easy to see anywhere else in the country at the height of the migration as from the paths winding among the trees and bushes on the steep slopes and lakeside of the Ramble, which lies midway between the two sides of Central Park very nearly abreast of the American Museum of Natural History. Even Kieran (very much a Van Cortlandt man) acknowledges that as many as twenty-nine species of warblers have been seen in the Ramble on a single day (May 13, 1955). That 260 species have been recorded from Central Park—I learn from Roger F. Pasquier of the Linnaean Society—gives an idea of the possibilities. As a boy I saw an American Bittern in the Ramble and on another morning walk in spring a Whip-poor-will alighted on one of its paths in front of me, splayed out and looking up at me with its large, dark eyes. These are as nothing, however, compared with many windfalls (in a literal, perhaps, as well as figurative sense), such as Louisiana Heron, Chuck-will's-widow, Swainson's and Black-throated Grey Warblers and Western Tanager, all, according to Pasquier, added to the park's rolls between 1969 and 1974.

But then unlikely birds may turn up almost anywhere in the city. In spring, from the streets of mid Manhattan, I have seen a Green Heron in the rain on the roof of one of a block of four-story buildings and an Osprey alight momentarily on a chimney. If, during migration, you keep your eyes on the sky there is no telling what you may see. (Or hear: "Hey, whyncha look where yer goin', Mac?") The spectacle of lines of

Snow Geese moving northward beyond the antenna of the Empire State Building is recorded in a sketch forming the frontispiece of *A Natural History of New York City*. Kieran, who has seen such a sight, tells how, too, during the course of a football game at the northern tip of Manhattan he counted eighty-eight hawks working westward, those low enough for identification being Red-tails with a minority of Red-shoulders.

Before the calamitous decline of the species in the 1960's, the city was even the haunt of Peregrines, attracted to it by the pigeons and Starlings it offered hunters of their speed and dispatch. Probably it seldom contained more than a few at any one time, but they could be looked for throughout the year. The craggy buildings being not too dissimilar to the cliffs that afforded them ledges for their aeries, Peregrines have even nested above the hectic thoroughfares, and perhaps more often than realized; a nest on the St. Regis Hotel was removed on the grounds that the fierce homemakers were threatening guests on the penthouse roof. Several times in the 1930's I was electrified by the sight of a Peregrine winging among the chasms of the financial district, a corsair king trimmed for the chase among the fat merchant pigeons.

Of all raptorial invaders of the city, the most astonishing, however, met the eyes of Allan Cruickshank and Joseph J. Hickey in the course of a baseball game at Ohio Field on 181st Street, when they looked up to behold a Swallow-tailed Kite sweeping about over the diamond.

That was on April 30, 1928. I well remember how, a few years earlier, Cruickshank and Hickey and other *enfants terribles* of the Bronx County Bird Club, which included Roger Tory Peterson, had swept with their youthful *élan* and startling reports into the sedate Linnaean Society, in which I was one of a foursome of participants who were even more *enfants* but not *terribles* at all, quite the opposite. They were hawks themselves in the pursuit of birds. Cruickshank, Hickey and Peterson went on to distinguish themselves as ornithologists, Roger probably to see more of the world's avifauna than anyone else ever has. Yet I venture to believe that the fervor kindled in the heart by a May morning at the height of the migration, which they first knew before adolescence, was hardly to diminish for them in the course of the years.

## The Full Tide of Spring, and the Warblers

Not all Mays are alike. It takes a certain pattern of weather to produce the "wave" that is what the addicts look for, when Nature empties the jewel-box of the wood-warblers into the trees and there is not a lull in the effervescence of song. The term is misleading if it causes one to picture a peak of avian numbers that travels up the continent like a swell. A wave is a static, rather local build-up, the outcome of a combination of meteorological factors occurring in the period of ten days or so when the maximum numbers of birds may be expected to come through. Among these would seem to be a warming trend to stimulate the movement, a few days of low ceiling to bring the migrants down out of the sky as they arrive and a cold front moving in to bar their passage northward. A different combination, and one that might produce a wave elsewhere, will send the sky-borne hosts winging on through a given area. The arch-birders do not, however, hold off until conditions appear propitious. They go afield as they can, hope for the best and make the best of what there is. Those who aim at spectacular lists, when at the outset they find that it looks like the Big Day, are likely then to go all out.

I have never heard of a May anywhere in the East, however poor compared with some, that was not a delight—a delight in birds in a landscape given over to beauty, as if there were not another care on earth but beauty. The early spring flowers are in decline, like the violets, or have vanished—except the indefatigable Spring-beauties—as the great fortnight begins, but the woodland floor is still sky-flecked with Wild Blue Phlox, beside which the orange-yellow of the Golden Ragwort banishes shadow, and clumps of orchid-pink Wild Geranium tempt the covetous transplanter. Front yards by the square mile are stage-shows of blossoming azaleas. The woods along their borders break in a surf of still-flowering dogwoods—trees that were all in white the morning those reflective phrases of notes more than flute-like in richness told the listener: the Wood Thrush has come! Still waters reflect the limbs of the misnamed Redbud crowded with purplish pink pea-blossoms. Every day now makes a perceptible difference in flowers and foliage. The new leaves are out sufficiently to stipple the woods in the liveliest green but not so much as to mask the structure of the trees or shut off the vistas through the glades: the perfect time. And the birds . . .

The truth is that one is not in condition, without a conscious effort, to say how many birds are making their presence known. By now, in relish of ever new fare, the ear has come to filter out the commoner voices. One simply does not hear Cardinals, Song Sparrows, Robins. Instead . . .

Those few mellow whistles, slightly halting (a hint of syncopation) from on high in an elm in which Goldfinches and Purple Finches are feeding on the new seed: a Baltimore Oriole. And the two swinging, Robin-like songs, one more blurry, the other clearer and more melodious than the Robin's (and without the Robin's habit of hitting a broken note): Scarlet Tanager (a brand of incandescent red in the greenery) and Rose-breasted Grosbeak (you would think the white underparts stained with cherry juice). The three have been household names as stellar beauties among our avifauna ever since the Arm and Hammer company started distributing picture cards of birds in its packages of baking-soda in my childhood. Should one take the time to seek them out in the treetops for the visual treat? (One is at best a window-shopper without the possibility of acquisition however the juices of one's appetite may flow.) What with the little capriccios of warbler songs in the trees about one, the three famous beauties can go till later. But that "P'chickoo chitoo"—a descending call —must be followed to its source, surely a Summer Tanager! (And so it proves to be. It precedes me up the Canal, appearing in plain view in a Redbud, a strawberry in raspberry mousse.)

There are experts who have little trouble putting a name

to any warbler song, even the most inconsequential—and few could be called consequential. This facility requires much practice, however, and yearly; it is hard enough to keep the little refrains all in mind even over a twelvemonth. But the commoner, which have passed a certain point of familiarity, seem to remain with one. The little buzzy running up the ladder and tipping over at the top, as it has been called: that can be only the little Parula of grey-blue head and yellow breast crossed by an orange band and a slaty. That monotonous reiteration, slightly up and down: a Black-and-White, too perpetually busy working its way around a tree-trunk or limb to put much conviction into its performance. The Chestnut-side, with yellow crown and black eye-patch running down into the chestnut flank, puts rather a lot into its "Weech weech weech weech *wee*-choo!" Hearing it, I am back on a sunny, brushy hillside in endless boyhood with the joy of private discovery. The Black-throated Blue's fuzzy, ascending "Pweeoo pweeoo *pwee*" takes me back to youth, too, and to the consciousness of romance in being in the mountains of North Carolina; a drawling but sweet little insinuation, it always seemed to me in the cool, moist woods above the rhododendron thickets. There is no warbler resembling the male, whose pattern of blue above, black on face, throat and flanks, and white below, makes you understand how it could have started the young John Burroughs—who became the first to find its nest—on his lifelong passion for birds.

The Myrtle's song tends to fade in and fade out. A typical one, descending in pitch to the last three notes, sounds like "Wee wee wee witch witch witch." The male now in nuptial dress of bluish, black and white with yellow on crown, rump and sides of breast, the Myrtle must be our most vigorous and successful warbler. (The Audubon's Warbler of the western states is now considered of the same species.) Breeding across Canada and Alaska farther north than any of its kin, it exchanges the bluish and black of its plumage for browns to winter as far north as the coast of New England, subsisting principally on Bayberries. The related Wax-myrtle of the

Maryland and Virginia coastal country supplies swarms of Myrtles with similar fruit. But it consumes other berries, too, along with insects' eggs and larvae, being an outstanding example of a species' profiting from a catholic dict. Such a robust warbler, a little heavier-looking than most of its kin, should have a more decisive song. The vagueness and variability of the offering complicate the problem of making sure that Myrtle Warblers are not something else when they may outnumber all other migrant warblers combined by three to one, even ten to one. I have near put a permanent crick in my neck craning at Myrtle Warblers.

"Did you ever see such a flood of Myrtle Warblers!"

That is a safe utterance when you meet your fellow birders on one of these May mornings that bring us all out—and the Myrtles. Another is: "Have you seen anything good?" The awkwardness comes in replying to that question if the other party gets in with it first. (So don't let him.) You are loathe to produce your trump only to meet with the rejoinder—rendered diffidently so that it will not seem rubbed in—"Oh, yes, I meant to say we did see that, too. Three, as a matter of fact."

*But this year I have seen a Mourning Warbler*—and I care not who knows of my joy in it. Even if it can be topped with a rarer warbler—a Connecticut? an Orange-crowned?—none so uncommon can be so beautiful as it, in blue-grey hood becoming scaly black on the breast, abruptly canary below.

Having someone with you who can identify all the singers from their songs is of course a great convenience; but there is nothing like having to run them down yourself for the satisfaction it brings you or for fixing the song in your mind. When you have followed that insistent "Chick, weeoo chee weeoo, chick!" with the unknown little fidgeter attached to it through hummocky swamp—"Chick, weeoo chee weeoo, chick!"—and tangled thickets as the singer keeps retreating, disappearing— "Chick, weeoo chee weeoo, chick!"—getting between you and the sun when it does come in sight again—"Chick, weeoo chee weeoo, chick!"—and finally you get that crucial one good view and nail it, beyond possibility of a doubt, you know you have earned your bird. You are enlarged to the extent of the White-eyed Vireo. (Like the Brown Thrasher, which also has a black pupil in a round, pale iris, the jerky little clockwork singer looks as if it had just been struck wide-eyed by a revelation.) The familiarization course in North American bird-song is a time-consuming one, though simplified by the many recordings of birds' voices put out in recent years, and the more of it you can get behind you in your early years, when you need not be miserly of the hours, the better. Some songs have to be learned over and over again, others happily bear an unforgettable and unmistakable signature. Of these, that of the White-eyed Vireo, though it varies from individual to individual in other respects, is one, with its emphatic *chick* at the end and usually—like the exclamation-point in Spanish, Vera says—at the beginning, too.

*What's that?* "Pweesh pweesh wee chee chee chee." From well up in a tree it comes. "Pweesh pweesh wee chee chee chee." The first two notes are nasal, the remaining four clear and faster. *I see you! Stay where you are, you little rascal.* One is always in desperate anxiety, it has so often happened that the mystery-vocalist has flitted heartlessly off and away. (In this case I need have no fear, for an hour later I find the singer in the same tree, still, or again, repeating its two-second song every seven seconds.) "Pweesh pweesh wee chee chee chee." *A Cerulean! Oh, you sapphire! You delicacy, you animated morsel of imagination's candy, you fancy's child of the ultimate artist's palette, you fairy-lovely!*

Well, the Cerulean is in truth not likely to be mistaken for a sapphire, and all the warblers are no less deserving of those other effusions. The task of an honest Paris among them would be a thankless one. The Blackburnian, fortuitously yet so felicitously named, is like a fire in a black woods; none is more brilliant. Yet to Edward Howe Forbush, writing in his *Birds of Massachusetts*, "that bright front is its chief glory, while the Magnolia's beauties are distributed to every part of its graceful little form." Yellow beneath, black-streaked, and on rump, grey-blue on crown, the Magnolia was to him "the most strikingly beautiful warbler that makes its home in New England." Yet it could be argued that the Cape May, similarly colored but buttercup-yellow to the Magnolia's more lemon-yellow, has all that the Magnolia has and more besides, being cinnamon-cheeked where the Magnolia is black-cheeked and adorned with a brilliant yellow collar. In his *Warblers of North America*, Frank M. Chapman wrote that he could "still recall the particular tree and hour in which, over twenty years ago, I discovered with uncontrollable exultation my first Cape May," an "exquisitely colored spring male." As he noted, "the beauty and rarity" of the species made it "eagerly sought for." The Cape May was indeed once a rarity, as was the Chestnut-side and, on the eastern seaboard, the Cerulean, a bird of the Mississippi Valley.

The Yellow Warbler, whose continent-wide distribution below the arctic and charms of person make it probably the most generally beloved of the family, was to Chapman one "in whose plumes dwells the gold of the sun," as it is to me, too, to whom, also, the light streaking of orange-brown on its flanks gives its sunny yellow a sultry cast. There is gold equally in the Hooded Warbler, set off by the jet of its crown, throat and breast, and in the cheeks of the Black-throated Green in the dusky conifers. It was this latter that "was my first real introduction to the wood warblers," Forbush wrote: "a brilliant male . . . his green back, yellow cheeks and black throat fairly gleaming in the morning sun, and the white markings of his wings and tail flashing in and out as he moved among the dark branches. I thought it the most beautiful bird in the world and longed to possess it."

It is time to call a halt—except that I cannot let pass without mention that absolute darling, in color an inlay of costly woods, the Bay-breasted Warbler, its face of ebony set in mahogany. And then there comes Maurice Broun, writing in *A Natural History of North American Birds*, with an apostrophe of that fiery coal, the black warbler picked out in orange-red patches, with white underside, of which Chapman wrote: "If a bird exists which is more constantly in motion and in a greater variety of ways, I have yet to see it. . . . With what dainty grace he spreads his tail, half opens his wings, and pirouettes from limb to limb like a village belle with coquettishly held skirts tripping the mazes of a country dance!" Says Broun: "Every bird lover has at some time been asked 'Of all the warblers, which one is your favorite?' And he has probably answered—the Redstart!"

But enough. No more.

May is the month of the Big List. Working with one or two others, covering as much ground as they can with profit, my friend Paul G. DuMont and David A. Cutler of Philadelphia each manages to record between 160 and 200 species in a day at the height of the migration. For a single person in a good locality, that would be a very respectable year's list. Although a party of four or five in Texas scored 229, Paul doubts that anywhere in the East it would be possible to beat the best days on the mid Atlantic seaboard. Here you can pick up the species at the fall-line—a boundary between habitats and therefore likely to be especially productive—the coastal plain with its estuarine waters and marshes, and the ocean shore. In this mid region, moreover, at the right time you can get both the full roster of arriving migrants and the rear ranks of the withdrawing winter birds.

### —And the Shorebirds

On the ornithologically fruitful mid Atlantic seaboard, the number of warblers and the number of shorebirds that may be looked for in the course of a year are about the same: something like thirty-eight. (Looked for, but by no means necessarily found.) And as much as May is warblers to the birders it is sandpipers and plovers. It brings the height of their migration, too. Though they are not as many as in autumn, they are charged with the fresh vigors of spring and are now in brighter and more distinctive garb (with few exceptions), males and females alike.

The tidal rivers, mudflats and short-grass marshes inland of

the barrier islands can look like water-bird exhibits. At Assateague, it is nothing unusual, I am sure, to see fifteen Snowy Egrets on a thirty-foot strip of channel shore, as I have, their plumes cascading down their backs from the tops of their heads to turn up above the tail. You follow a flock of peeps ripping by and where they flutter lightly to a landing find the field of your glasses crawling with their kind—Least and Semipalmated Sandpipers. Whimbrels, which are curlews and among the largest of the sandpipers, stand above the grass; on their long legs they could wade among the peeps. Their small, dark-striped heads taper to a long, down-curved bill, a caricature of a proboscis, which they bear with dignity. The least likely of the shorebirds to be overlooked are the Willets. They are at home here, breeding on the East coast from New Jersey southward (also on the northern prairies—an odd combination) and seem altogether so. About as big as the Whimbrels, and less shy, they are the most vociferous of all and the most conspicuous when they fly about, as they are continually doing, flashing their wings, which are black divided by a longitudinal white stripe, and displaying their white rumps. (Folding their wings on alighting, they simply disappear.) "Pill-will-willet," or "Prrr wee wee-wee"; their calling is incessant, mingled with the equally incessant cries of the Laughing Gulls.

The Laughing Gulls are also at home here and very much so. They are everywhere, baying at one another, ranging and romping over marsh and river; their flight is fluid and dextrous, their energies boundless. "Kee awk" or "Kee wawk," they call nasally as they wing by. That famous laugh of theirs is nasal, too, high and staccato, trailing off into a mocking "ha ha ha ha." Snowy of body, they seem irreverent of their own comeliness, which, with their heads now slate-colored and darker even than the mantle, their bills red, is striking. The Common Terns rise from the inevitable billboards to shear the air with that weightless grace of theirs, as if flight were a kind of impromptu song. But even after this I feel I have never seen a seabird so visibly an exemplification of what is called a state of grace as the three Gull-billed Terns we watched coursing over the outer beach and dunes at Assateague last May. I cannot believe there has ever been a purer white or more flawless modeling than that of their wind-sculptured bodies, a softer grey than that of their mantles, a bird of more elegantly turned head than theirs, black-capped with a black bill—short for a tern's—just proportioned to it.

You see Whimbrels on the beach at Assateague standing about in loose congregations facing the breeze, quite patrician, and sometimes, flying north just outside the surf, a flock you may first mistake for small brown ducks, as I did. A few Willets may be among them and two or three big Boat-tailed Grackles picking about for food; these, in the pines back at the campground, keep up such a loud converse of buzzy or beedy ejaculations, some sounding like questions and answers, that you could imagine them a flock of parrots.

The outer beach is less popular with shorebirds, however, than the sandy margins of the bay formed by the hook in which the island ends in the south. You may hear them as you approach this before you see the forms flitting over the water—

for shorebirds call mostly from the wing: the broken warble of a Dowitcher, the burry *beeeeep* of a Dunlin, the *kee-un* of a Turnstone, the *wheet wheet wheet-wheet* of a Semipalmated Sandpiper. The plump Dowitchers, pallid in autumn, have turned a russet salmon beneath and the droopy-nosed Dunlins, which despite their short legs like to go out in the water and switch about, are quite transformed: writing of the courtship pursuit of a female Dunlin by several males, Herbert W. Brandt observes that "as they all twist about, in and out, twittering all the time, the alternate flashing of their reddish backs and black lower parts seems like the signals of a telegraphic code."

The Dunlin in breeding plumage reverses the law of nature that creatures shall be darker above than below, the better to escape detection: the lower half tends to fall into shadow and if dark to begin with would be conspicuously so. A species that Arthur Cleveland Bent calls "an aristocrat among shorebirds, the largest and strongest of the plovers," does so even more boldly; for where the Dunlin has a black patch on its underside, the Black-bellied Plover in spring becomes a solid, absolute jet from its facial mask on down and back. The effect is to add to the bird's apparent stature and, as it were, to dramatize it. I wish it were called the Silver Plover, for the Golden Plover is equally black beneath in spring and, as it is chased above in black and gold, so is the Black-bellied in black and silver; in both birds the back resembles chain mail. My friends and I in boyhood, when questions of relative prowess mattered much, used to try to gauge the comparative speeds of shorebirds when their flocks took to the air together. Since we decided in favor of the Black-bellied Plover, I am glad to see that Brandt calls it "the fleetest racer of the air among a field of highly developed specialists," swifter even than "the graceful Long-tailed Jaeger." But the Silver Plovers still have the poignant shorebird voice. "Pee-a-wee," they call as they take wing. "Pee-a-wee," it comes back to us in farewell. They leave us to the company of a smaller, less wander-prone relative.

The Piping Plover is a paler version of the commoner Semipalmated Plover, being a bird of the farther out, of the beaches, specifically of the dry sands of the upper beach. Counting it and the similar Snowy Plover of the Gulf and West coasts (and the other continents) as one, it is among the only three *shore-bird* shorebirds breeding south of Canada, as it does here at Assateague. (The other two are the Willet and the Wilson's Plover, which also breed on the island. The witless slogan promoted by the Department of Conservation and Economic Development in Richmond, "Virginia is for Lovers," could better read "Virginia is for Plovers.") The Piping Plovers have a settled air here that goes with their being at home. We meet several as we walk along the shore of the bay. They give a short run, stop dead, cock the head like a Robin, tip forward if they locate a morsel, then repeat the performance. Each time they stop they become one with the sand, like the Ghost Crabs that share their habitat—probably would be quite invisible but for the dark collar and forehead mark they are now wearing as courtship ornaments. They are one of the birds that cannot but elicit the term *lovely*, so infectious is their air of refinement, delicacy and that innocent gentleness we associate with doves —an unwarrantable attribution that gave rise to many Victorian paintings of young women cuddling doves or laying them to their cheeks. Mentally one extends such caresses to the Piping Plover, which, moreover, with its large, rounded plover's head, in which its black eyes are wide set, has better proportions than a dove. The preciousness of life: that is what it makes one feel so acutely, so almost painfully at the heart.

### Summer Again, and Two Voices

To be away for only two days as May comes to its half-way mark is to find a changed world on being at home again. The season has turned from the lean to the lush part of the year. The Red Maples are fully foliated, the oak leaves half sized, the Whites still behind. After a thunderstorm the woods are fragrant and of a fertile, shadowy green. Buttercups have succeeded the violets. Yellow-centered, white waxen flowers hang like lamps beneath the May-apples' umbrellas. The first blackberry blossoms appear, more like small, chalk-white wild roses

—which is what they are—than you remembered. Now are heard the songs that mean the migration is at its last stage: the thin "Tsee tsee tsee *tsee tsee tsee* tsee tsee tsee" of the Blackpoll, our commonest warbler after the Myrtle—and the upward trilling, quite subdued, of the Olive-backed Thrush, an echo of the Veery's down-spiraling, but inverted. It is surprising that the Olive-back sings as audibly as it does, courting attention, for its world, one would judge, is full of perils, even, as in the case of some persons, imaginary ones. When it alights it remains motionless with attention, rapt with it, as if it were hearing voices. When it flies off it does so silently.

The Blackpoll and the Olive-back are with us nearly till the end of May, the former often into June. They see summer in. The last Spring-beauty closes, the last Flowering Dogwood petal falls. The Hollies come into bloom, those on our place, males and females, all on the same day—and how is it done? The Amelanchier—Shadbush—berries are purple-ripe. With Black Locust, Black Cherry, Blackberry, Japanese Honeysuckle, Multiflora Rose and Mountain-laurel all in bloom, the country-side is decked in white for the bridal month. The first Tree-frog trills by the back door, so loud it makes you jump, and the first minute lantern of a lightning-bug drifts across the darkening woods. The first crop of young birds is out of the nest while the late migrants are still coming through. June is only three weeks old when the revolving wheel brings Midsummer Day and the dismaying start of the progressive shortening of the days once more.

The hot weather has yet to come, however. The early mornings of hot days can be idyllic and I do not much mind the heat. To me it is an excess of a good thing as opposed to cold, an excess of a bad. Still, who would not go to warmer climes in winter, cooler in summer? I could well follow the Olive-backed Thrush and Blackpoll Warbler to their homes in the boreal forest where the cool shadows are redolent of conifer foliage warm in the sun. But more than to escape the heat it would be to hear two birds that touch emotions beyond reach of any but great artists.

The Hermit Thrush I came to know in Vermont hills, once pasture, where the firs and spruces of the invading forest stood amid undergrowth and weeds beaded with dew in the early morning; I would soon be drenched. I have not heard one sing since I attempted to set down some idea of it:

> Its voice is melodic and pensive, it sings in phrases, releasing them one by one to the wind. There is no lovelier sound. The elegiac periods, gently warbling, move up the scale, as if they would ascend to a higher realm, and fade away, the singer seeming to be drifting off into abstraction or falling silent to listen. You could believe it moved, as man may be moved, by the inexpressible.

Eugene P. Bicknell speaks of the Hermit Thrush's "tranquil clearness of tone and exalted serenity of expression," Forbush of "the mysterious, elevating character of the emotions with which the Hermit's song infuses us."

The Hermit Thrush is a musician, to our ears an instrumentalist, its tones between strings and wood-winds. The Loon is neither musician nor instrumentalist. It is a voice. From the forbidding waters off the coast it comes in May to northern lakes. There at evening in the dark reflection of the jagged forest, drawing behind it a V of waves that show as colored streamers of the sunset sky, it raises a cry that wells up out of the quiet in a clear falsetto and falls off to drift away into space:

"Ooo aaaaaaaaah oo."

To drift away into space and into silence, a silence profound and intense. God only knows what you would think if you did not know the origin of that voice. You wait, nerves drawn.

"Ooo aaaaaaaaaah uh." It floats out upon the gathering dusk as if to plumb its depths. You think you have never heard a sound more nakedly pregnant with the soul's mystery and compulsion. But your nerves are due for a further tightening of the screw.

"Oo ah eeeeeeee ah oo."

The cry breaks upward for the "eeeeeeee," abruptly descends to the "ah oo." The effect is devastating.

"Oo ah eeeeeeee ah oo.

"Oo ah eeeeeeee ah oo."

Other cries come from that half-human throat and another Loon or two across the water take them up: whinnies, softly fluttering and quavering—spectral voices calling up spirits—and a prolonged "Oooooooo-ah" rising with what in a human being would be hysteria, to a "We-ah we-ah we-ah we-ah" such as you hear from gulls, breaking downward between the syllables. It rives the night with its insistence, to some hearers suggesting lunatic laughter—hence the bird's name—or the demonic. And indeed, with Loons sounding from two or three quarters, each in the voice of two or three different beings, you could imagine yourself at a witches' Sabbath, a Walpurgis Night of the wilderness. But to me that broken, pealing cry is at once one of anguish and triumph such as life has surely earned the right to voice to the heavenly orbs as they come twinkling on.

I am of course presuming in interpolating emotions into the weird incantations of that veteran of the dreary seas and the chill sub-marine. And I cannot imagine what further fantasies I might be lead into if, "toward nightfall" at sea, I had, like Forbush, "heard his wild storm-call far out to windward against the black pall of an approaching tempest like the howl of a lone wolf coming down the wind; and . . . seen his white breast rise on a wave against the black sky to vanish again like the arm of a swimmer lost in the stormy sea." But when I hear that solitary voice rise and fall across the gloaming . . .

"Ooo aaaaaaaaah oo."

. . . and wait . . .

"Ooo ah eeeeeeee ah oo."

When I hear it I feel as I must. And what I feel is that in the voices of the Loon and the Hermit Thrush, each in its very different way, and not in them alone among birds, but in them as in the Veery in highest degree, there is both transcendence of circumstance and longing for what lies beyond it. When I am told that such an effect is purely coincidental and subjective on my part, I cannot argue. Neither can I bring myself quite to believe it. If it is not in the bird itself, a rendering—largely unconscious, admittedly—of what is in the very plasma of life, derived from who knows where, then, to me, it is a quality in the cosmos of which the bird is the—again, largely unconscious—agency of expression. Either way—and perhaps I have merely said the same thing in different words—it is the gift of birds not only to contribute immeasurably to the beauty that meets the eye in Nature, to which we turn for relief from the violence we do it as we spread our ugly and overbearing works across the landscape, but to allow us to believe, as we also see in Nature that which affrights and appalls us, that what meets the eye in Nature may not be all there is.

# BIBLIOGRAPHY

ALLEN, ARTHUR A. *The Book of Bird Life*. New York: Van Nostrand, 1961.

ANDERSON, BRUCE H., AND WALTER KINGSLEY TAYLOR. "Nocturnal Migrants Killed at a Central Florida TV Tower; Autumns 1969–1971," *The Wilson Bulletin*. March 1973.

ARBIB, ROBERT. "Of Art and the Nest," *Audubon Magazine*. November 1972.

ARDREY, ROBERT. *The Territorial Imperative*. New York: Atheneum, 1966.

*Audubon Magazine*. "Orgy at the Lek." May 1974.

AUSTIN, OLIVER L., JR., AND ARTHUR SINGER (ILLUS.). *Birds of the World*. London: Golden Press, 1961.

BARNES, IRSTON. "The Naturalist," *The Washington Post*. August 20, 1972.

BENT, ARTHUR CLEVELAND. *Life Histories of North American Birds*. Washington, D.C.: United States National Museum, Bulletin 113 (20 volumes). Republished beginning in 1963 by Dover Publications.

*Birds in Our Lives*. Washington, D.C.: United States Department of the Interior, 1966.

BOWEN, EZRA. *The High Sierra*. New York: Time-Life Books, 1972.

BRAND, ARTHUR R. "Vibration Frequencies of Passerine Bird Songs," *The Auk*. April 1938.

BROLEY, MYRTLE JEANNE. *Eagle Man* (Charles R. Broley). New York: Farrar, Straus and Young, 1952.

BROUN, MAURICE. *Hawks Aloft*. New York: Dodd, Mead, 1949.

BRUNN, BERTEL, AND ARTHUR SINGER (ILLUS.). *The Hamlyn Guide to Birds of Britain and Europe*. London: Hamlyn and Golden Pleasure Books, 1970.

BULL, JOHN, AND EDWARD R. RICCIULI. "Polly Want an Apple?" *Audubon Magazine*. May 1974.

Burrows, Carin. "The Fierce and Erotic Gods of Buddhism," *Natural History*. April 1972.

Chapman, Frank M. *Handbook of Birds of Eastern North America*. New York: D. Appleton, 1895, 1912.

————. *My Tropical Air Castle*. New York: D. Appleton, 1929.

————. *The Warblers of North America*. New York: D. Appleton, 1907.

Conway, William G. *Birds in Our Lives*. U. S. Department of the Interior, 1966.

Da Vinci, Leonardo. *Leonardo da Vinci*. Reynal. From edition by Istituto Geographica De Agostini S.p. A. Novara. 1956.

DeGraaf, Richard M., and Jack Ward Thomas. "A Banquet for the Birds," *Natural History*. January 1974.

Dorst, Jean. *The Migration of Birds*. Translated from the French by Constance D. Sherman. Boston: Houghton Mifflin, 1962.

Droscher, Vitus B. *The Mysterious Senses of Animals*. New York: Dutton, 1965.

Fisher, James, and Roger Tory Peterson (illus.). *The World of Birds*. Garden City, N.Y.: Doubleday, 1964.

Forbush, Edward Howe. *Birds of Massachusetts and Other New England States*. Boston: Commonwealth of Massachusetts, 1925. Republished, condensed and extended in range, with additional species by John B. May, under the sponsorship of the Massachusetts Audubon Society, undated, by Bramhall House, New York, as *A Natural History of North American Birds*.

Frisch, Karl von. *Animal Architecture*. New York: Harcourt Brace Jovanovich, 1974.

Frith, Harold James. *The Mallee-fowl*. Sydney, Australia: Angus & Robertson, 1962.

Gilliard, E. Thomas. *Birds of Paradise and Bower Birds*. Garden City, N.Y.: Natural History Press, 1969.

Graham, Frank, Jr. "Man and Gull," *Audubon Magazine*. November 1972.

Halle, Louis J. *The Sea and the Ice*. Boston: Houghton Mifflin, 1974.

————. *The Storm Petrel and the Owl of Athena*. Princeton: Princeton University Press, 1970.

HARTING, JAMES E. *The Birds of Shakespeare*. Chicago: Argonaut, 1965.

HARTSHORNE, CHARLES. *Born to Sing*. Bloomington: Indiana University Press, 1973.

HARWOOD, MICHAEL. *The View from Hawk Mountain*. New York: Scribner's, 1973.

HAY, JOHN. *Spirit of Survival*. New York: Dutton, 1974.

HEINROTH, OSKAR AND KATARINA. *The Birds*. Ann Arbor: University of Michigan Press, 1958.

HEINTZELMAN, DONALD S. *Autumn Hawk Flights. New Brunswick*, N.J.: Rutgers University Press, 1975.

HINDE, R. A. *Bird Vocalizations*. New York: Cambridge University Press, 1969.

HOGG, PETER. Report on birds migrating through an oil company camp in the eastern Sahara. *Ibis* (London), October 1974.

HOOKER, T., AND BARBARA. *Bird Vocalizations* by R. A. Hinde. New York: Cambridge University Press, 1969.

HOWARD, LEN. *Birds as individuals*. Garden City, N.Y.: Doubleday, 1953.

JOHNSON, DAVID W., AND T. P. HAINES. "Analysis of Mass Bird Mortality in October 1954," *The Auk*. October 1957.

KEETON, WILLIAM T. "The Orientation of Pigeons," *Science*. August 29, 1969, and April 3, 1970.

KIERAN, JOHN. *A Natural History of New York City*. Boston: Houghton Mifflin, 1954.

LACK, DAVID. *The Life of the Robin*, Rev. ed. London: Penguin Books, 1953.

LAWRENCE, D. H. *England, My England*. London: Martin Secker, 1927.

LINCOLN, FREDERICK C. *The Migration of American Birds*. Garden City, N.Y.: Doubeday Doran, 1939.

————. *Migration of Birds*, Circular 16. Washington, D.C.: Fish and Wildlife Service, U.S. Department of the Interior. 1950.

LORENZ, KONRAD. *King Solomon's Ring*. New York: Crowell, 1952.

MADSON, JOHN. "The Prairie Blizzard," *Audubon Magazine*. March 1970.

MARSHALL, A. J. *Bower-Birds*. New York: Oxford University Press, 1954.

MATTHEWS, GEOFFREY V. T. *Bird Navigation*, 2nd ed. New York: Cambridge University Press, 1968.

MATTHIESSEN, PETER, RALPH S. PALMER, GARDNER STOUT AND ROBERT VERITY CLEM (ILLUS.). *The Shorebirds of North America*. New York: Viking, 1967.

OGBURN, CHARLTON. "The Crow," *Atlantic Monthly*. April 1935.

————. "Birds in Java," *Audubon Magazine*. September-October and November-December 1949.

————. *The Southern Appalachians*. New York: Morrow, 1975.

ORR, ROBERT T. *Animals in Migration*. New York: Macmillan, 1970.

PARSONSON, G. S. "The Settlement of Oceania," *Polynesian Navigation*. Melbourne, Polynesian Society Memoir No. 34, 1962.

PASQUIER, ROGER F. *Recent Additions to the Birds of Central Park*. Proceedings of the Linnaean Society of New York, 1974.

PAXTON, ROBERT O. "The Changing Seasons," *American Birds*. June 1974.

PETERSON, ROGER TORY. *A Field Guide to the Birds*. Boston: Houghton Mifflin, 1947.

————. *Birds Over America*. New York: Dodd, Mead, 1948.

————. Introduction to *Birds As Individuals*, by Len Howard. Garden City, N.Y.: Doubleday, 1953.

————. With James Fisher, *The World of Birds*. Garden City, N.Y.: Doubleday, 1964.

POUGH, RICHARD H. *Audubon Bird Guide*. Garden City, N.Y.: Doubleday, 1946.

————. *Water Bird Guide*. Garden City, N.Y.: Doubleday, 1951.

PRATT, AMBROSE. *The Lore of the Lyrebird*. Melbourne, Australia: Robertson & Mullens, 1933, revised 1955.

ROBBINS, CHANDLER, BERTEL BRUNN, HERBERT S. ZIM AND ARTHUR SINGER (ILLUS.). *Birds of North America*. London: Golden Press, 1966.

SIELMANN, HEINZ. *Lockende Wildnis*. Gütersloh and Vienna. 1970.

SLUD, PAUL. "The Song and Dance of the Long-tailed Manakin," *The Auk*. July 1957.

SMITH, STUART, AND ERIC HOSKING. *Birds Fighting*. London: Faber & Faber, 1955.

STEINER, GRUNDY. *Of Men and Birds*. Prolegomena to *The Birds of Shakespeare*, by James E. Horting. Chicago: Argonaut, 1965.

STERLING, CLAIRE. "Taps for Songbirds," *The Washington Post*. April 16, 1974.

STONE, WITMER. *Bird Studies at Old Cape May*. New York: Dover, 1968. Republished from original edition of 1937.

STORER, JOHN H. *The Flight of Birds*. Bloomington Hills, Michigan: Cranbrook Institute of Science Bulletin No. 28, 1948.

THOMPSON, WILLIAM L. and KENNETH A. SHIOVITZ. "Song of the Bunting," *Natural History*. October 1974.

THORPE, WILLIAM H. *Duetting and Antiphonal Song in Birds*. Leiden, Netherlands: E. J. Brill, 1972.

TINBERGEN, NIKO. *The Herring Gull's World*. Collins *New Naturalist*. London, 1953.

————. *The Animal in Its World*. Cambridge, Mass.: Harvard University Press, 1972.

VOGT, WILLIAM. *Notes on the Eastern Willet*. Proceedings of the Linnaean Society of New York, 1937.

WALCOTT, CHARLES. "Explorations," *Harvard Magazine*. November 1974.

WALKER, BRUCE T. *The Great Divide*. New York: Time-Life Books, 1973.

WALLACE, GEORGE J. *An Introduction to Ornithology*. New York: Macmillan, 1955.

*Washington Post, The.* "Hunters Legally Invading National Wildlife Refuges." April 14, 1974.

WEIR, DONALD G. "Status and Habits of *Megapodius pretardii," The Wilson Bulletin*. March 1973.

WELTY, JOEL CARL. *The Life of Birds*. New York: Knopf, 1972.

WOOD-GUSH, DAVID G. M. *The Behavior of the Domestic Fowl*. London: Heinemann, 1971.

ZIMMERMAN, DAVID R. "That the Peregrine Shall Live," *Audubon Magazine*. November 1975.

# INDEX

Albatrosses, 54-55, 56, 71, 81, 82, 89, (Laysan) 275
Alcids, 40, 51, 77, 133
Alexander, W. B., 42
American Birding Association, 216
*American Birds*, 29, 130, 241, 248, 262, 263
Anserines, 132, 195, 229, 239, 241-243, 246
Antarctic, the, 39-41, 51-56
Appalachian Mountains, 137, 247-259
*Archaeopteryx*, 69, 80
Arctic, the, 39-40
Ardrey, Robert, 147, 150
Arnold, Matthew, 46, 48, 55
Assateague Island, 28, 261, 311-317, 361-364
*Atlantic Naturalist*, 28-29, 216
Audubon, John James, 217, 224
*Audubon Magazine* and Society, National, 63, 160-161, 217, 291
Auk, Great, 77
Austin, Oliver L., Jr., 43, 47, 79, 156, 162, 227
Avifaunas of the world, 43-44

Bailey, Florence Merriam, 349
Barbet, Crimson-breasted, 62
Barnes, Irston, 235, 237
Bellrose, Frank C., 272, 280
Bent, Arthur Cleveland, 223, 224, 317, 363
Biomes, 131-134
Bird-bath, 214, 297-298
Birds-of-paradise, 157, 158-159
Blackbird, European, 47, 181, 190-191
Blackbirds: Red-winged, 153, 316, 332; Rusty, 350
Blanchard, Barbara D., 338
Bluebird, 24, 292

Bobolink, 237, 238, 240
Bob-white, 125, 313
Bock, Carl E., 241
Bowen, Ezra, 137-138
Bowerbird, Archbold's, 163; Great, 162-163; Regent's, 164; Satin, 98, 163-164; Spotted, 163, 182-183; Stagemaker, 98, 162
Brand, Arthur R., 171
Brandt, Herbert W., 363
Brant, 298
Breeding-bird censuses, 130
Broun, Maurice, 215, 252, 257, 359-360
Browning, Robert, 50-51
Bry, Ed, 291
Bufflehead, 334
Bulbul, Black-capped, 61
Bullfinch, 182
Burrows, Carin, 15
Bustard, Great, 73

Cade, Thomas J., 260
Cape Charles, 226
Cape Henlopen, 226, 228-229, 321-322
Cape May, 226, 261-262, 319
Cardinal, 100, 184-185, 295, 300, 329
Carlson, Carl W., 216
Cassowary, 14, 75
Catbird, 102, 185-186, 205, 233, 302, 348
Central Park, New York, 329, 349, 351-352
Chaffinch, 116, 180, 274
Chapman, Frank M., 20, 26, 27, 41, 117, 173-174, 176-177, 184, 196-197, 207-208, 348, 359-360
Chat, Yellow-breasted, 128
Cheney, S. P., 167

Chickadees: Black-capped, 137, 301; Carolina, 23, 294, 297
Chicken, 113-115, 153, 187, 316
Chicken, Prairie, 92, 161, 162, 291
Chough, Red-billed, 37
Christmas censuses, 129-130, 216, 241, 309
Clare, John, 47
Clarin, 173-174
Clark, Sir Kenneth, 15-16
Coker, Robert E., 41
Colors in plumage, 111-112
Columbus, Christopher, 35-36
Condor, 193
Conrad, Joseph, 16-17, 31
Conway, William B., 293-294
Cowbirds, 205-207
Cranes, 156, 243-244
Creeper, Brown, 45
Crossbills, 45, 306, 307-308
Crows: Common, 104-106, 107-108, 113, 187, 272, 297, 330, 337; Fish, 315; Hooded, 104, 272
Cruickshank, Allan, 353
Cuckoos: European, 46, 65, 205-206; Long-tailed, 35, 269; Shining, 269, 276; Yellow-billed, 212
Curlews: Bristle-thighed, 222, 269; Eskimo, 224, 343

Decoration by birds, 163-165
DeGraaf, Richard M., 305
Diatryma, 14, 73
Displacement activity, 101-102
Distribution of birds, 36-41
Dodo, 76, 78
Dorst, Jean, 233, 245-246, 263, 267, 282, 339
Dovekie, 263
Doves: Collared Turtle, 140-141; Mourning, 123, 210, 291, 325
Dowitcher, 224-225, 363
Drayton, Michael, 47
Drongo, Grey, 185
Drury, William H., 231

Ducks: Black, 44, 311, 313, 314, 315; Tree-, Fulvous, 156; Ruddy, 286; Wood, 333
Duetting in birds, 188-190
DuMont, Paul G., 225-226, 360
Dunlin, 363
Durdin, Kent, 106-107
Dvorak, Antonin, 167

Eagles: Bald, 225, 258-259; Golden, 14, 106-107, 258; Harpy, 14
Edge, Rosalie Barrow, 252
Eel, 34
Egrets: Cattle, 60, 140; Great, 30, 211, 218-219, 314; Snowy, 60, 211, 314, 361
Eiders, 195, 318
Elephant-birds, 75
Emlen, Stephen T., 173; with John T., 278, 281
Evolution, avian, 69-73
Expanding populations of birds, 140-141

Falcons: Eleanora's, 233; Peregrine, 243, 259-261, 353
Farallon Islands, 236
Feathers, 67-73, 78-79, 81, 86-88, 111-112
Fedak, Michael, 79, 153
Feeding-stations, 22-23, 295-297, 298-302, 305, 308, 331
Finches: Darwin, 99; House, 305; Purple, 22, 139; Woodpecker-, 98-99
Fisher, James, 40, 43, 54, 73
Flicker, 262
Flightlessness, 73, 75-78
Flycatcher, Great Crested, 218, 349
Forbush, Edward Howe, 143, 224, 358-359, 366, 367
Frequency-range in bird song, 171
Frigatebirds, 74, 89, 90, 92, 268
Frith, Harold J., 201-203
Fuertes, Louis Agassiz, 26, 43, 359

Gadwall, 316

Gannets, 36, 40, 41, 271, 323-324
Gardener, Orange-crested, 164-165
Garuda, 14
Geese: Barnacle, 45; Blue, 311, 342; Canada, 209, 243, 275, 286-287, 309-310, 314, 341, 343; Snow, 243, 311-312, 314
Gilliard, E. Thomas, 158-159, 161, 163
Glands, effect on migration, 339-340
Godwit, Bar-tailed, 35, 222
Goldfinch, 22, 113, 210, 308
Goodwin, Clive E., 248, 255
Goshawk, 258, 306
Grackles: Boat-tailed, 362; Common, 113, 210, 234, 329, 350
Graham, Frank, Jr., 231
Great Lakes, 248-249, 351
Grebes: Great Crested, 156; Horned, 132, 286, 321; Western, 156
Griffin, Donald R., 34, 93, 271
Grosbeaks: Evening, 23, 305, 306, 308; Pine, 45, 306, 307-308; Rose-breasted, 355
Grouse: Blue, 138; Pinnated, 92, 161, 162, 291; Ruffed, 112, 138, 289; Sage, 109, 138, 161, 291; Spruce, 92, 109, 138
Gulls: Black-headed, 45, 155, 230, 318; Bonaparte's, 319; Great Black-backed, 320; Herring, 99, 317, 319-320, 345; Laughing, 362; Lesser Black-backed, 45, 230, 318; Ivory, 36, 109, 132; Little, 45, 230; Ring-billed, 319, 345; Ross's, 36
Gulls and terns (Laridae), 51-52, 98, 107, 132-133, 147, 154-155, 209
Gyrfalcon, 250, 259

Halle, Louis J., 31, 52, 55, 56, 95, 175-176, 186, 223
Harrier, 314
Harting, James E., 14, 49

Hartshorne, Charles, 166, 167-169, 170-171, 174, 182, 183
Harwood, Michael, 251
Hawk Mountain, 251-253
Hawks: Broad-winged, 82, 243, 248, 255; Cooper's, 255-256; Red-shouldered, 21, 258, 297, 328; Red-tailed, 187-188, 256-257, 258; Rough-legged, 258, 306; Sharp-shinned, 187, 233, 255-256, 261, 314
Hay, John, 123, 227
Heintzelman, Donald S., 248, 254
Herford, Oliver, 301
Herons: Black-crowned Night, 314; Great Blue, 310-311, 314; Green, 125, 352; Little Blue, 211, 325
*Hesperornis,* 76
Hickey, Joseph J., 353
Hinde, R. A., 181
Hoatzin, 58
Hogg, Peter, 244
Honeyguide, 108
Hooker, Barbara L. and T., 189
Howard, Len, 117-118, 191, 302-305
Hudson, W. H., 177
Humboldt Current, 41

Ibis, Scarlet, 31, 58
Imitation of sounds, 181 183, 185-186

Jaegers, 36, 229, 351
Jay-thrush, Himalayan, 189
Jays: Blue, 232, 233-234; European, 98, 169; Grey, 108
Johnston, David W., and T. J. Haines, 265
Junco, Dark-eyed, 286, 292, 337-338

Kakapo, 76, 78
Kea, 108
Keats, John, 48, 49
Keeton, William T., 283
Kemper, Charles R., 265

Kieran, John, 341, 352, 353
Killdeer, 44, 218, 219-220
Kingbirds: Eastern, 141-143, 147-149, 187, 233; Western, 235-236, 261-262
Kinglet, Golden-crowned, 43, 46
Kinglet, Ruby-crowned, 348
Kipling, Rudyard, 26, 57, 58
Kirkman, Frederick B., 147
Kites: Black, 58, 59, 82, 249; Brahminy, 12; Everglade, 109; Swallow-tailed, 65
Kittatinny Ridge, 250-254
Kittiwake, 263, 323, 324
Kiwi, 33, 76
Köhler, G., 107
Konishi, Masakazu, 116, 181
Kramer, Gustav, 278

Lack, David, 146
Lammergeier, 37, 109
Lark, Horned, 139, 291
Lascaux, 15
Lawrence, D. H., 16
Lawrence, Louise de Kiriline, 185
Leonardo (da Vinci), 82, 83, 85-86
Lepthien, Larry W., 241
Life zones, 134-139
Lincoln, Frederick C., 55, 238-243, 263, 292, 340
Linnaean Society of New York, 29-30, 32, 352-353
Longspur, Lapland, 292
Loons, 38, 234, 321-322, 366-368
Lorenz, Konrad, 98
Lyrebird, 119, 177-179, 182, 185

Macaw, Hyacinthine, 110
Madson, John, 290-291
Magpies, 45, 304
Malau, 201
Maleo Fowl, 201
Mallard, 281, 290-291, 311
Mallee Fowl, 98, 100, 202-203
Manakins, 159-160
Marler, Peter, 116, 180
Marshall, A. J., 163, 182-183

Martin, Purple, 212
Matthews, Geoffrey T. V., 273, 274-275, 276, 279, 281-282, 284-285
Matthiesen, Peter, 223
Mayr, Ernst, 159
McCabe, John Henry, 17-19
Meadowlarks, Eastern, 123; Western, 182
Megapodes, 98, 100, 193, 201-203
Mental attainments of birds, 103-108
Merlin, 261-262
Merriam, C. Hart, 134
Mewaldt, L. Richard, 275
Migration, aberrants during, 235-236
Migration, altitude of flight during, 233, 249
Migration, nocturnal and diurnal, 233
Migration routes: North American (flyways), 238-243; Eurasian, 243-247
Migration, stimuli to, 335-340
Milton, John, 48, 50
Moas, 75
Mockingbird, 100, 126, 127, 144-145, 154, 168, 174-175, 185-186, 302, 345
Murphy, Robert Cushman, 41, 52, 100, 153-154
Murre, 40
Musicality of birds, 166-168
Mynah, Hill, 116, 181, 182

National Wildlife Refuges, 312-313
Navigation, avian: by bearing, 271-274; by coordinates, 283-285; by goal, 274-277; by magnetic field, 283; by stars, 278-280; by sun, 278-280
Nighthawks, 112, 166, 219, 233, 234
Nightingale, 47, 48-49, 175, 186
Notornis, 76, 78

Nottlebaum, Fernando, 181
Nutcracker, 98
Nuthatches: Red-breasted, 137, 301; White-breasted, 23

Ocean City, Maryland, 318-319
Odum, Eugene P., 338
Oilbird, 93
Old-squaw, 38, 225, 318-319, 322
Oriole, Baltimore, 128fn, 226, 290, 355
Oriole, Black-naped, 63
Oropendolas, 117, 196-197, 207-208
Orre, Robert T., 236, 262
Osprey, 243, 244, 254, 352
Ostrich, 38, 75, 91
Ovenbird, 125, 236
Ovenbird, Rufous, 199
Owls: Barn, 61, 94, 116, 138; Barred, 21; Great Grey, 136, 138; Great Horned, 129, 138-139; Snowy, 15, 306
Oystercatcher, 109

Parakeets, invasion of U.S. by, 60, 305-306
Parrots, 57-58, 60, 104, 107, 116-117, 181-182
Parsonson, G. S., 35
Pasquier, Roger F., 352
Paxton, Robert O., 299, 300
Peacock, 58-59, 157, 158, 290
Penguin, Adélie, 95, 153-154
Penguin, Emperor, 37, 79, 153
Penguins, 38, 74, 75-78, 100
Perdeck, A. C., 272, 273-274
Perse, Saint-John, 19
Peterson, Roger Tory, 25, 29, 40, 43, 73, 166, 267, 303, 353
Petrel, Snow, 37, 54
Phalaropes, 132, 156, 222
Pheasants, 157; Argus, 159, 294; Ring-necked, 291
Phoebe, 120, 292, 330
Phororhacus, 73

Pigeons: domestic (Rock Dove), 268, 270, 271, 276-277, 278, 279-280; Fruit, 61-62, 110; Passenger, 39, 223-224
Pintail, 246, 316
Plankton, 40, 41
Plovers: Black-bellied, 363; Golden, 35, 36, 221-222, 224, 269, 342; Mountain, 220; Piping, 363-364
Polynesian navigators, 35
Poor-will, 349
Potoo, Giant, 176-177
Pough, Richard H., 142, 252
Pratt, Ambrose, 177-179
Procellarines, 51-56, 194
Ptarmigan, 136, 138
Pterosaurs, 71

Raven, 107, 257
Redpolls, 45, 291, 306, 308
Redstart, 359-360
Reed, Chester A., 27, 348
Releasers, 98-99, 100
Respiration, avian, 92-93
Robbins, Chandler, 254, 257, 264
Robin, American, 45, 145, 291, 297, 299, 329, 331
Robin, European, 46-47, 100-101, 146
Rook, 245
Rowan, William, 272, 337
Ruff, 45, 160-161, 222
Rüppell, Werner, 272

Sadovnikov, M. P., 103
Sahara, 38, 244
Sanderling, 317-318
Sandpipers: Curlew, 222; Least, 218; Purple, 318; Semipalmated, 218, 221, 223; Solitary, 218, 219; Spotted, 219, 348; Western, 218, 221
Sauer, Franz and Eleonore, 280, 281
Schmidt-Koenig, Klaus, 279-280
Schüz, Ernst, 272
Scrub-fowl, 201-202

Seton, Ernest Thompson, 26, 32

Shakespeare, William, 14, 47, 49, 50, 51, 65, 169, 295

Shearwaters, 40-41, 52, 55, 56, 89, 269; Manx, 274-275, 276

Shoveler, 246, 316

Shrikes: Bou-bou, 189-190; Northern, 45; Red-backed, 274, 278

Sierra Nevada, 137-139

Sight in birds, 94-96

Singer, Arthur, 43

Siskin, Pine, 22, 306, 308

Size, extremes in avian, 75

Skeleton, avian, 90-92

Skimmer, Black, 229-230

Skinner, B. F., 268

Skua, 36, 53, 99, 324

Skylark, 48, 50

Slud, Paul, 159

Smith, C. Percy, 35

Smith, Stuart and Eric Hosking, 206

Snipe, Common, 112, 165, 218

Social parasites, 205-208

Song, inheritance of versus learning, 179-181

Sonar in birds, 93-94

Sparrows: Chipping, 139; Field, 125-126; Fox, 26, 292, 341; Golden-crowned, 275; Harris's, 139, 236; House, 140, 153, 271; Pinewoods, 184; Song, 126, 180-181, 328; White-crowned, 180, 338; White-throated, 275, 285, 305

Spenser, Edmund, 48

Starlings: European, 102, 140, 168-169, 171, 187-188, 272, 273-274, 278; Glossy, 61

Steiner, Grundy, 15, 21-22

Sterling, Claire, 266-267

Stevenson, Robert Louis, 48

Stone, Witmer, 216, 261-262, 350

Storer, John H., 84, 87-88

Stork, 89, 193, 243, 272, 274, 339

Storm-petrels: Leach's, 274, 275, 276; Wilson's, 40

Swallows: Bank, 45; Barn, 45, 65, 123, 274; Cliff, 199, 274, 340-341

Swan, Whistling, 310, 316

Swiftlets, Cave, 61, 93-94, 200

Swifts: Chimney, 166, 200, 233; Palm, 200; Swallow-tailed, 200

Szoke, P., 167, 170

Tailorbirds, 58, 171, 198-199

Tanagers: Scarlet, 355; Summer, 236, 355

Tatler, Wandering, 222, 269

Taylor, Joseph W., 216, 225

Taylor, Walter Kingsley, and Bruce H. Anderson, 264

Teals: Blue-winged, 272, 350; Green-winged, 44, 246, 315, 345

Tennyson, Alfred Lord, 112

Terns: Arctic, 35, 227, 231; Caspian, 228; Common, 227-228, 231, 274, 362; Fairy, 194; Forster's, 229; Gull-billed, 362; Least, 227, 228; Royal, 228; White-winged Black, 229-230

Thomas, Jack Ward, 305

Thompson, William L., and Kenneth A. Shiovitz, 171, 172-173

Thorpe, William H., 189-190

Thrasher, Brown, 126, 185, 233, 348

Thrushes: Grey-cheeked, 342; Hermit, 167-168, 170, 174, 236, 366-368; Malabar Whistling, 182; Olive-backed, 246-247, 286, 365; Song, 47-48, 98; Wood, 170, 172, 174, 204

Tinamous, 177

Tinbergen, Niko, 102, 154-155

Titmice: European, 107, 117-118, 271, 303-304, 329; penduline, 197

Titmouse, Tufted, 23, 126, 294

Tool-using by birds, 98-99

Towhee, Rufous-sided, 126, 305

Townsend, Charles Wendell, 221

Turnstone, Ruddy, 322

Van Cortlandt Park, New York, 352

Veery, 137, 174, 236, 367

Vireos: Red-eyed, 123, 185, 226, 236; Solitary, 256; White-eyed, 358; Yellow-throated, 185, 212

Vision, avian, 94-96

Volume-surface relationship, 73-74

Von Frisch, Karl, 164-165, 167, 195-196

Vultures: Black, 219; Egyptian, 59, 98; Turkey, 25

Wall, G. L., 95

Wallace, Alfred Russell, 43

Wallace, George J., 102

Walton, Izaak, 47, 48-49

Warblers: Bachman's, 140; Bay-breasted, 236, 359; Black-and-White, 336, 356; Blackburnian, 214, 358; Blackpoll, 171, 340, 342, 365; Black-throated Blue, 356; Black-throated Green, 129, 359; Canada, 137, 214-215; Cape May, 298, 300, 341, 359; Cerulean, 358, 359; Chestnut-sided, 236, 356, 359; Connecticut, 236, 342; Hooded, 214; Kirtland's, 140; Lawrence's, 129; Magnolia, 359; Mourning, 357; Myrtle, 286, 315, 356-357; Palm, 349; Parula, 129, 231, 349, 356; Pine, 226, 292, 300, 332; Prothonotary, 350; Tennessee, 214, 231, 236; Yellow, 336, 359; Yellow-throated, 349

Warbler songs, 355-356

*Washington Post*, 29fn, 312-313

Waterthrush, Louisiana, 348

Wave, migration, 354

Waxwings, 93, 210, 306-307

Weavers: Buffalo, 198; Social, 198

Weaver-finches, 103, 197-198; Cassin's, 197-198

Webster, John, 47

Weir, Donald G., 201

Welty, Joel Carl, 68, 88, 89, 103, 107, 158, 161, 182, 268

WGBH-TV, 116, 180-181, 189

Wheatear, 35, 246

Whimbrel, 225, 361, 362

Whip-poor-will, 21, 183, 195, 349, 352

Wings, form and function, 88-89

Willet, 132, 149-150, 361-362

Wilson, Alexander, 219, 224

Wilson, Edmund O., 151

Wolcott, Charles, and M. C. Michener, 277, 282-283

Wolfson, Albert, 337-338, 339

Woodcock, 112, 165, 262, 292

Wood-Gush, David G. M., 114

Woodpecker-finch, Galapagos, 99

Woodpeckers: Acorn, 98, 99; Downy, 299; Pileated, 129, 297; Red-bellied, 299-300

Wordsworth, William, 46

Wrens: Carolina, 126, 184, 209-210, 212, 297, 300, 329, 330; House, 126, 210, 348; Marsh-, 197; Winter, 45, 137, 170, 286

Wryneck, 274

Yellowlegs, 218, 219, 344

Yellowthroat, Maryland, 128, 140

Young, condition of at birth, 192-194

Zoological parks, 293-294